An Illustrated Encyclopaedia

WONDERS *of* ANIMAL LIFE

also available by the same editor

An Illustrated World Gazetteer

Peoples of all Nations

Their Life Today and Story of Their Past

In 14 Volumes

Volume One
Abyssinia **to** Azerbaijan
Volume Two
Belgium **to** British Empire in America
Volume Three
British Empire in Asia **to** Canada
Volume Four
Ceylon **to** Dahomey
Volume Five
Danzig **to** England
Volume Six
Esthonia **to** France
Volume Seven
Georgia **to** Iceland
Volume Eight
India **to** Italy
Volume Nine
Japan **to** Mexico
Volume Ten
Monaco **to** Oman
Volume Eleven
Palestine **to** Rumania
Volume Twelve
Russia **to** Sin-kiang
Volume Thirteen
South Africa **to** The Ukraine
Volume Fourteen
The United States **to** Wales
with General Index

About the Editor

Sir John Alexander Hammerton (1871-1949) was an English statesman and author, best-known for his editorship of popular encyclopaedias published in the first half of the 20th century, such as the 10-volume New Book of Knowledge.

From 1914 to 1919, Hammerton was joint editor with HW Wilson of the periodical "The Great War: The Standard History of the All-Europe Conflict", published by the Amalgamated Press. It was lavishly illustrated with photographs and with realistic drawings which were sometimes hardly distinguishable from photographs.

He was also a contemporary and friend of Arthur Mee, about whom he wrote a biography.

An Illustrated Encyclopaedia

WONDERS
of
ANIMAL LIFE

by Famous Writers on Natural History

Volume Six

Edited by

J.A. Hammerton

Over Three Thousand Illustrations from Photographs and Thirty-three Colour Plates

LOGOS PRESS, NEW DELHI

ISBN -13: 978-81-7268-175-3 (Set)
ISBN -10: 81-7268-175-5 (Set)

ISBN -13: 978-81-7268-176-0 (Vol. I)
ISBN -13: 978-81-7268-177-7 (Vol. II)
ISBN -13: 978-81-7268-178-4 (Vol. III)
ISBN -13: 978-81-7268-179-1 (Vol. IV)
ISBN -13: 978-81-7268-180-7 (Vol. V)
ISBN -13: 978-81-7268-181-4 (Vol. VI)
ISBN -13: 978-81-7268-182-1 (Vol. VII)
ISBN -13: 978-81-7268-183-8 (Vol. VIII)

ISBN -10: 81-7268-176-3 (Vol. I)
ISBN -10: 81-7268-177-1 (Vol. II)
ISBN -10: 81-7268-178-X (Vol. III)
ISBN -10: 81-7268-179-8 (Vol. IV)
ISBN -10: 81-7268-180-1 (Vol. V)
ISBN -10: 81-7268-181-X (Vol. VI)
ISBN -10: 81-7268-182-8 (Vol. VII)
ISBN -10: 81-7268-183-6 (Vol. VIII)

Edition : 2008

Printed & Published by

LOGOS PRESS

Building No. 4788-90, Street No. 23, Ansari Road, Darya Ganj, New Delhi-110 002 (India)
Phone : 23272187

Foreword

Here is not a 'natural history' in the accepted meaning of that description. There exist many and excellent natural histories and more than fifteen years ago the present editor was associated with the publication of one which, in its authoritative letter-press and profuse illustration, had wide acceptance. But it is undeniable that the general reader finds large and exhaustive treatises on animal life, encumbered with Latin names, somewhat hard reading, however fine their illustrations, if they are arranged on the approved scientific divisions—order, family, genus, species—into which naturalists split up animated nature. A proper natural history, however, must follow this method of treatment if it is to form the basis of a scientific knowledge of the subject.

Does the ordinary reader desire such knowledge? Does he require it?

The answer to both questions is a negative: emphatic in the first and modified in the second case. No matter how slightly youth is drawn to the conventional study of zoology, not even the forbidding scientific approach to natural history can rob it of its inherent fascination.

A boundless curiosity about the infinite diversity of creatures that share the life of the globe with him is a deep and abiding and a most natural trait in man. The stories of a Adam naming the beasts, and of the animals, two by two, going into the ark are ancient evidence of man's interest in his fellow-creatures of the so-called lower orders. A study of the life-histories of many animals and birds, fishes and reptiles, or of the astounding social systems of certain insects, is calculated to limit man's pride in himself as the incarnation of the highest intelligence or the finest physical product of the animal world. Especially is it likely to extend his sympathy to all lowly things that are living out their little days with him upon this planet. It lies at the root of humanitarianism. Interest in animal life is never an idle curiosity, and it may prove more absorbing than any other interest that could be named.

Not, then, to add a new natural history to a list already adequate, but to meet this universal and most healthy interest in the astonishing realities and the mysterious ways of the animal kingdom is the purpose of WONDERS OF ANIMAL LIFE. Its title adequately suggests its scope: to enquire into and to illustrate all that is of uncommon interest in the life of the animal kingdom.

While the reader will find in our pages a constantly changing panorama of animal life, with no more apparent order than the naturalist finds in the Brazilian jungle, he can hardly fail to be interested and he is certain to be instructed, for though the only method that is observed throughout our chapters is a rough alternation of interest, now in mammals, next in reptiles, then in birds, fishes, insects, each chapter of this work is written either by one of the leading specialists on his subject or—where expert knowledge is less needed than vividness of descriptive style—by a popular author.

A glance at the list of contributors, their scientific and literary credentials, and the subjects allotted to them in our scheme, will indicate to the reader that though WONDERS OF ANIMAL LIFE is designedly popular in its appeal, it is not the less authoritative in being more entertaining than the conventional sort of natural history.

Never before has there been brought together so representative and so varied a collection of photographic documents covering the whole range of animated nature. In the last decade, and particularly within the latter part of it, naturalists have acquired an immense amount of new knowledge, and marked progress has been made in recording the wild life of the world by means of direct photography.

The exploits of the camera experts employed by the organizers of some of the great 'nature and adventure' films—'Simba' is a fine example—that have fascinated millions throughout the world in these years have produced so rich a body of material for illustrating such a work as this that editorially we are in a more favoured position than any of our predecessors in the same field and we hope the reader will agree with us in thinking that we have taken advantage of that fortunate circumstance for his entertainment and instruction.

J.A. HAMMERTON

Publisher's Note

We are happy to present the illustrated encyclopaedia—Wonders of Animal Life—to the learned readers. As its title suggests, it attempts to enquire into the astonishing realities and the mysterious ways of life of the animal kingdom—mammals, reptiles, birds, fishes and insects.

Presented in eight volumes, each chapter of this work is written either by one of the leading specialists on the subject or—where expert knowledge is less needed than vividness of descriptive style—by a popular author. The text is enriched with a representative and varied collection of photographic documents covering the whole range of animated nature. Our other notable illustrated encyclopaedias include *The Living Animals of the World* (4 volumes), *The Wonders of the World* (4 volumes), *Peoples of All Nations* (14 volumes), and *The Earth and Its Inhabitants* (8 volumes).

TABLE OF CONTENTS

Volume One

List of Colour Plates

Volume Two

List of Colour Plates

Volume Three

List of Colour Plates

Volume Four

List of Colour Plates

Volume Five

List of Colour Plates

Volume Six

List of Colour Plates

Volume Seven

List of Colour Plates

Volume Eight

List of Colour Plates

Chapter CI

The Golden Eagle: King of Birds

By Seton Gordon

Author of "Days with the Golden Eagle"

As I write these lines I have just returned from visiting an eyrie of the golden eagle far up a lonely Highland glen. The eyrie is built upon a rock, at a height of 1,500 feet above sea level, and with a little care it is possible to climb to it.

Three weeks earlier I had visited this nest. The eagle was then sitting closely, and I was able to take my departure without causing her to fly from her eyrie. I returned, accordingly, on the fifth day of May, the date on which the eagle hatched her young last year, hoping to see eaglets in the nest.

Walking quietly round the base of the rock I reached a point from where the eagle's nest was visible. On the crown of the eyrie a dark object was clear, and on looking through my telescope I was glad to see that the eagle was at home. She was brooding very high on her nest, and from this I surmised that the eaglets were hatched. For a few moments she watched me, then walked deliberately to the edge of her eyrie and after standing there magnificently awhile launched out on to the still air. Then from the eyrie came a welcome high-pitched call—the cry of a baby golden eaglet.

No more fitting domain for the king of birds could be conceived. Westward rose snow-covered hills on which sun and shade alternated. In the glen beneath a herd of stags was feeding, their young horns showing as small dark knobs against grey heads. On the eagle's rock alpine flowers were all in bud.

The first view into a golden eagle's eyrie is always an exciting moment. There, in its roomy home, stood a tiny eaglet clad in white down and a day or two old at the most. Beside it was a richly-marked egg, from which, later, an eaglet also emerged. In the eyrie lay a grouse and the remains of a very small rabbit. Although it was of such a tender age the eaglet showed marked individuality. A piece of heather beside it annoyed it greatly, and it made repeated pecks at it with its feeble bill. If all goes well with it that tiny eaglet, by the time these notes appear in print, should be a strong, fierce eagle, and in mid-July it should leave the eyrie for the limitless aerial plains of which the golden eagle is feathered monarch.

Seton Gordon

GOLDEN EAGLET IN ITS NEST

Here in surroundings typical of the wild country which is the golden eagle's last sanctuary in Britain, we see an eyrie or eagle's nest with a downy young bird crouched among the heather roots which line its home of twigs and pine branches.

Of all British birds the golden eagle is easily the most picturesque and magnificent, and is now found only in the wildest districts of the Scottish Highlands.

Much of late has been written on the present-day position of the golden eagle in the Highlands and some writers have expressed the opinion that this fine bird will soon become extinct. There is no doubt that many golden eagles are shot and trapped annually, but I do not think the species is in any danger so long as there exist large deer forests in the Highlands. In a deer forest the eagle is looked upon with friendliness. It keeps the grouse down, and grouse in a deer forest are almost as unpopular as eagles on a grouse moor, for the most careful stalk is often spoiled by an old cock grouse rising at the critical moment and by his lusty crowing giving the alarm to the deer.

But no bird can be considered secure. Take the sea eagle. About the year 1860 this bird was numerous along the sea coast of western Scotland. There is now not one sea eagle left. The bird's fondness for lambs brought about its wholesale destruction, for it was shot and poisoned ruthlessly, and is now but a name. Sea eagles were sometimes tamed as pets. MacLeod of MacLeod tells me that a sea eagle was formerly kept as a pet at Dunvegan Castle in the Isle of Skye. It was allowed its freedom,

Seton Gordon

Seton Gordon

EYRIE, EGGS, EAGLET AND PREY

In the lower photograph of an eyrie we see two of the kills made by the male for its young, a hare and a grouse. The grouse is just in front of the eaglet's legs and the hare is in the right foreground. Above we have a nest on the Atlantic coast.

yet was so tame that it would appear in the blue vault of heaven and plane earthward at great speed if MacLeod stood outside the castle displaying a rabbit for its dinner.

THE chief of MacLeod told me an amusing story about this bird. An old woman one evening was fishing in the sea for saithe, beneath the castle. As she caught the fish she threw them, one after another over her shoulder on to the grass behind her. At length, when she considered that she had caught a sufficient number, she ceased her fishing and turned about, meaning to gather up her catch. Imagine her feelings when she saw the old sea eagle, looking towards her expectantly as it stood on the grass, while not one single fish remained. The eagle had swallowed the saithe one by one as the old wife had thrown them considerately to it, as the bird doubtless thought.

The nesting season of the golden eagle takes up half of the year. Towards the end of January, if the weather be open, the eagles begin to repair their eyrie, and it is a fine sight to watch an eagle struggling against a winter gale while she carries in her bill a large branch. Eagles are particularly fond of pine branches for the construction of the eyrie, and they will fly considerable distances to the nearest pine tree. Some of the branches taken are as thick as a man's wrist. Nest-building goes on during February, and the eyrie is completed by mid-March, if the site be in any sense of the word a sheltered one. From the fifteenth to the twentieth of March the

E.N.A.

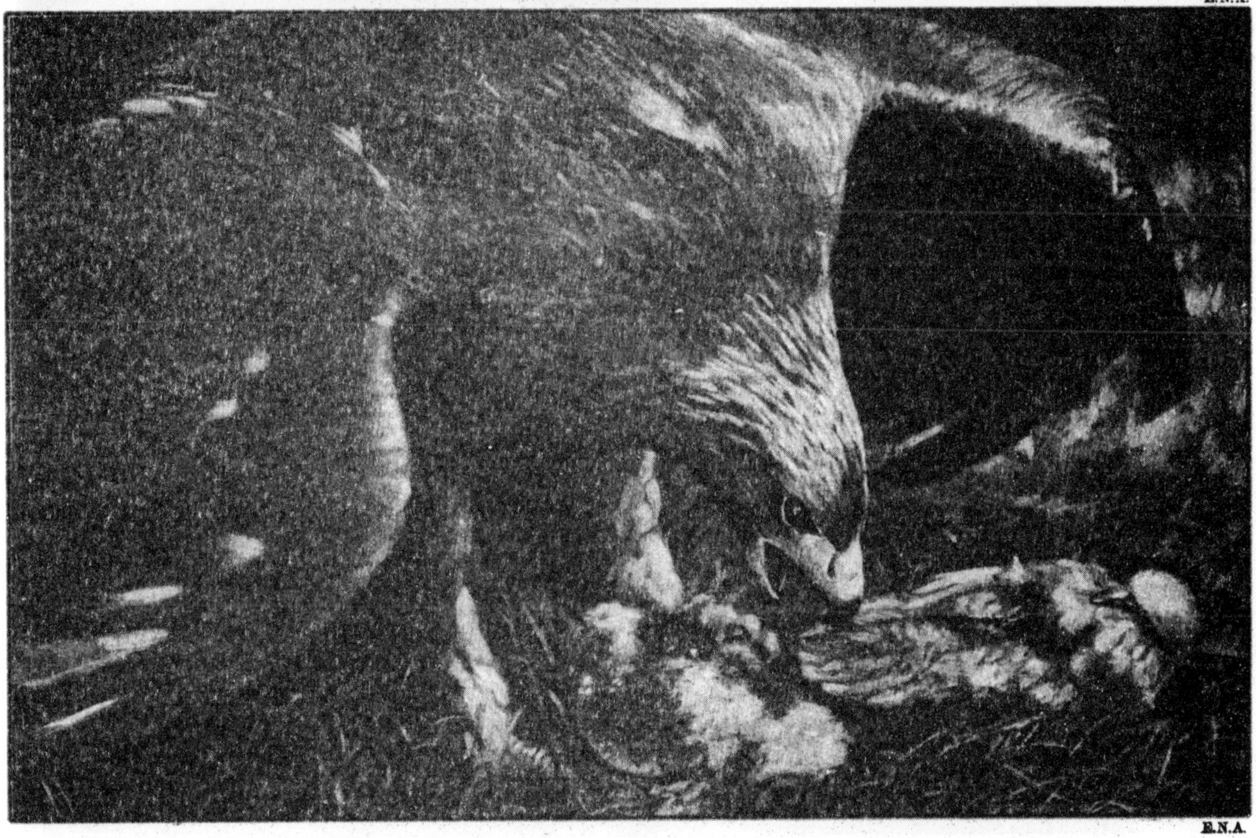

E.N.A.

EAGLE DEVOURING ITS PREY AND A FINE SPECIMEN TRAINED FOR "HAWKING"

Some people still carry on the ancient practice of hawking with all its fine art of training wild fierce birds to obey the will of the falconer. But to train hawks is one thing and to hawk with eagles quite another. Yet human ambition has achieved even this. In the upper photograph is an eagle on the heavily gloved fist of a daring falconer. The great bird is about to be flown at a quarry. The lower photograph shows the head of an eagle as it hungrily eats the prey which it has caught.

Capt. C. W. R. Knight

HOW THE GOLDEN EAGLE LOOKS WHEN IT IS IN A REALLY ANGRY MOOD

With a dead rabbit in its great curved talons the golden eagle prepares to enjoy the quarry it has caught (bottom). This is the same bird as appears in the upper photograph in page 1137, and it has one of several rabbits which it caught in a day's hawking in Kent. Notice the angry attitude of the wings and ruffled crest feathers. Above is a photograph of an eyrie with two birds in a quarrel. When really annoyed the golden eagle gives a very fine exhibition of temper.

Arthur Brook

MATERNAL CARE: SHELTERING THE YOUNG FROM THE RAIN AND FEEDING THEM

When bad weather comes—and on the west coast of Scotland the rainfall is very heavy—the eaglets must be protected from damp and cold. The mother bird, therefore, covers her little ones with a wing. In the lower photograph we see an example of this maternal care, the eagle standing with its head to the crag against which the eyrie is built, to lessen the discomfort of the driving rain. Above is a family being given its dinner which a hard-working and swift-winged parent has been procuring for it.

Seton Gordon

EAGLE CONVICTED OF LAMB STEALING: A TREE EYRIE OF THE HIGHLANDS

For the most part the golden eagle feeds on mountain hares and, failing hares, grouse. It is only where both these are scarce that the bird will carry off lambs. Many golden eagles pass their whole lives without lamb-stealing, a habit only occasionally formed, but which has got the whole family a bad and largely undeserved name. In this page is a very remarkable photograph of one of these culprits caught in the act. The lamb has been carried up to the nest and is being torn in pieces for the young. Above is an eyrie in a tree.

Arthur Brook

EAGLE AND THE GROUSE FOR WHOSE DESTRUCTION IT IS BOTH PERSECUTED AND PRESERVED

Many people have lamented the probable extinction of this the largest and noblest of British birds. But while gamekeepers on the grouse moors do undoubtedly shoot and trap and poison these great birds of prey on account of the damage they do to grouse, which are preserved for men to kill, in the deer forests the golden eagle is not molested as a rule. This is just because it helps to keep down the grouse which often betray the stalker to the deer by getting up in alarm and noisily proclaiming danger. Here is an eagle with a fresh killed grouse.

Seton Gordon

Seton Gordon

EAGLET GROWS UP AND MAKES A START IN LIFE

About eleven weeks after hatching the eaglets leave the nest for their first flight. The lower photograph shows an eaglet that has safely reached the ground after the first adventure into space. It has now to start life on its own, after weeks of care and protection. The upper photograph shows the bird a week or so earlier in its career.

two eggs are laid. They are somewhat rounded in form, and are usually covered with a profusion of rich brown spots and blotches. The earliest hatching date for the eaglets that I have known is April 29th. Usually they first see the light during the opening days of May. When they are hatched they are clad in white down, and after a time this baby coat is replaced by a second downy coat. At the age of a month the eaglets commence to show their feathers, and the young quills grow rapidly. The eaglets fly from the eyrie eleven weeks after they have left the egg.

A few years ago my wife and I spent thirty-one days in a hiding tent set up some thirty yards from a golden eagle's eyrie built in an old pine tree, and during that time, taking watch and watch about, learned many interesting things about the home life of the golden eagle. At first the birds were full of suspicions of the hide, carefully camouflaged though it was, and we spent more than one fruitless watch

Seton Gordon

GOLDEN EAGLE WHOSE COLOUR IS WHITE OR BROWN ACCORDING TO AGE

One of the first things to realize about the golden eagle is that it is not golden. The general colour is dark brown, the tail being marked with dark grey. Only on the neck is there anything approaching a gold tint in the plumage. The young when first hatched are clad in white down. This first coat is moulted for a second, and at about four weeks old the feathers begin to show.

without seeing anything of the eagles. But after a time they became more or less used to us, and a fact in our favour was that the nest was in a moderately thick wood, so that the eagles could not keep so careful a watch on us as they would have done had the nest been built upon an open rock. The female eaglet—always the larger of the two hatched—was in this instance of an unusually bullying disposition, and led her wretched brother a fearful life, tormenting him day after day. She used to chase him round the nest and aim blow upon blow at him, so that every day we feared lest she should kill him.

It was only his greater agility (he was half-starved, as his sister took his share of the food) that saved him, for he was often able to elude her onslaughts by sprinting round and round the eyrie while she followed in pursuit. But when the eaglets had reached the age of a month they lived quite amicably together.

This pair of golden eagles fed their young sometimes on squirrels, and we often wondered how they were able to capture these nimble animals. The eaglets were always disappointed when they saw father arrive with a squirrel. They hated the long dry fur of a squirrel, and they were not able to skin the animal. And so they swallowed fur and flesh together, making exceedingly comical wry faces as they did so.

THE mother of this pair of eaglets hardly ever brought prey herself to the eyrie. The cock did the hunting, and the female used to watch his arrival from some viewpoint near, and within a few seconds of his taking wing (he usually remained only a few seconds at the eyrie) she sailed down to the nest and commenced to tear up the prey he had brought and feed the eaglets on it. It was noticeable that she never fed the small male eaglet until his large and bullying sister had been satisfied.

No lamb was ever brought to this eyrie, but a golden eagle of the west of Scotland, which we photographed at home, brought several lambs to her young. And this brings me to the interesting and much-debated question: Is the golden eagle destructive to lambs? To this question I would answer. "Yes and No." Let me explain. Under ordinary conditions golden eagles do not prey on lambs. On a moor or forest where the mountain hare is plentiful, eagles prey on the hares. As a matter of fact, they prey habitually on grouse and ptarmigan and rabbits, if these are present, and in a country where any of these species—hares, rabbits, grouse, or ptarmigan—are found in any numbers, lambs are as safe as if they were in Hyde Park. But in the north-western Highlands there are stretches of wild country where not a living thing except a sheep may be seen during a day's walk. Here the golden eagle does at times prey upon lambs—for the sound reason that it has nothing else to prey upon.

I live in a golden eagle country, and I do not think that any of the golden eagles of my acquaintance—and at least half a dozen pairs nest within easy motoring reach of my home—have ever taken a lamb. Perhaps a lamb-eating eagle might be placed in the same category as a man-eating lion.

Seton Gordon

BACK AND FRONT VIEWS OF A GOLDEN EAGLE AS IT FEEDS ITS EAGLETS

To obtain such photographs as these, or to make intimate observations of this very shy and formidable bird, such as are recorded in this chapter means not hours, but days of watching and waiting, and the spirit which can cope with disappointment. A " hide " is constructed sufficiently near the nest for a good view and yet not so near as seriously to alarm the eagles. In only the wildest parts of Scotland is the golden eagle now found, although until about the 'sixties it was known in the Lowlands, and a century before that in the Lake District.

Arthur Brook

EYRIE AND ITS TENANTS ON A HIGH CRAG IN A SCOTTISH DEER FOREST

With the golden eagle the female is larger than the male and seems to require more food in infancy. At least, it has been observed that, of two eaglets in a nest, the female ate her own share and most of her brother's and only the effects of gluttony kept her from inflicting severe damage on her more hungry but more agile brother. The male bird does most of the hunting, the female receiving the prey—grouse, hare or perhaps squirrel—and tearing it to pieces for her ravenous and rapidly growing progeny.

Seton Gordon.

LONELY TREE NESTS THAT ARE BUILT AND REPAIRED FROM JANUARY TO MARCH

Eyries are usually built on inaccessible crags, and, very occasionally, on the ground. Sometimes a tree is used, as we see in the above photographs. Sticks and twigs are collected together about the end of January, quite large branches, as thick as a man's wrist, being picked up and carried to the selected site. A grand spectacle it is to see one of these fine birds battling with a winter gale and coping, at the same time, with a large branch. Pine branches and twigs are especially favoured, and the birds make long journeys, sometimes, for the sake of securing the wood they want. The closely made framework is lined with heather and tufts of grass.

Seton Gordon

MAJESTIC HUNTERS OF THE WILD SCOTTISH HIGHLANDS PHOTOGRAPHED AT HOME

Fond of soaring and circling at a great height with its wings and tail outspread to the utmost, the golden eagle has also been seen to hunt low down near the ground. It pounces upon its prey, but does not, as a rule, chase it. The young deer are occasionally carried off, and the bird is not at all above eating carrion upon occasion. Traps can accordingly be set for it, and considerable numbers of golden eagles have been killed in this way because they were considered a menace either to sheep or to grouse. The female, when full grown, is three feet long and the male about three inches less. In Scotland the bird is often more appropriately called the black eagle.

Seton Gordon

EAGLE PROTECTS ITS FLEDGLING FROM SLEET

Eaglets are born when winter weather may be still about and the mother must lend the shelter of her wing if the eaglet is to survive. This photograph gives us an excellent idea of the remote and inaccessible sort of place that an eagle usually chooses for its nesting site—a ledge in the face of a precipice on a lofty Highland mountain

It may be of interest to mention here the life observations of a sheep farmer of western Inverness-shire. He is a skilled, and exceptionally observant naturalist, and he has never once during his long life either seen a golden eagle attack a lamb or seen a lamb in a golden eagle's eyrie.

MUCH has been written of the speed of a bird's flight, and it is usually believed that the peregrine falcon is the swiftest flier. My own opinion is that the golden eagle upon occasion is faster. I will narrate an experience I once had. I was watching from a hide an eyrie of a pair of eagles. The afternoon was hot and sultry, and I put my head out at the back of the hide to get a breath of fresh air. I happened to notice what, for a moment, I thought was an insect against the blue of the sky. Then, to my astonishment, I saw that it was one of the eagles. It was the male, and he was travelling like a thunderbolt, rushing down from the high ground with a ptarmigan held in one foot. For an eagle to be mistaken for an insect he must be at least a mile off and that mile was covered in well under half a minute. It was the most spectacular flying I have seen.

There is nothing sadder to see than a golden eagle caught in a trap. Not long ago I happened to be passing a wild corrie where a pair of eagles have nested from time immemorial. The eyrie was unoccupied, and I was wondering where the birds were nesting, when I saw, placed on their favourite resting knoll, a large steel trap. The trap had been sprung, and there was nothing in it, so I imagined that the eagle had escaped. But the friend who accompanied me for some reason looked over the cliff (he told me afterwards that he had felt an impulse to do so), and saw there a magnificent male golden eagle hanging with outspread wings at the end of a steel chain, its leg held in a trap.

With little difficulty we hauled the bird up. He had been some days a prisoner, and all hope of escape had evidently gone from him, for when we pulled him up he lay exhausted at our feet. The snap of the jaws of the trap had broken the bone of his leg; all that held the leg to the foot was a few tendons. These we cut through, and, carrying the eagle to a safe place away from the rocks, laid him upon the short heather. For a few seconds the great bird remained motionless. We began to think he was incapable of flight, when suddenly he seemed to realize that he was free, and stumblingly half-flew, half-hopped across the hill. He was heading straight for the precipice, and my friend, thinking that he would be dashed to death on the rocks, made as if to follow him. But he had scarce moved when a wonderful thing happened. The eagle felt the uprushing current of air at the edge of the cliff. Wide he opened his great wings, and mounted vertically into the sky at incredible speed. After sailing awhile serenely, he came to rest on a snow field farther up the corrie.

I will end this article with a plea for the golden eagle. I would urge that leniency should be shown towards it, for it is without doubt the finest of all British birds, and should it share the fate of the sea eagle, the loss to a nation of bird lovers would be great indeed

Chapter CII

Changes of Habit Among Living Animals

By Prof. J. Arthur Thomson

Regius Professor of Natural History, Aberdeen University; Author of "The Study of Animal Life"

ONE of the characteristics of life is plasticity, but it is not always in the same way that living creatures become suited to new circumstances. Sometimes an intelligent change of habit is effected very rapidly. Thus it is only about a century since sheep were established in New Zealand, but the naturally vegetarian or frugivorous kea parrots (*Nestor notabilis*) have learned in that time how to tear away the fleece from the loins and get at the fat and flesh above the kidneys. They usually attack sickly or fallen sheep, but they sometimes kill normal animals; and in either case the new habit is a very remarkable one. The bird may have begun by pecking at the fat adhering to skins pinned out to dry. Many discoveries among animals, as in mankind, are made half fortuitously, and intelligence is shown in the way the discovery is appreciated and utilised. Big-brained birds like parrots are not slow to take a hint, and the new device would probably spread by imitation.

The herring gull and the lesser blackbacked gull are characteristically fish-eaters, but it has been known for a long time that they are not averse to eating corn in the harvest fields. This tendency to vegetarianism has become increasingly marked in Scotland during the twentieth century. Two or three hundred gulls may be seen busy among the stooks on a single field of corn, and they also gouge out the insides of turnips in a systematically disastrous way. They will also dig up potatoes near the surface. The chief reason for this inland vegetarian feeding is probably that the numbers of herring gulls and lesser blackbacks have greatly increased, partly through protection, and partly because the birds of prey that used to devour the young gulls have become scarce. The white-tailed sea-eagle is no longer to be found in Scotland; the raven has practically gone; and the peregrine falcon is rare. It is probable that the increase of trawling has restricted the readily available fish-supply for herring gulls and lesser blackbacks: and this would naturally suggest to shrewd birds the exploration and exploitation of other fields. So there has been, to man's loss, an intelligent and rapid change of habit. It may be noted in passing that the multitudes of small black-headed gulls often seen in the fields are mainly to the good, since they are predominantly insectivorous, and destroy huge numbers of injurious pests.

It is easy to put a date-limit to the kea parrot's change, namely, the introduction of sheep into New Zealand. There are also many observations to show that the herring gull and the lesser blackback have changed their diet in increasing numbers of recent years. But there are other cases of similar changes which must have taken a much longer time. The robber-crab (*Birgus latro*), common on Christmas Island and the like, is a giant relative of the hermit-crabs in shore waters. But it has become terrestrial and does not require to go to the sea except to spawn. This change of habit from water to land must have required a very long time, for it is associated with a change in the breathing organs—a change which could not be effected quickly. The robber-crab has to breathe atmospheric air, not the air mixed in the water as ordinary hermits do. But what we are concerned with at present is something different, namely, the robber-crab's novel habit of climbing the stems of the coco-palms in order to secure the nuts. With its heavy claw the crustacean makes a hole in the nut and spoons up the flesh. The broken shell may be afterwards used, in hermit-crab fashion, as a shelter for the tail.

ROBIN THAT BUILT A PAPER NEST

Robins, favoured by man as few birds have ever been, have learned to profit by picking up his unconsidered trifles. In this case a robin found a heap of paper in a farmyard and made a nest entirely of paper save for the horsehair lining.

Now, this extraordinary habit of climbing the coco-palm could not, we think, be learned in a day, and yet it must have been learned, and not so very long ago, for the coco-palm is not a native of these parts. The coco-palms of Christmas Island must have sprung from nuts wafted by currents from distant shores. Let us be clear at this point that hermit-crabs have an instinct—an inborn, hereditary, racial predisposition or prompting—to shelter their vulnerable sensitive tails in some borrowed house, usually the shell of a whelk or some other sea-snail. The robber-crab's tail is not soft as in hermits, yet *Birgus* is true to the ancestral instinct to seek some extrinsic shelter, such as the personally secured shell of a coconut, or the fortuitously discovered empty beef-tin. This is an instinctive prompting, but the climbing of the coco-palm is surely an intelligent response to a new situation. We take it as an instance of a new habit adopted intelligently but probably requiring generations of testing before it became part of the orthodox routine of life. Organic evolution is a long-drawn-out commentary on the text: Test all things and hold fast that which is good.

THE case of the robber-crab and the coco-palm seems to us to illustrate well, what is so often ignored in conventional biology, that all robust, resolute animals share in their own evolution. They are not inert items that are being sifted against an inexorable sieve; they are rather individualities which struggle and strive. They are not mere pawns, moved by a callous environment; they are living creatures that insist on sharing in the game. No doubt each receives by heredity its particular hand of cards beyond which it cannot go; but it is more or less open to each organism to play the hand for all it is worth.

Inborn in many animals are certain reactions which always occur in answer to a particular stimulus. When the earth vibrates the worm jerks itself back into its hole; and when the action is as simple as this it is called a reflex. The brain is not needed and the action is involuntary. A message from the outside world is received by superficial sensory nerve-cells (S); the thrill passes to associative nerve-cells (A) in the nerve-cord; it is shunted to motor nerve-cells (M), also in the nerve-cord, which command the effector (E) muscle-cells to contract. We may compare the sensory nerve-cells to scouts; the associative nerve-cells to general headquarters; the motor nerve-cells to the executive officers; and the muscle-cells, or "effectors" (E) to the 'men' that do the work. Taking the first letters of the words, we may indicate a simple reflex action by the letters S A M E (sensory, associative, motor, effector); and as it often happens that one reflex action sets another at work, as sucking is followed by swallowing, this might be conveniently indicated by S A M E, followed by S A M E, followed by *S A M E*.

SUCH chains of reflex actions form instinctive behaviour, considered from the physiological side; but many instincts have probably more or less of a psychological aspect as well, being suffused with awareness and backed by endeavour. A hive-bee forces its way into a difficult flower, it collects the pollen, it stows it away in its pollen-baskets, and when these are full it makes a bee-line for home. It does not need to learn to do these things the capacity for doing them is part of its hereditary make-up. An instinct is an inborn, ready-made power of doing apparently clever things.

Now the meaning of this digression is to suggest that in new surroundings or circumstances animals have very little power of changing their instincts; what they may be able to change are their intelligent habits or their individually learned associations. This difference makes the whole problem of change or no change more intelligible. When a young partridge or redshank hears its parent's danger signal it is bound to squat and remain motionless. This is instinctive behaviour. But when a mother otter is teaching her cubs how to behave when the hound's bark is heard, she is establishing an association; and when she is teaching them how to catch trout or how to eat frogs, she is appealing to their intelligence. The habits built up on the basis of association or of intelligence are more or less changeable if the conditions of life change. In short, the more instinctive an animal is, the less plastic it is; and the more intelligent an animal is, the more educable it is. When the schoolboys in Italy adjust a moving Indian file of processionary caterpillars so that the head of A is brought round to touch the tail of Z, the larvae may go on circling for hours, obeying their instinct, unable to break the spell. But everyone knows that intelligent mammals can be trained to do all sorts of unusual things, and to adjust their behaviour to altered circumstances.

THE word "modification" is applied by naturalists to individual changes of structure and function that are directly due to some change or peculiarity in surroundings, food or habits, and that persist after the inducing cause has ceased to operate. If a man goes to the tropics for some months, he may become very brown and freckled. This means that an unusual amount of a dark pigment called melanin, familiar in Negroes, is deposited in the skin. There is an advantage in this, for it may save the skin from being burnt in the glare. This kind of change is very common, and it is called an adjustment, the point being that it does not last. After a few months at home the extra pigment has been absorbed, and the man is as he was. But if he stayed thirty years in the tropics, he might become so thoroughly tanned that he would remain brown after he returned to England for the rest of his life. This would be called a modification, or an individually acquired character. It persists after the inducing cause has ceased to operate, but there is very little evidence that it can be entailed on the offspring in any representative degree. This is a separate problem which cannot be briefly discussed; let us rather give some examples of modifications.

If sheep be taken to a much colder climate, they sometimes grow a thicker and longer fleece, a useful protective modification. In the next generation the wool is still longer and thicker, and this is natural enough, since the offspring are under the influence of the cold from birth onwards, whereas the parents

W. S. Berridge

F. W. Bond

KEA PARROT OF NEW ZEALAND THAT ALTERED ITS DIET FROM FRUIT TO FLESH

While habits may take thousands of years to change, they may also alter very quickly as has been the case with the kea parrot of New Zealand. This was an entirely vegetarian bird until sheep were introduced from Europe. It has since formed the habit of perching on the backs of sickly or fallen sheep and tearing away the fleece from the loins so as to get at the fat and flesh above the kidneys. This habit possibly began by a chance finding of a fleece with some meat adhering to it and imitation, so strong in parrots, may have helped to spread the habit.

experienced it only after their arrival. It has not been shown that there is any further increase after the first generation.

Similarly, if plants are transported from a low-lying region to the high Alps, they may develop a thicker skin or more hair on their leaves, a protective modification which their offspring may show even more markedly. If the plants are taken back again to the low grounds the individual leaves may retain the characters they acquired on the mountains, but the new leaves and the leaves of the offspring may be entirely of the low ground type. The Alpine modification does not last, and the same is true of the changes that follow exposure to desert conditions or the like. Some cases are intermediate between "adjustments" and "modifications."

THE experimental evidence of plasticity or modifiability is often very striking. In the caves of Carinthia and Dalmatia there lives a wan, blind newt called proteus, mentioned in another chapter. It is about six inches long, and shows no colour except where the red blood shines through the three pairs of external gills. The eyes remain arrested in development and do not reach the surface. But if proteus is brought from the cave to the new environment of a well-lighted laboratory it begins to develop spots, and in a week or two it is dark-coloured, like a common newt. And if a larval proteus is reared under red light its eyes grow larger, reach the skin, and become seeing eyes. The reason for red light is that white light would evoke a dark skin, thus shutting out the light from the re-awakened eye.

An experiment in the opposite direction illustrates what may be called a minus modification. A goldfish was kept for three years in complete darkness, care being taken to secure abundant food and freshness. The result was complete blindness, which was indicated in the structure of the eye by the degeneration of the rods and cones, the percipient elements of the retina. This proved that the normal stimulus of the light is required in this animal to keep the structure of the eye up to the mark. The experiment would have had even greater interest if it had led to some knowledge of the state of the eyes in the blind goldfish's offspring; but there are not as yet any data on this subject.

MANY of the animals, for example, fishes, crustaceans and insects, that live permanently in caves are more or less blind. They find their way about by their other senses, especially touch and smell. There are many different gradations in the state of the eye in different cave-inhabiting types, but some species are entirely blind. To some naturalists it seems justifiable to say that the blindness illustrates the hereditary accumulation of the results of disuse and darkness, but it is necessary to proceed cautiously. As we have already explained, part of the blindness of proteus is the outcome of an influence operating on each successive crop of individuals, for under the red light in the laboratory the usually arrested eyes may become seeing eyes. Therefore the sense of sight is not actually lost to the proteus race. Perhaps the same is true of other blind cave-animals. They are certainly walkers in darkness, but it is possible that they may recover their sight. No one knows, for no one has tried with sufficient care or for long enough, what may follow restoration to the light.

But there is another way of looking at the facts. Eyes are very variable structures; that is to say, they may be better or worse from birth onwards, apart from the direct influence of illumination or of darkness. A variation is an inborn peculiarity whose origin is still obscure; it is the outcome of some germinal change and is quite different from a bodily modification. It may be due to some disturbance or rearrangement, some strengthening or weakening, of the hereditary items or 'factors' that make up the inheritance carried by the egg-cell and the sperm-cell. Albinism, or the absence of pigment, as in a white blackbird, may be mentioned as an example of minus variation; the appearance of long Angora hair in various types of mammal, such as rabbits, is a plus variation. In regard to many new variations we know that they are readily entailed by heredity on the offspring; and this is more than we can confidently say in regard to modifications.

NOW let us return to the cave. It may be that the frequent blindness of cave animals illustrates the hereditary accumulation of the results of disuse and darkness; but there is little experimental evidence in support of this possibility. It requires fewer assumptions to suppose that variants, changing in the direction of poor sight a smany variants do, found their way into the grateful shade of the cave, and continued to vary in the same direction. The passage towards complete blindness would be assisted by Nature's way of sifting out all useless organs.

Darwin was much interested in the beetles of Madeira, because they illustrated so well his theory of Nature's sifting or natural selection. As is well known, his theory was that new departures or variations, which are always cropping up, are sifted in the struggle for existence. Any variation that gives its possessors some appreciable advantage will tend to secure their survival, while a variation that handicaps its possessors will tend to their elimination. Thus, the fitter, which simply means the better suited to particular conditions of life, will automatically tend to survive. The struggle for existence, which does the sifting, includes all the answers-back that living creatures make to environing difficulties and limitations; it means much more than internecine competition among fellows; it may be a struggle against a changeful environment, or against foes of an entirely different type; it may be other-regarding, as well as self-regarding.

As to the beetles in Madeira, the peculiarity is that so many different kinds are wingless. Out of the 580 species of beetles that were known in Madeira when Wollaston made his study, over 200 are so far

CRAB THAT HAS ADOPTED LAND HABITS AND CLIMBS TREES FOR FOOD

The robber crab of Christmas Island has entirely forsaken the sea, where its ancestors lived, save for spawning. Furthermore it has formed the habit of climbing coconut palms for the sake of the nuts, whose kernels it eats and whose shells it uses as armour for its tail. This change happened at no very remote period, for coconut palms are not indigenous to the island.

deficient in wings that they cannot fly. Moreover, of the twenty-nine genera peculiar to the island no fewer than twenty-three have all their species flightless. What is the meaning of this? It has no doubt something to do with the fact that Madeira is wind-swept, so that there is great risk of flying beetles being blown out to sea. But it is necessary to be more precise. The beetles did not intelligently shed their wings so as not to be blown away, for they are hatched out from the pupa-state without wings or with no more than vestiges of wings. It is an old-established constitutional peculiarity, we may be sure of that; and it is seen in many beetles which live in haunts where they are *not* exposed to any dangerous wind.

FATAL INABILITY TO CHANGE A HABIT

In the case of the processionary caterpillars seen above instinct is too strong for adaptation to suddenly altered circumstances. The instinct to follow the next caterpillar ahead is so powerful that if the individual at the head is joined to the one at the tail of the procession, the whole company will walk round in a circle for hours.

Another possibility is that the native beetles of Madeira learned to lie low, and in the course of generations lost their wings by disuse. But, as we have said, there is little evidence that the results of disuse can be hereditarily entailed. On the whole, the probability is that Nature's sifting favoured germinal variations in the direction of wing-reduction. To be quite fair, let us quote Darwin's careful sentences from "The Origin of Species" (1858). "Several conditions make me believe that the wingless condition of so many Madeira beetles is mainly due to the action of natural selection, combined probably with disuse. For during many successive generations each individual beetle which flew least, either from its wings having been ever so little less perfectly developed or from indolent habit, will have had the best chance of surviving from not being blown out to sea; and, on the other hand, those beetles which most readily took to flight would oftenest have been blown to sea, and thus destroyed."

MAN has taken many plants and animals to new countries where they have done well, and this is best called naturalisation.

Acclimatisation, in the strict sense, means that the introduced plants and animals have become in the course of generations adaptively changed to withstand climatic influences which were at first unfavourable. This is generally believed in, but there is surprisingly little evidence of its actual occurrence. The whole question is very carefully considered in G. M. Thomson's "Naturalisation of Animals and Plants in New Zealand" (1922), and the conclusion is that there is actually very little to indicate acclimatisation in the strict sense, that is, fresh adaptation to new conditions of climate and surroundings.

When plants or animals get a footing in a new and different country, what happens? First there is often great increase in the number of individuals in a given area, witness rabbits in Australia and skylarks in New Zealand. This may be due to very favourable conditions and to the absence of the enemies and other natural checks which kept the numbers down in the old country. Secondly there may be a marked increase in individual size and vigour, as seen in the gigantic dimensions attained by the European water-cress in New Zealand streams. But, contrary to widespread opinion, there is very little evidence of increase in variability or of change in habit. The big fact is that animals successfully naturalised in a new and different country remain very much the same as they were at home. There are probably subtle constitutional changes, such as the increase in the number of red blood corpuscles in men who settle at high altitudes, like Johannesburg, but there is not much visible change either in structure or in habit. Rats may take to tree-climbing in one country and to sewers in another, but these are trivial changes. And the same may be said of changes of diet in insects that invade a new area where the old food-plants are absent. Necessity is the spur of nutritive experiments. When a bird nests in a very strange place, such as a scarecrow, we should remember that it is not so strange to the bird as it seems to us.

The barnacle goose (*Bernicla sandwensis*) of the Hawaiian Islands has become entirely a land goose during the breeding season. Moreover, it shows an obstinate rigidity in always going back to the same breeding-place, an attachment which enemies, including hunters, recognize to their own advantage. Moreover, the parents are moulting when they lead the goslings about, so that they cannot fly away; and they have left the vicinity of the sea in which they used to find refuge. There are many instances of this sort of imperfection in habit-change. And the apparent imperfections become striking, though fallaciously so, when man enters into the plot. Thus the now much reduced elephant seal, once very abundant on Californian coasts, persisted in being

F. W. Bond

W. S. Berridge

WHITE-TAILED SEA EAGLE WHOSE DISAPPEARANCE AFFECTED THE FEEDING CUSTOM OF GULLS

At one time the sea or white-tailed eagle was common in the Isle of Man, on the Cumberland coast, in Ireland, and South Scotland, but during the latter part of the nineteenth century it became gradually killed off. The effect in so far as Great Britain is concerned of doing away with this strong bird, which is only a little smaller than the golden eagle, has been a multiplication of the creatures on which it fed, such as gulls. The gulls, fish-eaters pure and simple, being not only more numerous but having their convenient fishing grounds disturbed by intensive steam trawling, have taken to going inland to feed and have changed their diet of fish for seeds and grubs.

Arthur Brook, Builth

RAVENS, A DIMINISHING RACE THAT PREYS ON YOUNG GULLS

Just as the sea-eagle went, so is the raven going while the ten times more harmful rook has been encouraged to multiply tenfold. The raven, a dweller among cliffs, has a great liking for young gulls in the season and in former times helped to keep the gull population within reasonable limits. But owing to the comparative ease with which the bird can be trapped it has now become numbered among those British species that are diminishing. This is one more reason for a surplus of gulls which must seek food inland.

unafraid of man. But how can one expect giant animals to have a tradition of timidity? How can one expect animals that have held a position of security for tens of thousands of years to react adaptively to man's mischievousness in the course of a century? For thousands of years they have known no fear—is it any imperfection that they remain unafraid of a few men intruding from a ship's boat? We do not absolve them, so to speak, from being somnolent in security, but we cannot, with justice, think of them as stupid.

There is no doubt that animals can adjust themselves, and sometimes adapt themselves, to new conditions of life. There may be changes in structure and changes in habit. But since some animals are profitably plastic and others are fatally stereotyped, we wish to emphasise our suggestion that those "habits" that are based on reflexes and instincts are very hard to change; while those that are based on intelligence and on individually-learned associations remain effectively plastic. The instinctive line of evolution leads to extraordinarily effective results, as in ants, bees, and wasps; but the intelligent line of evolution is the open path of educability.

Oliver G. Pike

SEA GULLS WHICH VISIT THE FARMER'S FIELDS AND DESTROY CROPS

Herring gulls have become noticeably vegetarian in Scotland since 1900 owing to the diminution of their natural enemies. They, together with the lesser black-backed gull, shown in these photographs, are often seen in the harvest fields among root crops. The lesser black-backed gulls seen in the fields do a lot of good by eating harmful grubs but the herring gulls will dig up potatoes and eat the hearts out of turnips in a manner highly exasperating to the farmer who thus finds new pests added to the old list which was already too long.

F. W. Bond

E.N.A.

CRABS THAT HAVE FORSAKEN THE SEA FOR A LIFE ASHORE

It must have taken the robber crabs and other land crabs many centuries to change from a sea habit to a land habit. We have two examples of the change here. In the lower photograph is a land crab on Enderby Island, off the coast of West Australia, perched upon a plant. The upper illustration shows us a robber or coconut crab which has climbed a tree, fetched down a coconut, broken the shell and is scooping out the inside. And yet the ancestors of this creature, allied to the hermit crabs of the sea, were exclusively of the salt-water.

F. Martin Duncan

J. J. Ward

HOUSE-FLY, CARRIER OF FILTH, AND THE COMPLEX TONGUE WITH WHICH IT FEEDS

House-flies, though not entirely unfriendly to man's interests, do so much more harm than good that they may be regarded as foes. The good they do lies in their consumption of decaying animal matter when they are in the larval stage. But these scavengers, when they reach the winged stage, still feed on filth and fly direct from it to perch on a baby's mouth or the food laid ready for a family meal. Apart from their revolting association with dirt, the house-flies are really dangerous as carriers of disease. Filth adhering to their legs is trailed across our plates and our lumps of sugar. The right-hand photograph (much magnified) shows the complex tongue of the house-fly through which it takes all its food. On the left is the fly itself magnified.

Chapter CIII

Flies That Are Foes and Flies That Are Friends

By John J. Ward

Author of "Insect Biographies"

THE true flies have but one pair of wings, and belong to the order Diptera. Their hind wings are represented by a pair of tiny, stalked organs of drum-stick shape, known as halteres, or balancers. These rudimentary organs are conspicuous in the crane-fly, or daddy-long-legs, but are more or less concealed in some of the common flies; as in the case of the house-fly and the blow-fly, where they are covered with membraneous lobes, appendages of the upper pair of wings.

Apparently, these curious remnants of the lower pair of wings are an essential feature of the two-winged flies, for when they are removed the insect is no longer able to balance itself in the air. The name "balancers" is, therefore, well applied; so, indeed, is "halteres," it being the scientific name for the balancers, or weights, used by the Greek athletes while leaping. Since these balancers are so small that they can scarcely play any part in actual flight, it is probable that they function as sense organs; and there is some evidence to prove that they are used for auditory purposes.

Two other features worth noting regarding dipterous or two-winged flies are that they are not provided with biting mouth parts, and none is armed with a tail sting. Some people will maintain that they have been bitten by a house-fly, or stung by a gnat, both of which are impossible things, because the house-fly has only a sucking proboscis which cannot bite anything, while the gnat is entirely stingless. The female gnat, or mosquito (for the terms are synonymous), can, however, suck blood, for in addition to its sucking proboscis, like other blood-sucking diptera which we will consider later, it is provided with a beak consisting of six piercing lancets and probing instruments. These mouth parts, though, are entirely different from the lateral pair of biting mandibles which characterise beetles, wasps, bees, and other true biting insects, all of which bite sideways, not from above and below as mammals do. Many of the two-winged flies will be found to have a sharp-pointed tail of sting-like appearance, but that is an ovipositor, an organ used exclusively for egg depositing.

IN point of numbers the dipterous flies hold precedence over all other kinds of insects, and when we are out in the garden, or in the fields, or woods, and are unmercifully attacked by a swarm of flies of numerous species, nearly all of which will be of the two-winged order, it is obvious that the intentions of the various species may be entirely different, for while some are out for blood, others may merely intend to absorb some of the perspiring moisture from our face or neck, and still others are probably joining in the chase for mere amusement and the joy of life.

It is plain, therefore, that it is difficult to know who is who in the fly world. A gadfly that looks like a large house-fly may alight on your hand that is holding a fishing-rod, and, while you watch it, drive into your flesh its piercing lancets with so slight a prick that you scarcely know you have been wounded, yet you may have a badly poisoned hand in consequence, owing to the lancets introducing poison germs into the wound from the carrion on which the fly has been previously feeding. The drone-fly, of similar size, may also select your hand holding the rod just for a temporary resting-place; but, as it looks so bee-like, you quickly sweep it off, yet it is perfectly harmless, for it has only a tongue adapted for gathering pollen and nectar from the flowers.

Who, then, are friends, and who are foes in the motley crowd? They turn up each summer season from somewhere, but to discover that somewhere means much persistent, and often unremunerative, work by some hard-working entomologist. It was two young medical men who, in 1898, proved that in malaria-infested districts residents were quite safe from the disease so long as they protected themselves from the attacks of mosquitoes.

VAST tracts of the earth's surface are rendered uninhabitable for civilized man by malaria and yellow fever, and, in 1897–98 Major Ross (now Sir Ronald Ross) made the discovery that it was not the common grey gnat, or mosquito (*Culex*), that conveyed the parasite of malaria, but the spot-winged gnat (*Anopheles*). He found that the malaria parasite, when in the blood of a human being, developed to a certain stage, and then needed the body of the mosquito to complete its life cycle. The mosquito that sucked the blood of the infected person could then convey the germ in its saliva to a healthy individual. The disease was, therefore, proved as not contagious, or infectious.

After this definite proof by Ross regarding malaria, eminent medical men of the United States of America proved that the terrible yellow fever was, likewise, not conveyed by infected persons, but solely by the brindled gnat (*Aedes calopus*, or, as it was then named, *Stegomyia fasciata*). As a consequence, in 1900–1901, during the American occupation of Cuba, Major Gorgas, in one year, changed the city of Havana from a hotbed of disease with an annual death-rate of 750 to a healthy town with the death-rate figure as low as six. In 1904 he set to work in

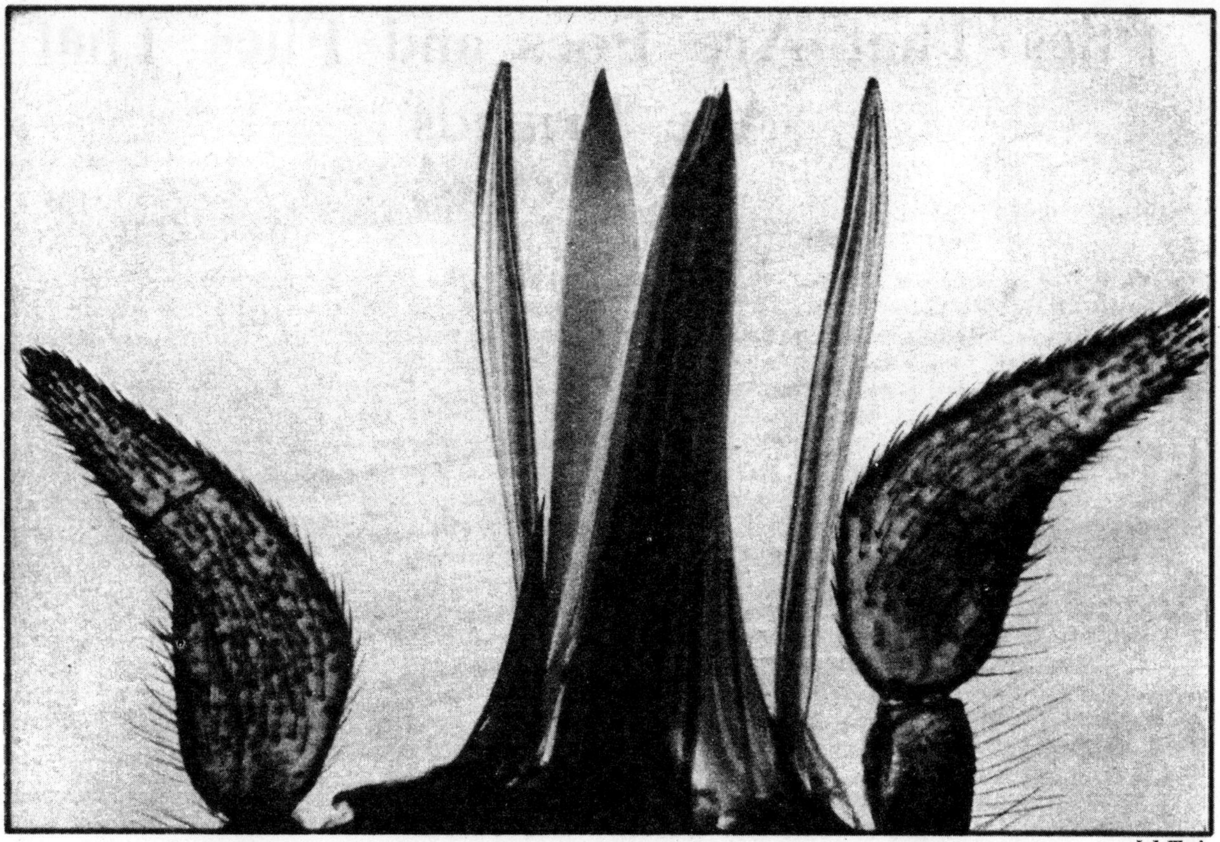

J. J. Ward

MOUTH PARTS OF THE GADFLY THAT ATTACKS BOTH CATTLE AND MEN

When a gadfly bites a distinct stab is felt in the flesh, and this photograph shows the apparatus which the fly—only the female "bites"—uses to produce the stab and the subsequent and very irritating swelling round the puncture. On the outside are the hairy antennae not unlike the claws of a crab to look at. Then come the probing instruments and lancets for making the puncture. This fly, which looks like a house-fly save that it is grey and an inch long, buzzes loudly. But its smaller relative, the cleg, arrives upon one's hand in silence.

the malaria and yellow fever infested area of the Isthmus of Panama. The French had failed in their efforts to cut the canal, with an estimated cost of 25,000 lives, and enormous financial losses, owing to these diseases. Then Colonel Gorgas took the situation in hand. He made it a crime for anyone to leave unscreened anything in the nature of puddles, shallow pools, or utensils containing standing water where aquatic gnat larvae could thrive. With drainage of land, and oil floating on the surface of water that could not be drained, and screening hospitals of fever patients with gauze, the battle was fought—and won. The diseases were effectually stamped out, and the army of some 40,000 labourers had, at the end of 1913, safely cut a connecting way of fifty miles length between the Atlantic and Pacific Oceans, saving a voyage of 8,000 miles round Cape Horn. To-day, the area of the Panama is free from yellow fever and malaria, and its people are robust and healthy.

These same malaria mosquitoes (*Anopheles*) in England may meet and attack us any summer evening, but, since they have not the connecting link of the malaria patient, they can do no more than inflict a painful puncture like that of our common grey gnat (*Culex*). There are twenty or more kinds of British gnats, some of which never appear to attack human beings and seem harmless enough; although we have to remember that all their life stories have not yet been fully investigated.

There are other blood-sucking insects known as midges (*Ceratopogon*), barely visible to the eye, which can cause us much pain and inflamed swellings that may trouble us for days afterwards. On the other hand, there are numerous midges whose only crime is that they may get into our eyes while we are motoring; but whether that is the fault of the midge-fly, or otherwise, is a very debatable point.

When we consider the larger flies of the gnat-like type, we turn to the crane-flies, or daddy-long-legs (*Tipulidae*). The long legs of these insects always seem to be more troublesome than useful to them when we see them come indoors and fly round the lights up against the ceiling, or when climbing a window pane. To appreciate their utility we have to see the fly at work in its natural home amongst the grasses in the fields—or more particularly on the lawn.

The female insect may be readily distinguished by her sharp-pointed tail, that of the male being blunt with a pair of lappets. When laying her eggs, she digs her sharp ovipositor into the ground while

J. J. Ward

F. Martin Duncan

TWO FLIES THAT ARE FRIENDS OF MAN: FLESH-FLY AND DRONE-FLY

In these photographs we have two flies that are friends. Below is a specimen of *Sacophagia carnaria*, the common flesh-fly, which in its larval stage preys upon locusts. Above are two photographs of the drone-fly (left) showing it seeking its food on a flower and (right) among plants on the ground. This belongs to the large and interesting family called *Syrphidae* none of whose members is harmful, while many are distinctly helpful in devouring plant lice. In all these photographs, of course, the insects are shown magnified.

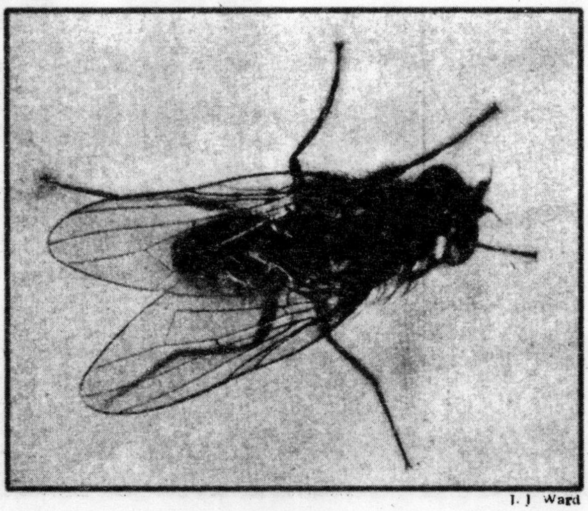

I. J. Ward

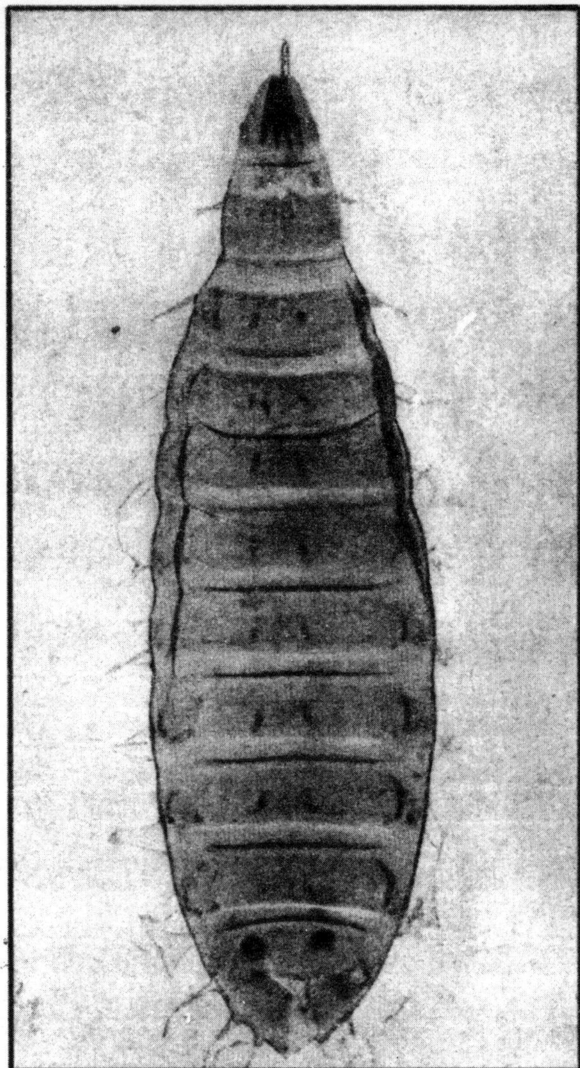

H. S. Cheavin

LESSER HOUSE-FLY AND LARVA

In the early summer small flies appear in houses and these insects are often thought to be "young" house-flies. But, of course, flies do not grow, and these little flies belong actually to another and smaller species. (Photographs enlarged.)

holding herself in an upright position. Then, twisting round amongst the grass blades by means of her long legs, she drills the hole and places several eggs about one quarter of an inch below the surface. She then travels a short distance with the combined action of her "stilts" and wings, and selects another spot for a further batch of eggs.

Since she has to deposit between 200 and 300 eggs, it is obvious that these long legs are just the right working tools for this occupation. There is always the danger, too, that a toad or a lizard may discover the crane-fly while she is egg-depositing. With so much leg action going on, the chances are that the food-catching tongue of those creatures will most likely get a stray leg, which the crane-fly can afford to lose with but little inconvenience, and, while the enemy is discovering that it has secured the "shadow," the substance is able to make its escape.

The eggs eventually hatch out the grubs which, later on, we recognize as "leather jackets," which gnaw away at the roots of the grasses with their horny jaws, often doing enormous damage to grass-land. We therefore have to regard the familiar daddy-long-legs and all his tribe (for there are various species) as being amongst our foes, even though we cannot bring any charge of blood-sucking against him.

When we turn to the flies of the more ordinary type we find ourselves up against a host of species that vary considerably both in colour and size. The largest is the gadfly (*Tabanus bovinus*), of grey colour, and nearly an inch in length, looking like a very large house-fly. This insect possesses formidable mouth-parts which consist of strong blades and probing instruments for blood-sucking purposes, all of which are ensheathed in the gutter of a fleshy, sucking proboscis. Both man and beast are attacked by means of these instruments, and they readily pierce Scotch tweed or flannel clothing.

THERE is a smaller and commoner gadfly, known as the cleg-fly (*Hoematopota pluvialis*), which is much slower in flight, and it approaches you in the woods without the fierce buzzing sound of its larger relative. It is therefore able to get in its puncture quite unsuspectedly. As in the case of the mosquitoes, it is the female insect that is the blood-sucker, the males not being provided with lancets.

Bot-flies (*Oestridae*) are always dangerous foes of our domestic animals, each species having its particular host. They are not blood-suckers, indeed, their mouth parts are often so much reduced that they cannot feed at all. Their business is to place their eggs, and sometimes their living larvae, into their host animals; the sheep bot-fly into the nostrils of that animal; the horse-bot fly on the hairs, so that the horse can lick them off and pass them to its stomach; and the ox-bot, or warble-fly, beneath the hide. They are some of the worst foes of the stock-owners; while the damage to hides from the "warble" (which is a hole made by the fly larva for breathing purposes) is estimated for Britain at from three to six million pounds annually.

House-fly with eggs just laid

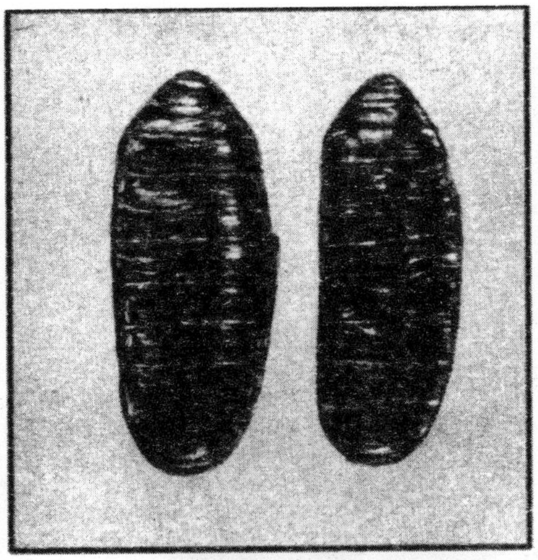

Pupa of house-fly, magnified

House-fly larva, enlarged

House-fly, much magnified

Antennae of feelers of house-fly

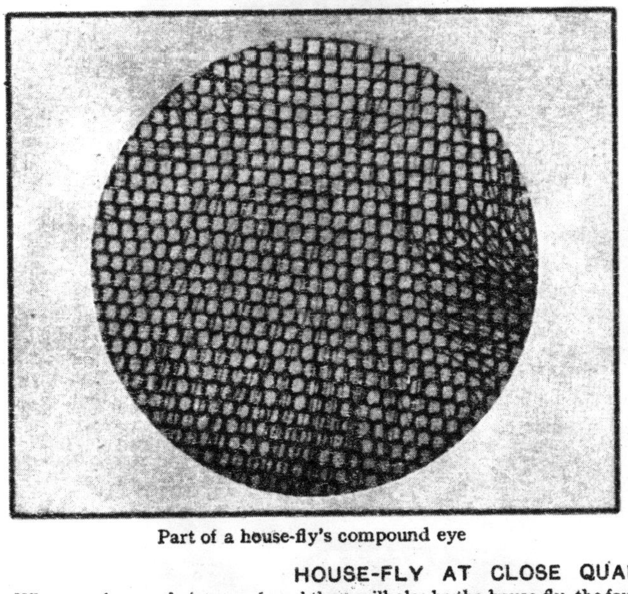

Part of a house-fly's compound eye

Magnified foot of house-fly

HOUSE-FLY AT CLOSE QUARTERS AND ITS LIFE STORY

Wherever human beings are found there will also be the house-fly, the foulest of living things. Attracted by means of its keen sensitiveness to odour, it goes straight to any filth or decaying matter there is about and from thence it may fly straight to human food. Milk is especially attractive, and being a medium in which bacteria breed very fast, is the means of quickly spreading infection. Notice the bottom right-hand photograph of the foot of a house-fly. There are special claws for rough, and pads for smooth, surfaces. These enlarged photographs are by J. J. Ward and H. Bastin.

A. H. Willford

F. Martin Duncan

BLOW FLIES BANQUETING OFF A STINKHORN FUNGUS: ANOTHER MEMBER OF THE "BLUE-BOTTLE" FAMILY

One of the most annoying of the flies that pester humans in their homes is the blow-fly, or "blue-bottle." This possesses a remarkably keen sense of detecting the presence of dead meat—it may be the corpse of a mouse or rat, or the family joint. The female blow-fly seeks out the meat in which to lay her eggs, which she can do at the rate of seven a minute. If baulked from alighting on a joint by a wire-gauze cover she will drop her eggs through the mesh of the wire so that they fall on the meat. Blow-flies are also very fond of the fungus called stinkhorn, and in the left-hand photograph we see a number of them gorging themselves with the rotting stuff. On the right is another member of the family—*Calliphora vomitcria* (enlarged).

The blow-fly, or blue-bottle (*Calliphora erythrocephala*), is the largest fly that is usually found in our houses. Its loud buzzing generally announces its arrival, and its keen sense of smell directs it to seek our dinner joint. Should the meat be unprotected, the blow-fly loses no time in getting to work. I can personally testify that it will deposit seven eggs in one minute. The eggs are of a pale cream colour and, under a magnifying lens, remind one of skinned bananas, excepting that they have a glossy surface.

J. J. Ward

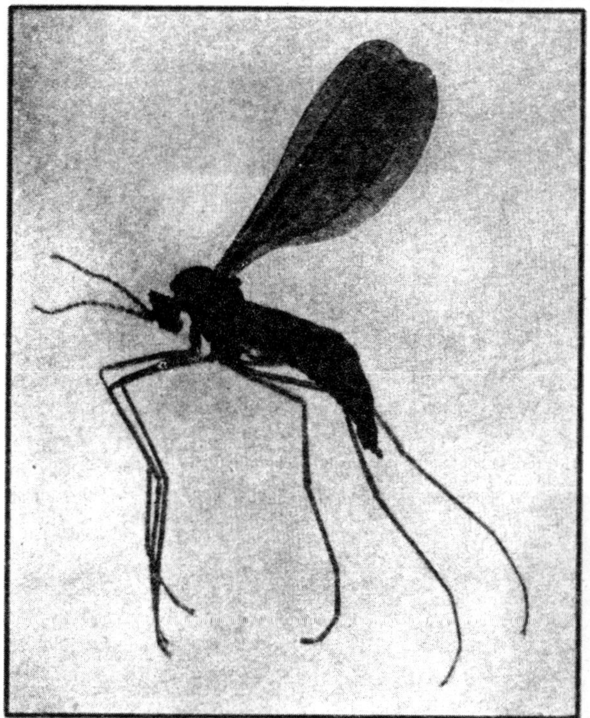

J. J. Ward

HESSIAN AND ICHNEUMON FLIES

The Hessian-fly (bottom) attacks the barley and the wheat while the long-tailed ichneumon-fly (top) has a specially long ovipositor which it inserts into the borings and lays its eggs on the bodies of the grubs inside. The photographs are enlarged.

The eggs hatch in about twelve hours during summer weather, and the maggots (the " gentles " of the fisherman) at once proceed to devour their food supply. In just over a week they are full-fed, and change to the pupal stage, which lasts about fifteen days. A new generation appears in from three to four weeks.

Belonging to the same family (*Muscidae*) are the green-bottle flies (*Lucilia*) with much the same habits, but some species of which deposit their eggs on the wool of sheep that are badly kept, causing much trouble to the stock-keeper. There is also the flesh-fly (*Sacrophaga carnaria*) which does not produce eggs but live maggots. These flies are more often found in the open, but will enter houses that lack cleanliness and contain animal food.

The ordinary house-fly (*Musca domestica*) in England is but rarely seen before the end of June; although a slightly smaller species (*Fannia canicularis*), with a jerky flight, may be quite abundant indoors during May and June. These smaller flies are often mistaken for young flies, but flies, like all other winged insects, do not grow; their growth is finished when they attain the winged state. Later in the summer the common house-fly is represented at about ninety per cent to each hundred found in the house. Both these flies have similar habits, the eggs being deposited very largely in stable refuse; probably ninety per cent of them are reared in stable manure heaps. In towns of late years flies have become more and more reduced in numbers, owing to stable yards being replaced by garages. Whenever flies are found in abundance in a town area, it is almost certain that there is a stable in the near vicinity; although a few are reared during warm weather in rubbish heaps of vegetable and other garbage where fermentation is going on.

Should the meat food in the larder be covered with a wire gauze cover, and be near the network, the blow-fly will drop its eggs on, and between, the wires. It is obvious, therefore, that the best use of wire netting is at the larder window, rather than on the meat itself, as then the blow-fly cannot enter.

In the open the blow-fly is not only able to find dead animals on which to deposit its eggs, but, by some marvellous instinct, it is able to anticipate the death of its quarry; for trapped animals such as hedgehogs, rabbits, stoats, birds, and what not, while still alive, are sometimes covered with blow-fly eggs.

Under favourable conditions the maggot of the house-fly will mature in about six days, and the pupal stage lasts another four or five days. So that from egg to fly stage is only some ten or eleven days. In hot weather new generations appear at about fortnightly intervals: and as each female fly can deposit more than one hundred eggs at one laying, and during

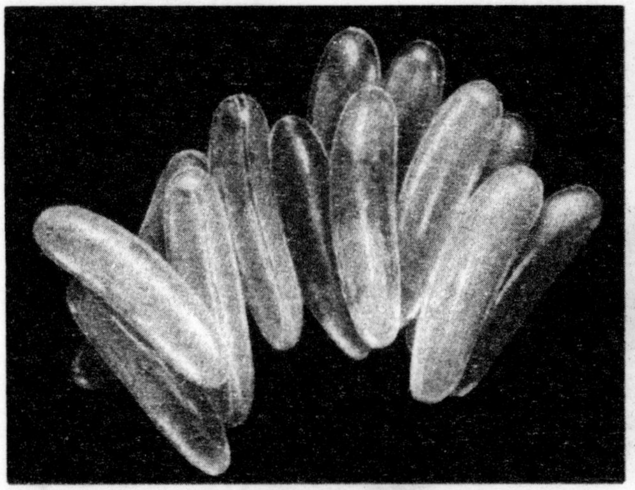

Eggs of blow-fly, magnified

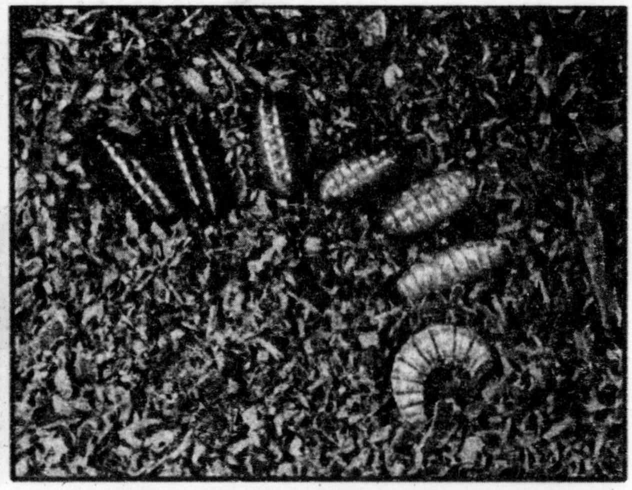

Changes of blow-fly pupa (left) to maggot (right)

Blow-fly maggot or " gentle "

Blow-fly just emerged, magnified

Blow-fly ready for flight

Head of blow-fly much magnified

Base of blow-fly's wing

Foot of blow-fly

MICRO-PHOTOGRAPHY SHOWS THE BLOW-FLY IN FULL DETAIL

The blow-fly or blue-bottle has wonderful compound eyes in its head (bottom left) and a long, sucking proboscis. The bottom centre photograph shows the base of a blow-fly's wing. The ribs in the wing are hollow tubes and the wing membrane is spread over both sides and covered with minute hairs. In the middle row of illustrations the centre photograph shows a specimen which has just emerged from its pupa skin. Notice the inflated skin of the " face." The fly blows this up in order to break through the pupa skin. Photographs by J. J. Ward

F. Martin Duncan

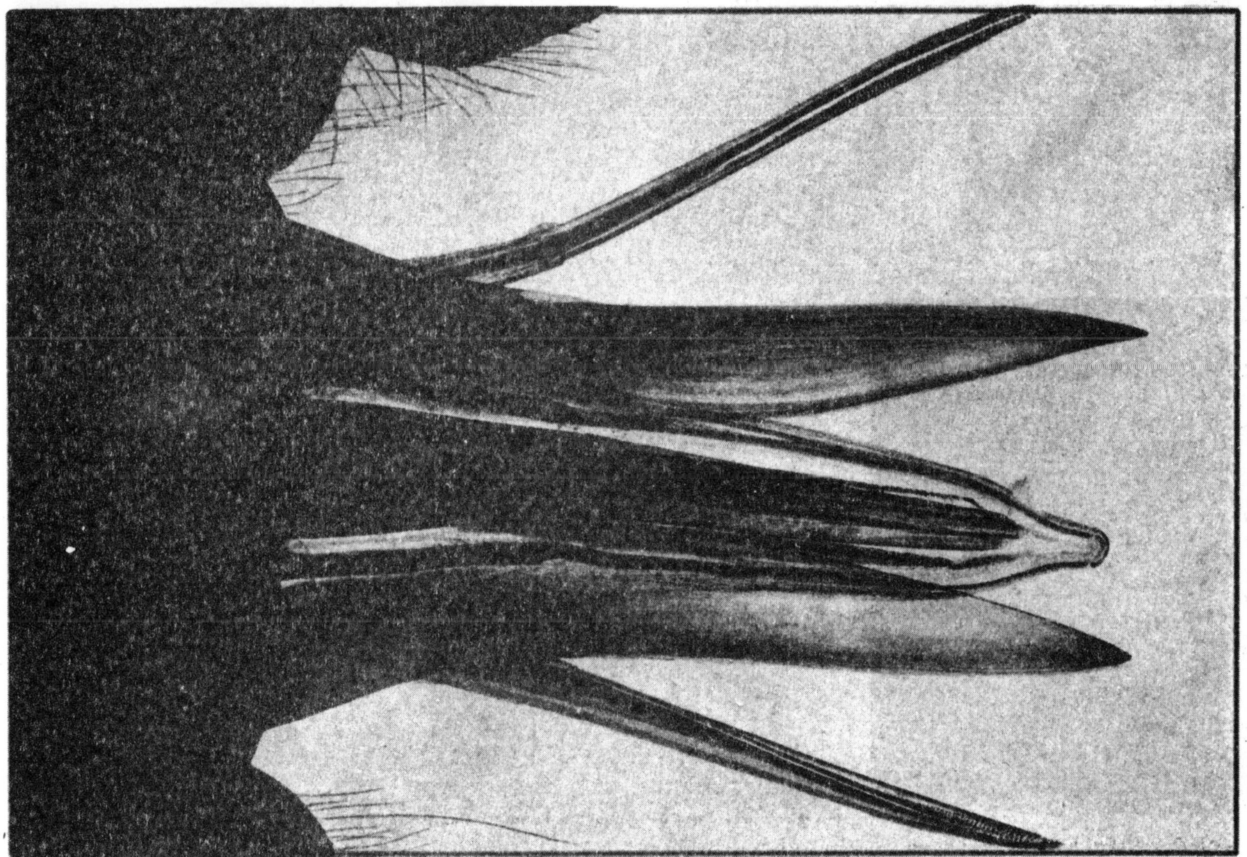

E. A. Botting

GADFLY AND THE SHARP LANCET WITH WHICH IT DRAWS BLOOD

Since it is made for piercing the thick hides of cattle the lancet of a gadfly (bottom) can very easily pierce a sock or a stocking and cloth as well. A photograph on page 1160 shows the entire mouth parts of the gadfly, but here we have a more highly magnified photograph to show the detail of this remarkable organ which is the cause of so much discomfort to man and beast. In Britain, luckily, the bite does not usually leave an infected wound. The upper photograph shows the whole insect and is considerably enlarged.

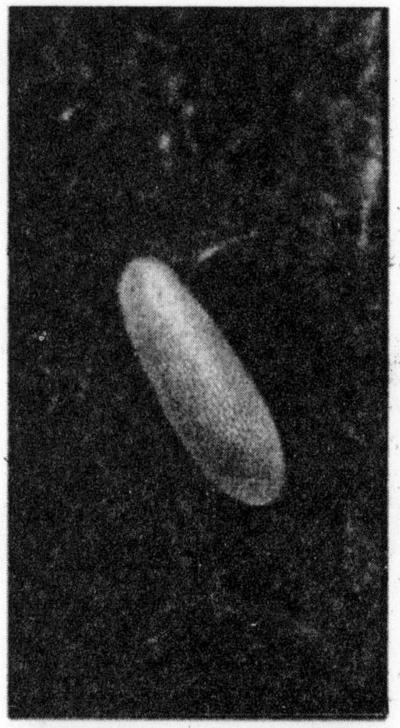

Egg of hover-fly, magnified

Larva capturing aphid

Lifting aphid from flower

Extending body for feeding

Larva of hover-fly on chrysanthemum leaf

Young hover-fly feeding on aphid larger than itself

Hover-fly grub with captured aphid

Hover-fly just emerged from pupa

Hover-fly feeding on poppy pollen

HOVER-FLY WHOSE LARVAE ARE WONDERFUL EATERS OF GREEN-FLY

In a country garden on a bright day a number of small flies may be observed which hang in the air, with rapidly vibrating wings, make a dart out of one's way and hover again. These are the hover-flies, and some of them are banded in black and yellow like small wasps. They feed on pollen and flower nectar, but their larvae, flat-bodied blind grubs, do immense good by wandering about on plants and spearing green-fly with their nose-probes. We see one (bottom left) in the act here. Photographs by J. J. Ward.

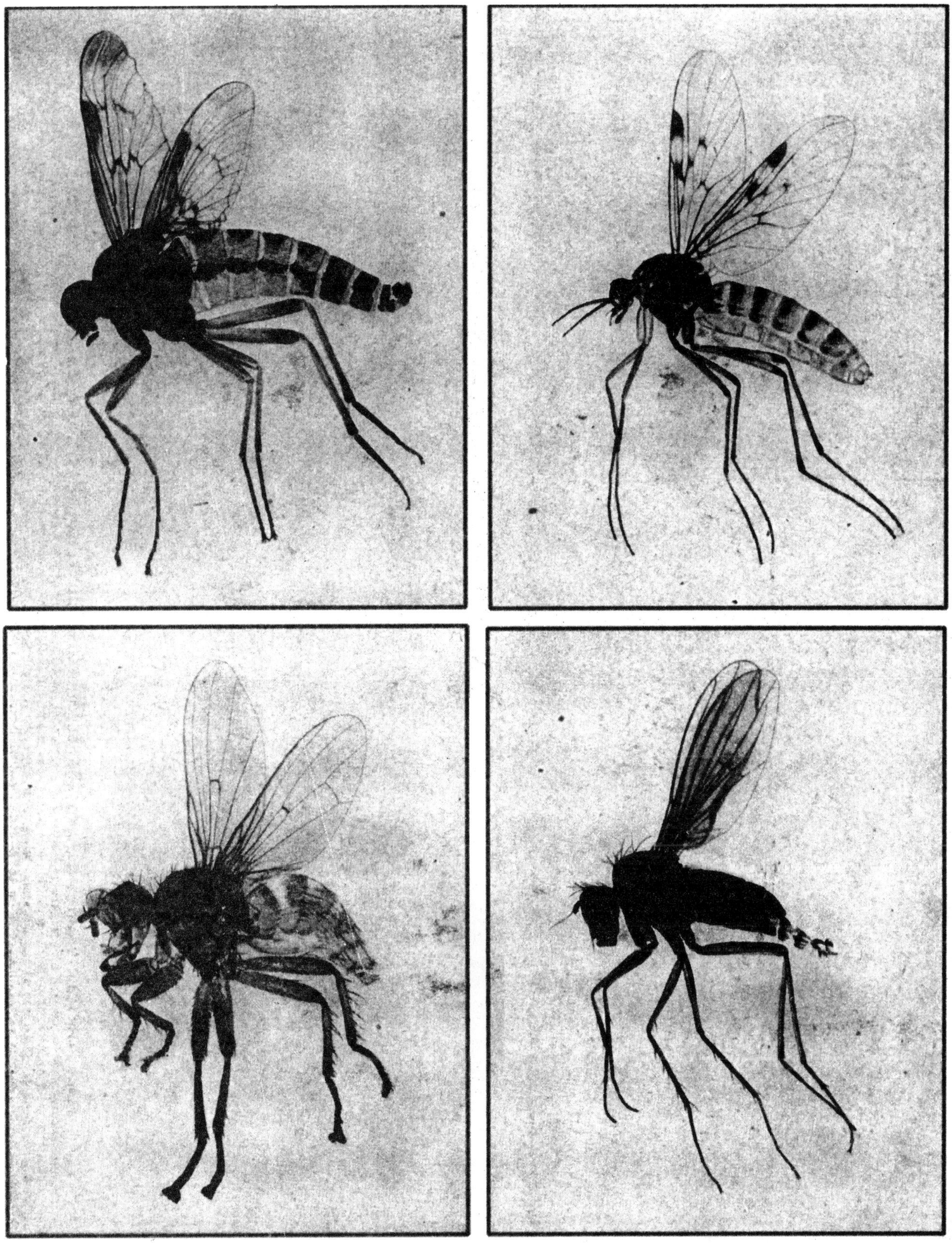

MARSH, BOG, DOWNHILL, AND WINDOW FLIES THAT ARE FRIENDS

The marsh fly (bottom left), whose scientific name is *Scatophaga stercoraria*, is one of the dung flies, and lays its eggs in the droppings of horses and cattle. Here are also the bog fly, *Campsiconemus curvipes* (bottom right), the downhill fly, *Leptis scolopacia* (top left), which is found beside streams and ditches in early summer and preys on harmful insects, while its larvae attack grubs; and the window fly, *Rhyphus fenestralis* (top right). This last is found on windows in houses and outhouses, the larvae being manure scavengers. Photos by H. S. Cheavin.

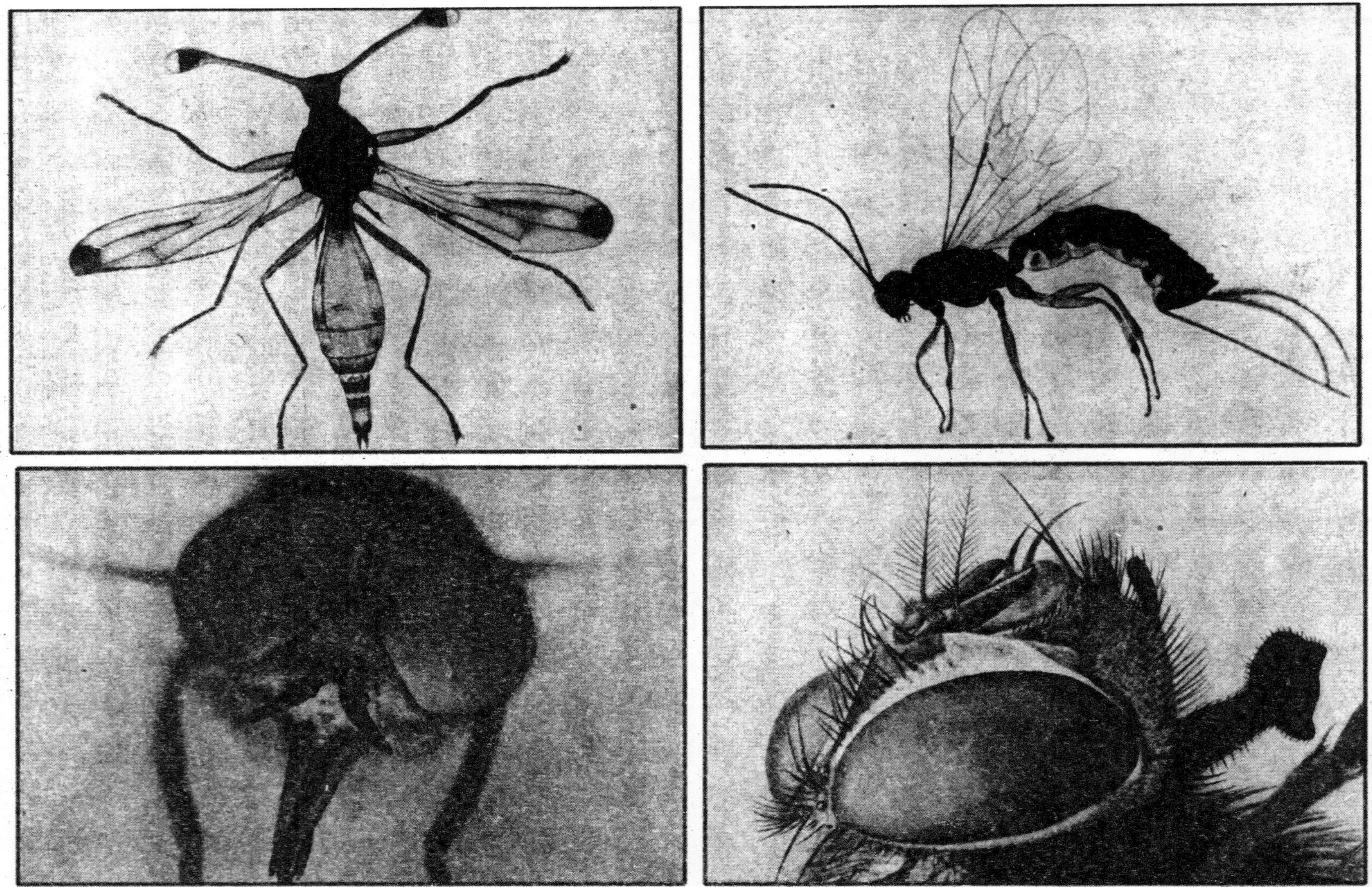

H. Bastin & H. S. Chavin

FLIES THAT PREY ON MAN AND HIS BELONGINGS AND FLIES THAT PREY ON OTHER FLIES

Painful and sometimes even poisonous are the bites of the blood-sucking great gadfly (bottom left). This is a large grey insect about an inch long whose lancets can pierce cloth quite easily, since they are constructed for getting through the rough hides of oxen. The right-hand bottom photograph gives us a side view of a blowfly's head. The stalk-eyed fly (top left) which comes from Natal, has its head produced into two lateral stalks which bear the eyes. On the first pair of legs there are toothed edges used for crushing the insect's prey. The ichneumon fly (top right) comes to the aid of man by laying its eggs on the bodies of various destructive grubs so that, when the larvae hatch they eatup the grub. Photographs much magnified.

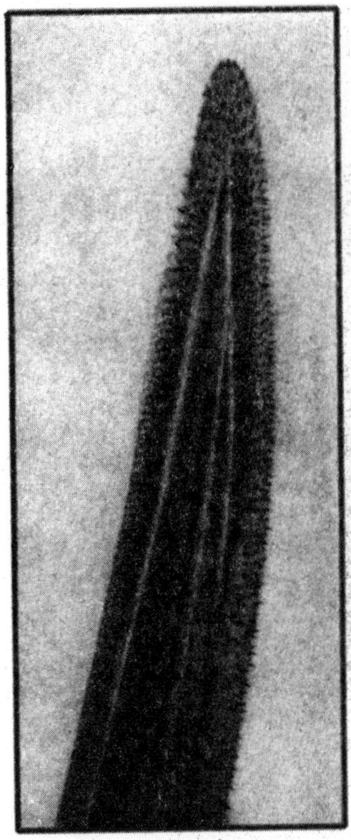

its life can repeat that effort some five or six times, it is obvious why flies become so abundant as the summer advances.

In a limited way and in certain circumstances we may regard both house-flies and blow-flies as friends, for in their larval stage they are powerful scavengers whose work is purely that of removing dead animal and other decaying matter, which, if left, would become a potent factor in disseminating disease germs. There is, however, the difficulty that they possess a taste for food that is similar to our own, and that they visit our dining-tables immediately after leaving the unsavoury material which they utilise in their economy. We have, therefore, to regard these flies as enemies to prevent contamination of our food.

As previously stated, the house-fly's mouth-parts cannot inflict any injury to our skin, but there is its relation the stable-fly (*Stomoxys calcitrans*), of outdoor habits, and very like a house-fly in appearance, but which is provided with piercing mouth-parts, and it occasionally comes indoors. It is this fly that sometimes causes people to think that they have been bitten by a house-fly. The stable-fly is nearly related to the tsetse-flies (*Glossinia*) of tropical Africa, which are carriers of the parasite of the sleeping sickness disease.

J. J. Ward

"CLOSE-UPS" OF THE HOVER-FLY AND THE GADFLY

The lower photograph shows the delicate antennae of a hover-fly, which resembles a little wasp. The upper photographs show (left) the deadly probe of a gadfly and (right) the head and huge dark eye of the same insect. These photographs are much enlarged

If we enter the garden, we are at once confronted by flies of innumerable species. We may disturb a buzzing mass of what look like house-flies from the top of a gooseberry bush; but, if we investigate more closely, we find that these flies are more hairy on their bodies. They are tachnid-flies (*Tachininae*) and, if we search the branches of the gooseberry bush, we shall probably find them infested with the caterpillars of the destructive magpie moth, and these tachnids are engaged in placing their eggs on the bodies of these larvae. The maggots that come from their eggs burrow into the tissues of the caterpillars, which are usually able to pupate in their cocoon of threads; but, instead of developing into the pupa of the moth, the cocoon more often produces from two to three pupae of these parasitic flies. Here, then, we have a fly which, to all appearances is an ordinary house-fly, but this time it is a real insect friend of man. Amongst the flowers all sorts of flies are busily occupied, and these, for the greater part, are again our friends, for they assist in the pollination of the blooms. Always conspicuous amongst them are the bee-like drone-flies sipping the sweets of all kinds of flowers. If we have a quick eye we may see a still more bee-like insect hovering over the primroses and probing their depths with its long, stiff proboscis while still on the wing. It is one of the bee-flies (*Bombyliidae*), which have hairy bodies and resemble humble bees. They possess marvellous powers of flight, and, at the slightest movement, they seem to vanish into space from the flower on which they may be feeding.

On every side, too, we shall find the abundant hover-flies (*Syrphidae*), many of them poised in the air almost motionless on rapidly vibrating wings. Some of them are striped black and yellow, looking like small-sized wasps. They feast on the pollen and nectar of the flowers, and their eggs are placed on the foliage of their food plants. The grubs that emerge from the eggs prowl about the plant and capture aphides; they are flat-bodied, and both blind and footless, but can loop their way about the leaves. As they move about, they are continually thrusting their pointed foreparts here and there with considerable rapidity; and sooner or later they spear a green-fly with their nose probe. When the capture is made, the grub lifts the aphid clear of the leaf and elevates it in the air, while it sucks its juices like drinking from a bottle. It then casts aside the empty skin of its victim and goes in search of another. When hungry, it can drain green-flies dry at the rate of one per minute, and it feeds both day and night.

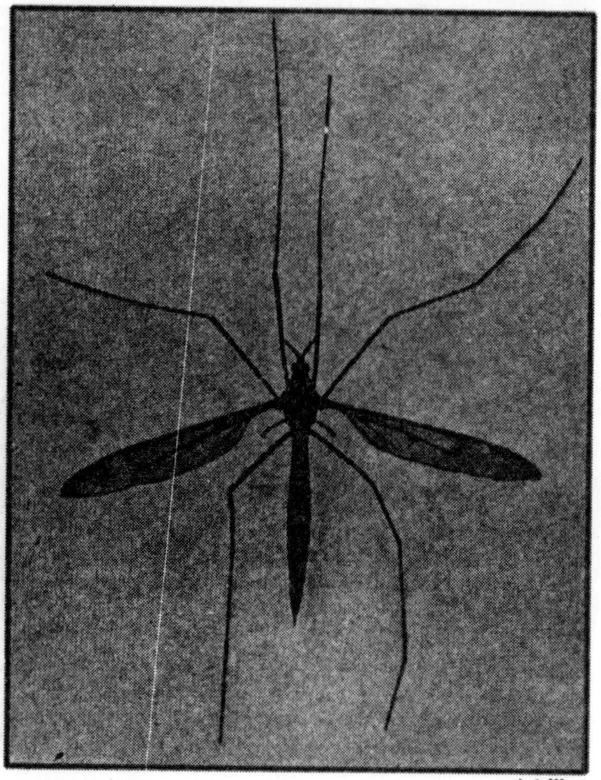

J. J. Ward

CRANE-FLY THAT BREEDS A DESTRUCTIVE GRUB

A way of getting rid of the "daddy-long-legs" grub was accidentally discovered at Bournemouth. A hose was left running on a rubber mat on a bowling green. The grubs to avoid saturation sheltered under the mat when they could be easily destroyed.

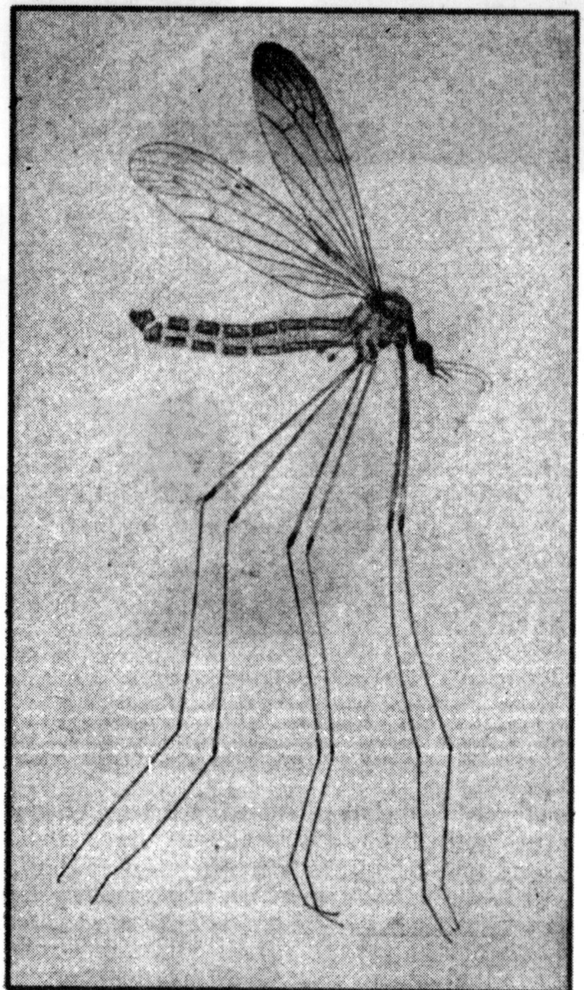

H. S. Cheavin

A MALE "DADDY-LONG-LEGS"

Leather-jackets—the white, fat grubs which eventually grow into the clumsy insects we know as "daddy-long-legs," do immense harm to turf and crops by eating away the roots. Here we see a view of the adult male from the side, magnified.

FROM what has been written here, it will be obvious that there are good flies and bad flies, but to make sure of their identity presents a very difficult problem. As it is, the flies that are the friends of humanity are often confused with the flies that are foes, and worse still, the harm done by the latter is not generally recognised to the extent that it should be. Identifying the true nature of these insects is, of course, only possible after careful study. More than forty thousand species of the two-winged flies have been recognized, and it is estimated that the unrecognized groups will eventually make the total fully three hundred and fifty thousand species. Perhaps I need offer no further apology for the omission of some species from this chapter.

Chapter CIV

The Universal Fight for Food

By J. R. Ainsworth-Davis

Formerly Professor of Zoology, University of Wales

THE aims of animal life may be summarised in the phrase "Meals and Mates," in other words the preservation of the individual and the conservation of the species. We are here concerned with the former only. Food is essential for repair of waste, growth, and the production of the energy enabling movement and all other vital actions. Hunger warns when food is necessary, while the senses of taste and smell make feeding pleasurable; otherwise no animal would bother about eating.

The world is one vast larder, providing an immense variety of bills-of-fare appealing to the most varied tastes, but not to be enjoyed without serious competition. Everywhere we can observe a strenuous "fight for food," much of it tragical in nature, for many animals prey upon their fellows in the most relentless fashion. The shape, structure and habits of any particular animal have been evolved with reference to securing food of some sort, and there are three kinds of diet—meaty, vegetable and "mixed," with the first of which this chapter deals.

Ground feeders include many flesh-eating or carnivorous animals that depend on living prey, none more so than some members of the cat family, which are very perfect engines of destruction. Lions and tigers, for example, in every detail of their structure, are adapted to a predaceous life. The specialised teeth include powerful canines for seizing and holding victims, blade-like flesh-teeth for cutting, and small front teeth used as scrapers in conjunction with the rough rasping tongue. Auxiliary weapons of offence are found in the strong claws, and these are kept sharp by being drawn back into sheaths when not in use. In spite of their enormous strength lions and tigers adopt a stealthy method of approach, relying on the sense of sight, and when sufficiently near a victim secure it by a sudden spring. The khaki colour of a lion and the striped markings of a tiger harmonise with their surroundings so perfectly as to make the owners extremely inconspicuous to those animals that are being stalked. Though these lordly cats take pride of place among flesh-eating forms that seek their meals upon the ground, they are more than equalled in ferocity by some of the carnivorous mammals inferior to them in size. The foussa of Madagascar, the snake-destroying mongooses (the "rikkitikkis" of Kipling), and the British weasels and stoats, were they as large as lions, would be far more awe-inspiring, and test to the utmost the courage of big game hunters. Wolves and their kind have discovered the value of co-operation, hunting as they do in packs, and following their prey by scent rather than sight.

Some ground mammals are specially adapted for feeding on insects, a striking example being the great ant-eater of South America, which raids ant-hills with its curved, powerful claws, and secures their denizens by means of a long sticky tongue protruded from the long toothless snout.

Many of the carnivorous birds are also ground feeders, one of the most notable cases being that of the secretary bird of East Africa, which destroys large numbers of venomous serpents. Lizards and snakes, among reptiles, glide and slither through dense vegetation in search of prey. Some of the large ground lizards are formidable creatures, especially the Komodo dragons, described in an earlier chapter of this work, of which examples can now be seen in the London Zoo.

E.N.A.

FOOD FOR THE HAWK

Rabbits are regarded by humans as creatures to be killed—for sport or because they are a nuisance to farming. But to other creatures, the hawk for instance, they are a necessary part of the available "menu."

For such a life the limbless snakes are well adapted, and with them the practice of "bolting" food is carried to an extreme, as when a loudly protesting frog is slowly swallowed as a meal by a common grass-snake.

The frog himself, and his cousin the toad, slimy-skinned amphibia which begin life as aquatic tadpoles, also affect a meat diet. They possess a long sticky tongue, attached to the front of the floor of the mouth, and this can be shot out with lightning speed to secure unwary insects.

Upon the ground we also find many rapacious insects, such as the tiger beetles, while the driver ants of tropical Africa travel across country in dense columns, devouring small

DIFFERENT PHASES OF THE FOOD FIGHT: LEOPARD, PIG, OTTER AND RABBIT

Getting food is either a case of struggling with other members of the same kind or with the cunning of the prey selected. Our left-hand bottom photograph shows a leopard which has succeeded in capturing a bird. By this act, perhaps, the lives of a thousand caterpillars or flies are saved and the doom of so many plants sealed. Quite another kind of fight is also exemplified here (bottom right). The young draw their life from their mother, but she makes no attempt at "fairness." If the stronger brother shoves aside the weaker, she takes no notice. Above are (top left) an otter with a fish and (top right) a rabbit browsing grass. The latter in coming out to feed often becomes food for human beings. Photographs by E.N.A.

mammals, caterpillars, and so forth. Highly carnivorous, too, are hunting spiders, scorpions and centipedes.

Many peaceful vegetarian forms, of varied kind, have endeavoured to escape from the pitiless struggle for existence to which they were exposed on the surface of the ground by taking to the trees as a refuge, where, too, the homes of many birds are constructed as a relatively safe shelter for helpless nestlings. Predaceous animals, following their example, have invented climbing devices of many kinds for taking advantage of this overhead dinner table Leopards and smaller creatures of the cat kind have adopted such a mode of life, and they often possess spotted coats harmonising admirably with the dappled pattern caused by sunlight shining through foliage. The leopard, too, and this also applies to some of the large climbing snakes such as anacondas, finds his mode of life doubly advantageous, for not only are arboreal animals available as food, but also ground forms which come near enough to his lurking place aloft to be secured by a spring just at the psychological moment.

GIRAFFE AND ITS PROTRUSIVE UPPER LIP

There seems no end to the ingenious ways of assisting the art of food-getting among animals. The giraffe has not only an amazingly long neck for reaching the upper foliage of trees that no other animal can get at, but also a protrusive upper lip which adds a few inches "reach" to this already grotesquely tall animal. Here we see the lip in operation.

Insect life abounds in trees, and is eagerly sought by climbing lizards, including the sluggish, colour-changing chameleon with its sticky tongue, and such birds as tits and woodpeckers. Many of the insects are themselves predaceous. The great bird-eating spider of South America also lies in wait for prey above the surface of the ground. The webs and snares woven by many of his smaller relatives are found at various heights, and their construction is often elaborate. In this respect the common garden spider is a mistress of craft, and her web is extremely beautiful. (The male is an idle waster.) Vegetation in hot countries may also be infested by blood-sucking leeches and ticks.

Mother Earth has been sought as a refuge by many vegetarians, but here again they have been followed by relentless foes. Rabbits and field voles are pursued underground by weasels, while earthworms and grubs have no peace. Many birds in particular probe for them from above, and here we see the practical value of the long bill of a woodcock or kiwi. That "little gentleman in velvet," the mole, is no mere prober, but a thoroughgoing underground hunter of untiring and ferocious nature. Shaped like a rounded wedge, he ploughs his way through the ground by means of powerful digging extremities, and the short glossy fur offers the minimum of friction, for it has no "set," the hairs growing out at right angles to the surface. A mole devours more than its own weight of animal food every day, and furnishes a kind of "larder" for the benefit of its young, this consisting of earthworms whose heads have been bitten off.

The conquest of the air was first achieved by insects, who began as parachutists and ended as aeronauts. After vainly endeavouring to shake off their enemies by learning to climb, they took to flight as a final resort. Some of them, however, became carnivorous, and adopted the reprehensible

Neville Kingston

Neville Kingston

TAME AND SEMI-TAME ANIMALS AND HOW THEY GET THEIR FOOD

Feeding is a serious business and hence it is remarkable that even dogs can be trained to take food without " snatching " at it. The task of feeding animals in captivity is one which needs all the keepers' wits. An alligator (bottom left), even when young, can snap uncomfortably so as to include both the food and the hand that holds it. The other illustrations show (bottom right) a party of penguins ; (top left) a bear of British Columbia which has found a " can " ; and (top right) a young hippo.

E.N.A.

E.N.A

PYTHON AND YOUNG LION SUCCEED IN GETTING SUPPER

From the banks of the Zambesi comes the lower photograph and, indeed, in such a place one might expect to see almost anything. Here is a huge python which has had the luck to come across a number of antelopes which have been drowned and washed ashore. The giant snake has already devoured one and is about to turn its attention to the other six—or as many of them as suit. Above is a young lion "snapped" while chewing the carcase of an aard-vark (see also p. 1078).

James

Photopress

INSTINCT TO FIGHT FOR FOOD SURVIVES EVEN YEARS OF CAPTIVITY

The instinct, deep down in the animal mind, to take no chances is shown in the lower photograph of a lion at the London Zoo taking its afternoon ration from the keeper. When the meat comes and a bar is removed from a special part of the cage to admit the meal, the animal cannot wait until the food is poked inside. It must stretch out an eager claw and seize what has to do for its " prey." Above are a brace of pelicans striving to eat the same morsel. Note the attitude they have to adopt in order to pick up the piece of food.

Mondiale

E.N.A

STRIVING FOR SUSTENANCE AGAINST DIFFICULTY: WILD BOAR AND ELEPHANT

When winter comes, those animals that do not get over the difficulty of the food-shortage by going to sleep till the spring have a hard time of it. Our lower photograph shows a number of wild boars in one of the forests of Hanover, looking in the snow for such food as they can manage to get. The elephant is a gargantuan feeder for it has the largest frame of any land animal to sustain, and it all has to be done on grass. The illustration (top) shows a fine bull elephant of Rajputana which has snatched a trunkful despite the urgings of its mahout.

practice of preying upon their kindred. The dragon flies are a striking example, and can be seen hawking for prey over ponds and streams. They fly with extraordinary swiftness, and their legs are bent forwards for the entanglement of victims, which are speedily dealt with, inedible parts, such as the wings of a butterfly, being shorn off by their powerful jaws.

BATS, among mammals, have acquired the power of flight, and most of them are insectivorous. The solitary predaceous insects known as sand wasps are remarkable for the way in which they provide "larders" for the use of their young, which they are never destined to see. After laying their eggs in holes in the ground or specially constructed nests, they store these with caterpillars, adult insects, or spiders, previously stinging them in the nerve cord so as to paralyse but not kill them. The kind of victim selected for this storage varies with the particular species of sand wasp.

The little ichneumon-flies provide for their young in different fashion. By means of a piercing structure on the abdomen they lay their eggs in caterpillars, chrysalids, or even the eggs of other insects, so that the larvae hatch out in actually living larders.

The innumerable hosts of blood-sucking insects make themselves peculiarly objectionable in the fight for animal food. Mosquitoes spread malarial diseases in tropical and sub-tropical regions by infecting their victims with microscopical parasites belonging to the animal kingdom, while the dreaded tsetse flies of Africa set up the fatal "fly disease" (nagana) in cattle and horses, and the no less dangerous "sleeping sickness" in human beings, in somewhat similar fashion.

Birds, evolved from a branch of the reptilian stock, followed insects into the air, and many of them have become adapted to the pursuit of these pioneer aeronauts. Swallows, martins, and goat-suckers, to mention no others, take heavy toll of insect life. If all the insectivorous birds were suddenly to become extinct the world would soon be over-run by insects, and the existence of man himself would be seriously threatened.

The birds of prey, provided with powerful hooked beaks and strong talons, eagles, hawks and falcons, and owls of many sorts and sizes, devour vast numbers of other birds, small ground mammals, and sundry reptiles. Storks and the like turn their attention to frogs and other amphibians. Shrikes, or "butcher

SPOON-FEEDING THE CRAB, A DAUNTLESS SCAVENGER OF THE SEASHORE

Feeding a crab with a spoon seems rather a domestic sort of business. But there is no fiercer fighter for its food than the crab. One may get a very convincing example of this in setting a night line for fish. When the tide is out and fresh bait is put upon the hooks it is quite likely that one may be interrupted by a scurrying over the rocks and there will then appear a dozen or more crabs with claws raised, and they will go at once, without hesitation, to the hooks and tear the bait from them, unafraid.

Lynwood M. Chace

AMERICAN RED-TAILED HAWK DEVOURING A DUCK

At first sight it seems that—as between bird and bird—the odds are all on the hawk. But, upon closer study, it is found that the hawk has to work very hard for most of its meals. Weak or sickly birds fall a comparatively easy prey, but to secure a healthy specimen takes all the strength and cunning of which the bird of prey is capable. A wild duck does not waste time on the wing. But here is a crafty hawk which has contrived to catch one for supper. The photograph was taken in America.

birds," of which one species is common in Britain, are notable among larder-makers. They impale mice, small birds, lizards, frogs, and chafers on thorns near their usual feeding places, thus creating a miniature shambles. Hence their common English name and also their scientific one of Lanius, which is simply the Latin for butcher.

The struggle for existence is rather less strenuous in rivers, lakes and ponds than elsewhere, so that many refugees from land and sea have taken to fresh water, while numerous insects spend there the earlier stages of their lives. But complete tranquillity and repose form no part of the scheme of life, and the fresh waters of the land are happy hunting-grounds for a great variety of extremely predatory creatures.

Arthur Brook

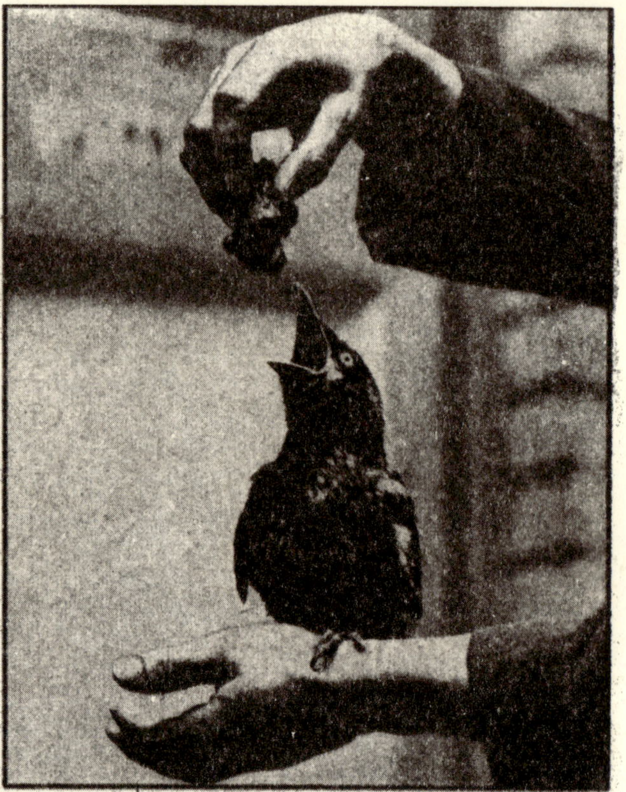

Neville Kingston

Capt. C. W. R. Wright

GOSHAWK AND THE RARE CARRION CROW, HUNGRY FOR THEIR MEAL

Gamekeepers, who habitually shoot the goshawk on sight as a destroyer of game and therefore an implacable enemy, might well observe the bottom photograph in which a goshawk is seen with a stoat that it has just struck down and killed. Above we see (left) a carrion crow feeding on a drowned sheep which it has found washed to the bank of a river; and (right) a carrion crow being fed in captivity. This was the first of its species ever to be seen in a zoological collection and was obtained because a nest was blown down in a gale.

Arthur Brook

BUZZARD AND KESTREL FEEDING THEIR YOUNG IN THE NEST

Both these photographs were obtained in Scotland where there is still much really wild territory where Nature is little interfered with. The lower photograph shows a buzzard and her young in the nest while above is a kestrel or windhover, as it is also sometimes called. The first is regaling its offspring with a couple of moles which it has caught while the kestrel has secured a rat. The young have to strive as best they can amongst each other for "first come first served" is the rule in Nature, and especially in a nest full of young birds.

Oliver G. Pike

C. W. Teager

C. W. Teager

BRITISH BIRDS FIGHT FOR FOOD IN WINTER AND ROUGH WEATHER

When the snow covers the ground the birds of our gardens and countryside have a hard time, and the survival of the fittest—both as regards health and efficiency at food-finding—is the rule. At such times, when worms and grubs are buried many inches out of reach, the bird has learned that the homes of man may be productive of life-saving victuals. Above we have (bottom) a company of hungry chaffinches and sparrows in a garden; (top left) a thrush that has found a likely garden; and (top right) a song-thrush with a discarded apple.

The otter, for example, that notable destroyer of fish, is really a large weasel specialised for an aquatic existence; and much the same is true of the fur-bearing minks, native to Europe, Siberia, and North America, though these also prey on small mammals and birds. Many birds also seek living prey in fresh water, and of this the fish-eating herons and king-fishers are well-known examples. Ducks and swans are more modest in their requirements, and their broad bills are used as strainers by which worms and other small creatures are separated from the mud in which they dwell.

Reptiles are well represented among the hunters in fresh water, and of these the most formidable are crocodiles and alligators, which not only devour aquatic animals, but also forage along the banks in pursuit of mammals and birds. The gavial of the Ganges possesses a long, narrow snout forming an effective fish-trap. The large, snapping turtles, native to the fresh waters of North and Central America, are savage animals which seize fishes and water fowl with their strong hooked beaks. Some of the large rapacious lizards known as monitors are also quite at home in the water, and of these the largest, *Varanus salvator*, which attains a length of seven feet, is native to South Asia and the adjacent islands, also ranging into Australia. Many snakes are also good swimmers, and the common grass snake may often be seen pursuing frogs in ponds.

Some of the fresh-water fishes are tireless hunters of their feebler brethren; none more so than the pike, detested by the fly-fisher, but himself providing

Central News

Allier

GIANT TORTOISE, HUNGER, A STUPENDOUS EFFORT—AND THEN DISASTER

Even the giant tortoises are not remarkable for their activity nor are they suited to violent efforts. A little tragi-comedy was enacted at the London Zoo by one of these clumsy creatures. Emboldened by the desire for food it heaved itself up as we see in the upper photograph, so that its head was above the railing of its paddock. But the effort upset the tortoise in more senses than one (bottom), and when on its back there was no hope for it until a keeper came and turned it over. Otherwise the tortoise would be on its back still.

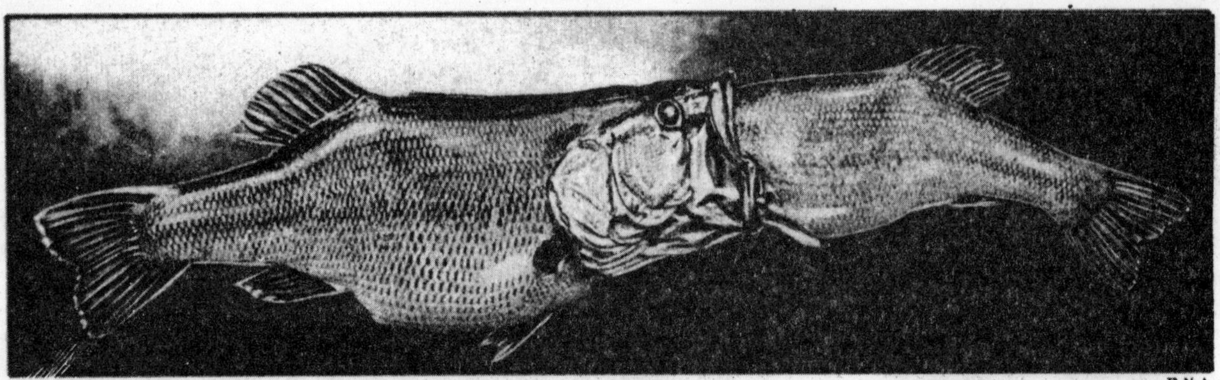

E.N.A.

AN ILL-JUDGED ATTACK IN THE FIGHT FOR FOOD

At its worst, the driving of hunger is the most unreasoning force in the world. Fish, not very high up in the scale of animals that possess any intelligence, are notoriously rash when hungry. Our photograph shows a couple of black bass that fell, one an innocent and one a guilty victim to unreasoning greed. The larger ran at the smaller and got the head well into its jaws and then found that it could neither swallow nor let go. The two were picked up, still struggling, in a Texas lake. Pike will also try to swallow fish too large for their throats.

exciting sport. He may attain a weight of sixty pounds, is a notorious cannibal, and varies his diet with water voles, frogs, and water fowl. Size, however, is no criterion of rapacity, and some of the smallest species are extremely voracious. A particularly interesting case is that of the West Indian "millions" fish, which preys upon all sorts of little animals and is particularly fond of the wriggling aquatic larvae of mosquitoes. This is probably the reason for the immunity from malarial diseases enjoyed by Barbados.

An ordinary pond, in spite of its tranquil appearance, is the scene of many small tragedies. Its inhabitants include rapacious water beetles and other insect forms of still more bloodthirsty character. Conspicuous among these are the aquatic larvae of dragon-flies, provided with a curious apparatus jointed like one of the old-fashioned extensible carriage-steps, and placed below the mouth. When not in use, this "mask" is folded up over the face, but it is in reality a seizing organ that can be rapidly extended. Any small creature

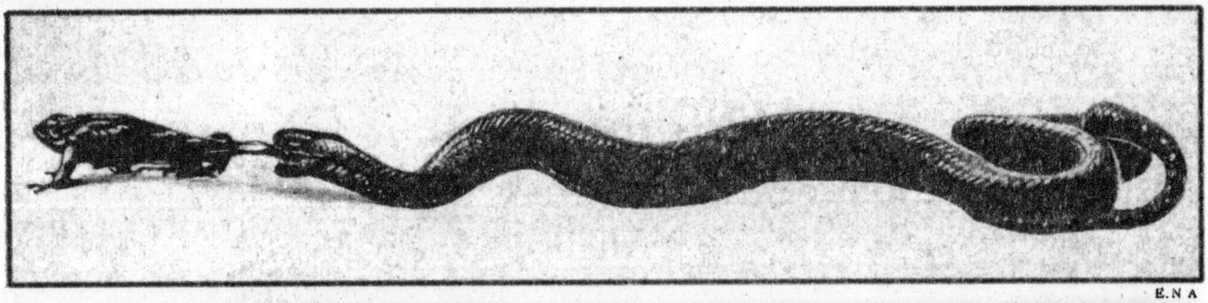

E.N.A

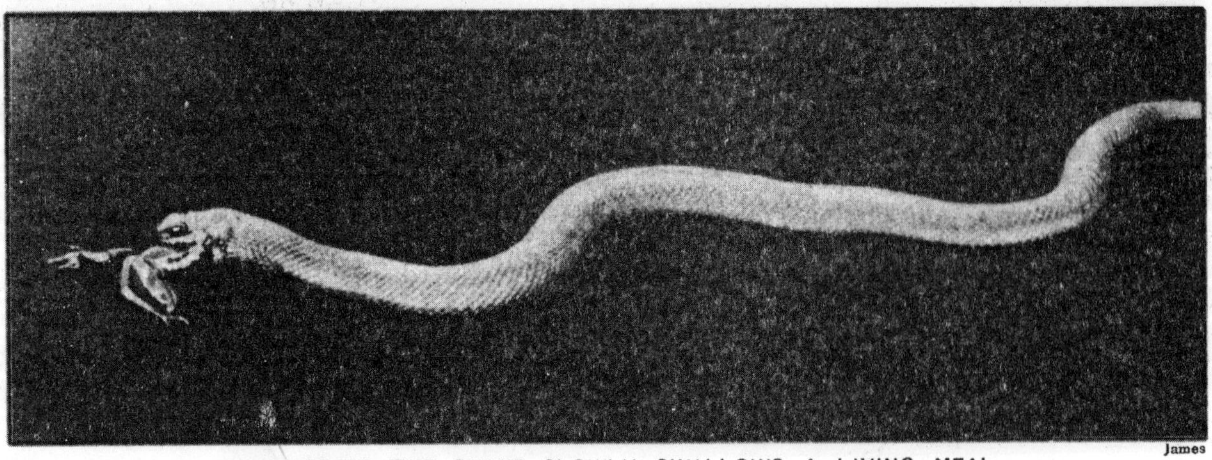

James

BY DEGREES THE SNAKE SLOWLY SWALLOWS A LIVING MEAL

When a snake decides to feed, its method is to have one good meal and then lie dormant for a time. Grass snakes may go some weeks between meals. In dealing with a frog or a toad the snake seizes its prey by one leg and proceeds to swallow steadily, the victim pulling the other way and protesting as violently as it possibly can. Slowly the meal is engulfed and swallowed despite violent struggles, which do not seem to worry the snake at all, for it proceeds stolidly with its business until the end.

H. J. Shepstone

E.N.A.

WONDERFUL BALEEN THAT FORMS A FILTER FOR A WHALE'S FOOD

It is impressive to remember that the whale, the largest of the mammals, feeds on tiny fish and marine organisms. The system of filtration by which the baleen whales extract food from the water is made possible by the plates of whalebone or baleen. These are formed from the mucous membrane of the palate and comprise a great number of horny plates suspended from the roof of the mouth, and covered on their inner edges with bristles. Here we have some baleen (top) and (bottom) a whale's mouth.

F. Vear

H. Wallace

Mondiale

Mondiale

WOODPECKER AND ITS NUTCRACKER: GREAT TIT AND MISSEL THRUSH

The two lower photographs give us an instructive insight into the habits of the woodpecker. On the left we see a bird peeping out cautiously from the hole it has drilled in a tree trunk for its nest and on the right a crack in the bole of a tree which has been ingeniously used as a nutcracker. Nuts have been placed firmly in the slit and the bird has then hammered them with its beak till they split. Above we have (top left) a great tit and (top right) a missel thrush both with good beakfuls of food.

F. Vear

E.N.A.

EXHIBITION OF LIZARD-SWALLOWING: CHAFFINCH'S NURSERY MEAL

Here is a remarkable photograph (bottom) from America. It shows two young road-runners, each of which has swallowed a lizard about a foot long and is now engaged in the lengthy process of swallowing. Notice that the birds have squatted back on their hocks and raised their beaks in the effort to get their meal down. Above is a cock chaffinch feeding its young.

can be grasped by a pair of toothed pincers situated at the end of this structure, and is then drawn back to be dealt with by a pair of powerful jaws.

The flattened bug known as a "water scorpion" is also a hunter of note, with piercing and sucking mouth parts. The front legs are turned forwards and used for seizing or holding on to living prey, among which tadpoles and small fishes are numbered.

Of great interest is the hydra, or fresh-water polyp, a living tubular stomach about one-sixth of an inch long, of which one end adheres to a firm surface. The mouth is in the centre of the free end, and from it radiate slender tentacles studded with microscopic structures known as "nettling cells," from which poisonous threads can be shot out. Woe to any little crustacean, such as a "water flea," touched by any of these, for it is at once paralysed, drawn to the mouth, and swallowed.

The sea is undoubtedly the original home of life, from which some groups of animals migrated to achieve the conquest of the land. Now and again there has been a return to this ancient abode, and a gradual re-adaptation to an aquatic existence. The sea lions, for example, notable hunters of fish, are distant relatives of bears in which the extremities have been converted into paddles, though the hind

F. Vear

Mondiale

F. Vear

Mondiale

HUNGRY BIRDS FEEDING OR BEING FED: FLY-CATCHER, RAVEN AND BLACKBIRD

In the bottom left-hand illustration we see a spotted fly-catcher, the male of the pair, feeding the hen. The individual struggle for existence becomes a joint one when the sexes mate, and private hunger is secondary to the needs of the new generation. The fly-catchers may be known by their habit of selecting a perch on gate or fence and making little erratic flights back and forth after insects and returning to the perch. The fly-catcher likes insects, but the rare raven (bottom and top right) likes stronger food. Here we see one with a young rabbit it has killed. Lastly, we have a cock blackbird (top left), the father of a family, returned home with a good supply for everyone

E.N.A.

ones can be bent forwards and used for a sort of clumsy progression on land. The true seals have gone a step further, for their hind flippers are turned backwards and united with the stumpy tail by folds of skin. Seals, though mostly marine, are also to be found in the Caspian, the Sea of Aral, and Lake Baikal, inland sheets of water which were once connected with the Arctic Ocean. Walruses are also marine carnivora, distinguished by the possession of huge upper tusks employed for digging up bivalve molluscs as food. The Cetacea (whales, dolphins, porpoises, and so on) are also descended from land mammals, and subsist on various kinds of animal food. The hind-limbs have been suppressed, the fore-limbs converted into paddles, and the tail spread out into a horizontal fin. Some are toothed, such as the porpoise, which devours large quantities of fish, often being a great nuisance to fishermen, and the dolphins are related forms, some of which have migrated up the estuaries of certain rivers of India and South America, to adopt a fresh-water life.

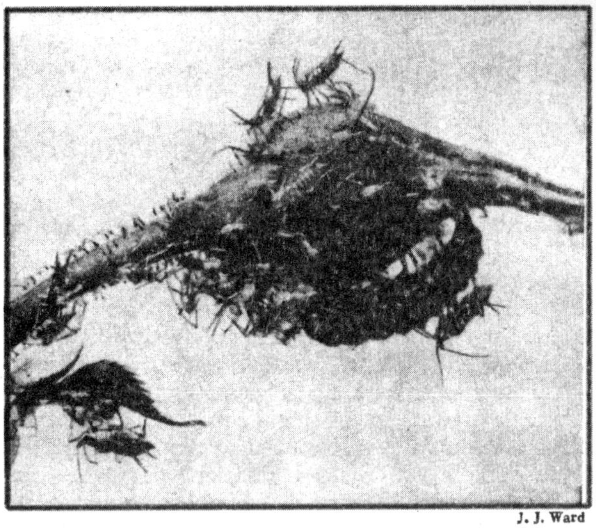

J. J. Ward

DESTRUCTION OF APHIDES AND FLIES

Rose growers should feel very affectionately towards ladybirds. The lower photograph is of a ladybird larva devouring a green fly, while another green fly walks unconcernedly over its back. Above is a coleopter beetle killing a fly.

There are also toothless Cetacea, such as the Greenland whale, which are curiously specialised for feeding on the shoals of small or minute creatures (plankton) of which vast numbers float in the surface layers of the sea. Numerous fringed horny plates (whalebone) hang down from the roof of the mouth to serve as a strainer. The whale, with open mouth, swims close to the surface, and swallows the little floating animals that stick to these fringes. There is no danger of suffocation, for the top of the windpipe is drawn out into a sort of cone that fits into the back of the nasal passages.

There are many birds that make the sea their home, and subsist on a fish diet, among these being gulls, cormorants, puffins, and divers. Most of these have retained the power of flight, but in the penguins the wings have been converted into effective paddles, enabling their owners, with the aid of powerful webbed feet, to surpass fishes themselves in their native element.

Marine carnivorous reptiles are relatively uncommon, though at an earlier geological period certain groups, now extinct, were the terrors of the sea. Although the " great sea serpent " appears to be fabulous, a few sea snakes are to be found in the Indian and Pacific Oceans. They are poisonous and prey upon fishes. The hawksbill turtle, the scales of which are the source of " tortoiseshell," are also flesh-eaters, their food consisting of fishes and molluscs.

The immensely numerous fishes which swarm in all parts of the ocean include a large number of species which pursue living prey of the most varied kind, largely belonging to their own class. Sharks, and their smaller relatives the dogfishes, are notoriously predaceous, their favourite hunting ground being the sea floor. Their tails are unsymmetrical, with a larger upper lobe, as a result of which unsteered swimming takes them downwards in a slanting direction. Large sharks often attain a length of from twelve to fifteen feet, but this may be greatly exceeded in certain species. The gigantic basking shark, for example, may be more than fifty feet long. One of the most remarkable fishes of this group is the much-feared hammerhead, in which the eyes are borne on lateral projections. The comparatively small Port Jackson shark has most of its teeth converted into crushing plates well suited for dealing with shell-fish. The thresher shark, with a greatly elongated tail, pursues tactics of its own, swimming round shoals of such fishes as herrings, and by splashing with its tail causes these helpless victims to huddle together instead of trying to escape.

The highly carnivorous rays or skates are modifications of the shark type, in which the body is flattened from above downwards, and there is a long narrow

C. W. Teager

THE REWARDS OF GOOD HUNTING

There is plenty of food in the summer when the birds are hunting for supplies to bring home to their nests. It is just a question whether or no they can see their family safely launched before they themselves become food for the hawk. Here is a male blue tit feeding its mate, who is too occupied with the nest to go far to find food.

tail. Certain species native to the Indian Ocean may be as much as eighteen feet broad, and weigh over half a ton. The sting rays can inflict serious wounds by means of poison spines on their whip-like tails, while the electric rays have converted part of their muscular system into batteries capable of giving severe shocks.

The vast majority of fishes now existing belong to the bony type, having well ossified skeletons, with which many of the edible forms, herrings in particular, have made us painfully familiar. They are for the most part flesh-eaters, living on a great variety of prey, which they secure in many interesting ways. In such a fish the tail fin is usually forked and symmetrical, as may be seen in a mackerel, so that unsteered swimming is "right ahead." Many rely on speed for the pursuit and capture of living prey, as in the case of the albicore and bonito, forms of about six feet in length closely related to the tunny, which chase flying-fishes.

SOME lie in wait for their victims, a well-known example being afforded by the sea angler, which remains almost buried in the sand, and relies on its "lure," a rod-like back-fin with a waving membrane at its end, to excite the curiosity of its smaller kindred. When these approach sufficiently near the angler makes a sudden snap, and they disappear in his enormous mouth, escape being prevented by numerous rows of backwardly directed pointed teeth, hinged at their bases.

The deepest abysses of the ocean are tenanted by a variety of weird-looking fishes of extreme rapacity, which prey on one another and also victimise deep-sea crustaceans and the like. This would result in wholesale and rapid extermination, were it not that the bill of fare includes sundry items that sink from above or are washed in from the adjoining shallower waters. No ray of sunlight can penetrate to the "abyss," and these nightmare fishes are either blind or provided with enormous goggle eyes, for which light is furnished by phosphorescent organs studding various regions of the body.

The familiar flat fishes, such as turbot, sole, and plaice, are quite different in structure from the rays and skates, for instead of being flattened from above downwards they are laterally compressed. For some time after hatching they swim about in the usual way, but then begin to tip over laterally, either to the right, as in the turbot, or to the left, as in sole and plaice, and very soon sink down to the sea floor, where they are destined to hunt for their living. Innumerable small creatures, many of them shrimp-like, float in shoals in the surface waters of the sea, providing abundant nutritious food for certain fishes. Among these the herring is prominent, and, like the whale, it possesses a straining apparatus for separating its minute prey from the water in which they float. The water, used for breathing purposes, flows out on either side through a series of narrow gill-slits, to bathe the scarlet comb-like gills and aerate the blood giving them their fine colour. But the shrimplets cannot get through the gill-slits, being prevented by numerous elastic fibres ("gill rakers") springing from their edges, and preventing the loss of a tasty meal.

The herring, in its turn, serves as food for many other forms, among which is the squid, a mollusc of the cuttlefish kind. This elongated creature can dart backwards through the water like an arrow by expelling water from its gill chamber, and possesses ten extensible seizing organs, two of which, known as tentacles, are much longer than the eight others called arms. Suckers are present on the thickened ends of the tentacles, and rows of them stud the arms. Once grasped by these structures, the prey is drawn to the mouth and dealt with by a horny parrot-like beak, from which a curious rasping organ is protruded for scraping away skin and flesh. The squid has large staring eyes, can change colour rapidly to match its surroundings, and is able to conceal itself by ejecting an inky fluid.

Gigantic species of squid exist on the American side of the North Atlantic, and these sometimes reach a total length of over fifty feet, of which forty-two are accounted for by the tentacles. Bathers are sometimes attacked by these formidable creatures.

Chapter CV

The Wonderful Little Earwig

By John J. Ward

Author of "Insect Biographies"

THERE are few people who can really appreciate an earwig. Superstition and lack of accurate knowledge have done their worst to produce an abiding aversion to that much-maligned insect; whose greatest crime, so far as I am able to ascertain, is that it has an annoying way of suddenly falling from flowers and garden produce, and causing a scare as "a horrid earwig." Why it is "horrid" is difficult to understand, since it does not bite, sting, or commit personal injury of any kind. Furthermore, there is not the slightest foundation for the widespread myth that it will penetrate the human ear. It would, surely, be a very unbalanced earwig that would seek an adventure of that kind.

I have reared the earwig from the egg stage to maturity, and photographed every phase in its metamorphosis. I have gone further and followed its development until the end of the third generation; and I am here able to state that, if ever a friendly and almost entirely inoffensive insect has been sadly misunderstood, that insect is the common earwig.

The gardener will tell you about earwigs; he will show you the damage they have done to the petals of his dahlias, phloxes, carnations, violas, and what not; he will bring you the ripest apricot, plum, or pear, and show you the holes they have made; and, should you doubt his word, he may even shake some of them from the holes in the fruit while he informs you that "Seeing is believing."

In a corner of my garden there is part of an old wooden post with a coil of rope round it, and when I want an earwig specimen I can generally obtain one by uncoiling a strand or two of that rope. Nevertheless, I do not charge the earwig with attacking the post, or the rope. So it is with the earwig in the fruit. I know quite well that the hole in the fruit was first made by wasps, and that the earwig, being of nocturnal habits, has simply found in the hole a cool and sheltered resting-place in which to hide during the hours of sunlight.

At the same time, I am fully aware that the earwig will sometimes sip up some of the ripe juices of the damaged fruit; but really it sleeps away the greater part of the day, and its activities and real feeding do not commence until after darkness has set in. The truth is, the earwig is really a carnivorous creature, and its vegetable diet is insignificant, and probably eaten largely to quench its thirst.

In the same manner that the earwig hides in the damaged fruit, it will more or less disappear into one of the curled petals in a dahlia flower-head, and there remain motionless throughout the day. Perhaps that same flower-head may have some badly damaged petals, eaten almost entirely by night-feeding moth caterpillars, which are hiding on or near the ground during the day; but as the earwig is found there, it is saddled with the whole of the damage.

IT is unfortunate that British gardeners rarely possess entomological knowledge. Their acquaintance with insects is mainly confined to attacking them with insecticides in order to kill them. They fail to appreciate the fact that many insects are their best friends, and much better destroyers of some of their worst pests than they themselves can ever hope to be. If the gardener better understood the ways and habits of the earwig, he would adopt an entirely different attitude towards it. The late Fred Enoch, who was a most skilled and careful entomological worker, says: "I have often, when preparing an earwig for microscopic examination, found its viscera full of the remains of hundreds of greenflies." To which may be added the fact that earwigs also feed on thrips, scale insects, tiny caterpillars, and baby slugs and snails; but their greatest virtue is that of devouring innumerable eggs of moths and other injurious insects. I can personally testify, too, that a family of baby earwigs will even eat up a batch of the comparatively large eggs of their own species, shells and contents rapidly disappearing, when they get the opportunity; but that opportunity is rare, for, as we shall learn later, the mother earwig

H. Bastin

COMMON AND LESSER EARWIGS

Of the three insects shown in this photograph the central one is a female of the lesser earwig while the other two are male (left) and female (right) of the common earwig. Notice the distinct difference in the forceps or hind pincers in each case.

The Wonderful Little Earwig

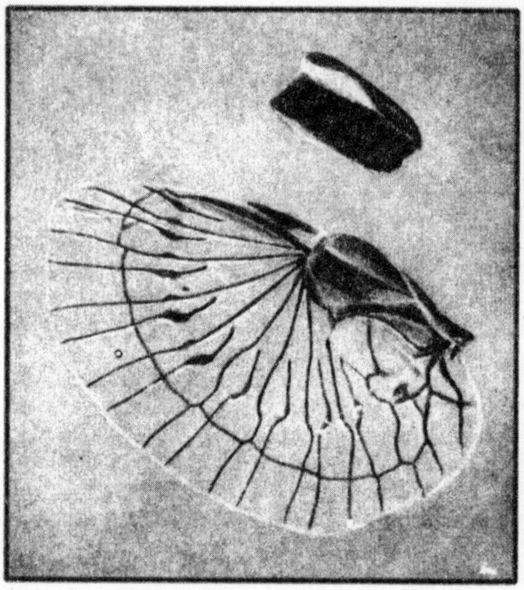

H. Bastin

WING CASE, WING AND PINCERS OF COMMON EARWIG

In the left hand of these two photographs are the wing case (top) and the wing, of a common earwig. When we compare the size of this beautiful wing with the case into which it has to be folded it is no wonder that, on the very rare occasions when the wings are used, the pincers (right) have to be employed in re-folding them. The pincers here are those of a male.

carefully guards her eggs against the attacks of such night-feeding families, which often move about with their mother in charge.

The earwig is first and foremost a scavenger, and after dark it becomes extremely active, rapidly moving over the stems and leaves of plants, occasionally stopping to lick up a splash of sugary fluid, or a few pollen grains scattered by the wind or by the numerous flower-feeding insects during the day. Such spots, if left, quickly provide a germinating area for a colony of bacteria, or microscopic moulds and fungi, all of which may result in injurious effects upon the plant and destroy its foliage. There is, too, a considerable amount of minute insect debris, such as cast skins, injured aphides, and dead insects, that accumulate on the leaves during the busy hours of sunlight, all of which the numerous earwigs eagerly search for as they forage about in small companies. It is while they are so occupied that they find insects' eggs adhering to the leaves and stems, and for these they have a particular relish. Such is, undoubtedly, the real function of the earwig, and I make the statement after much careful observation over a period of several years.

We should remember, too, that the earwig is probably the most prolific insect to be found in gardens. The reason is obvious—it is because the scavenger is there most needed. The strong and hardy plants of the wild do not need the services of the sanitary inspector nearly so much ; and in a newly-laid-out garden where everything is clean and tidy, but few earwigs will be found. This work of cleaning up the leaves, stems, and flowers of plants may seem trivial, but, actually, it is of the greatest importance in keeping the plants in good health ; especially during long spells of dry and hot weather when there is no rain to wash the leaves—always when the earwig is most active.

So much then for the valuable scavenging work of the little earwig ; but, surely, a reader will contend, the earwig does feed on the petals of flowers ? The answer is, certainly it does, and, on occasion, almost as much on tender green leaves. It does not, however, prefer that food, and rarely ever selects it during the early months of the season ; but as the months advance earwigs multiply in great abundance, each mother earwig being able to rear three or four families of an average number of forty each from April to October. The young attain full growth in about eight weeks, and, as they can increase at the same rate, it follows that, as the summer advances hordes of earwigs appear in all suitable places.

So effectively do these hordes carry on their scavenging work, that sooner or later there is a shortage of their normal food supplies ; and it is then that they supplement them with a vegetable diet. We must not fail to note, however, that whenever the earwigs are injuring the flowers, it is then that the plant is most free from aphides and other pests. Every worker in the garden is worthy of his hire, and, surely, it is better to have a few damaged flowers than unhealthy plants with shrivelled leaves, and filthy with greenflies.

Also, let us always make sure that the earwig is the real culprit. I have carefully marked perfect ox-eye daisies, phloxes, chrysanthemums, and other flowers early in the day, and those same flowers by evening have had their petals riddled with holes. I have watched in the bright sunlight tiny flies with biting mouthparts, together with tiny beetles, making those same holes ; but my gardener accuses the earwig of the whole of the damage. Furthermore, although earwigs will feed on over-ripe fruit, I have yet to meet the gardener who has ever seen an earwig break the skin of a sound plum, pear, apple, or other fruit. It certainly never does that.

Although one of the most familiar of British insects, yet its life-story has remained very inaccurately known. It is a charming and wonderful story with many quite unique features. As insects go, it is comparatively long-lived. Under normal circumstances it lives at least a complete year in the adult stage, and sometimes longer. Some of the females hibernate for the winter, but are not entirely dormant. They, like the queen wasp, are fertilised, and are

J. J. Ward

J. J. Ward

EARWIG AND ITS WONDERFUL AND RARELY USED WINGS

It is very rarely indeed that the common earwig opens its wing case and unfolds its wings. The lower photograph is of a common earwig displayed to show the opened wings. They are never used in flight, and not one in ten thousand individuals ever opens its wings at all. There are flying species of earwigs and also some without any wings at all, and it seems that the earwig is in a transition stage and is gradually evolving from a flying to a crawling life. The upper photograph shows an earwig with wings closed. Both illustrations are considerably enlarged

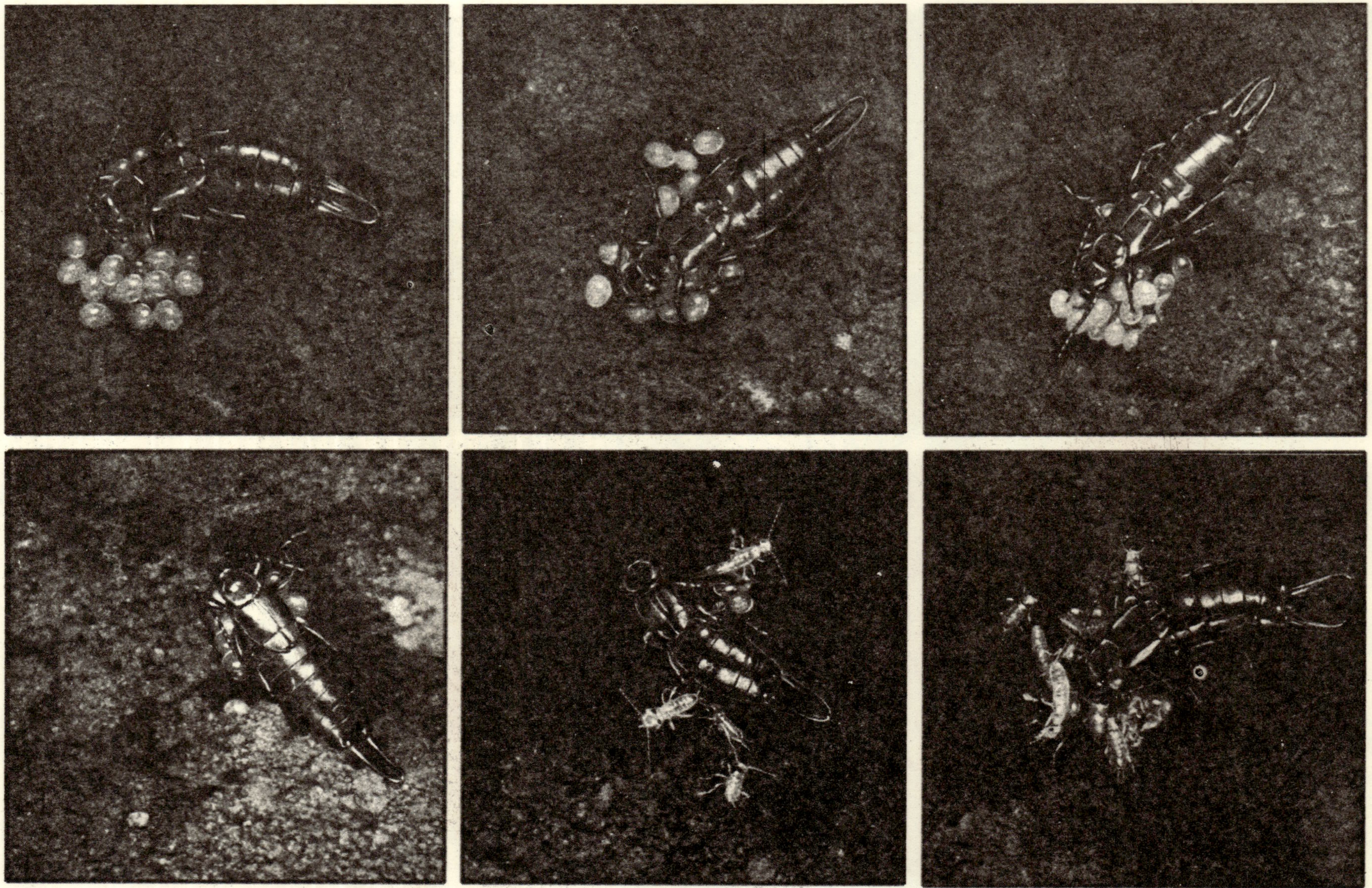

J. J. Ward

MUCH MALIGNED AND MISUNDERSTOOD INSECTS: THE HATCHING OF A BROOD OF EARWIGS

Earwigs, like spiders, are too often regarded with loathing and, at the best, can only expect indifference. Yet they are both extremely useful creatures and the earwig has qualities, hidden hitherto, that should serve to endear it at least to those who delight in gardens. This series of enlarged photographs, which should be studied from left to right beginning at the top, shows a glimpse of motherhood as it is practised among these curious and unjustly condemned insects. Having laid her eggs (top left) mother earwig sorts them with her mandibles until she has grouped them under her. She then broods over them until, after sixteen days or so the eggs hatch. This careful matron then helps her youngsters with the business of getting out of their shells.

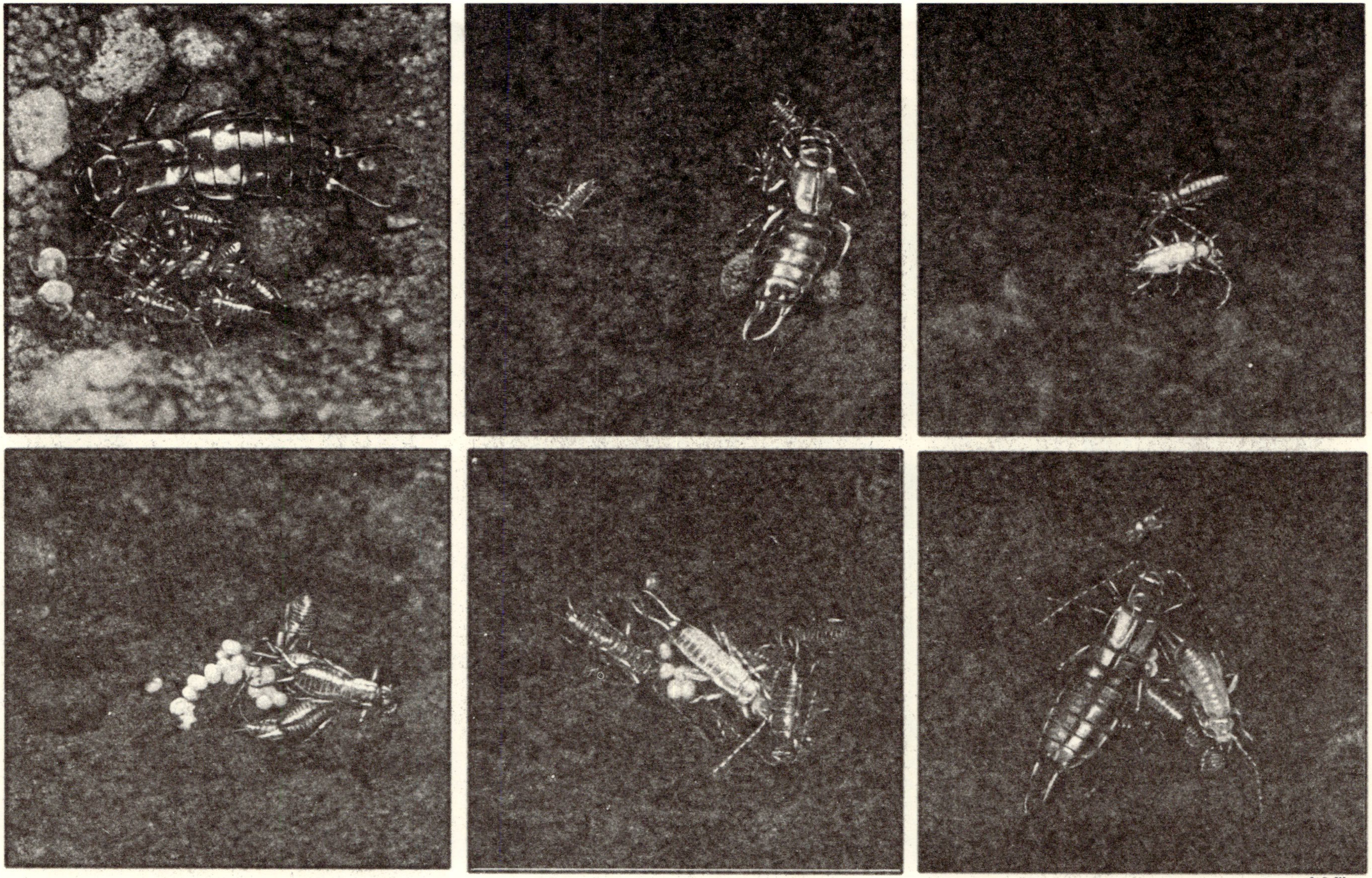

J. J. Ward

MOTHER EARWIG, ARMED WITH "KNUCKLE-DUSTERS," GUARDS AND BRINGS UP TWO FAMILIES AT ONCE

The remarkable tale of maternal solicitude, begun in the opposite page, is continued here. In about an hour the young are all free and the mother begins raking a hole in the soil (top left) into which her family of fifty or so immediately scuttle and begin to feed. The mother and her young are now half-buried (top centre) and she has now encased her hind pair of legs in lumps of mud. Any intruder she meets with a vicious sidelong kick, the mud lumps acting like knuckle-dusters in giving more power and effect to the blow. In two weeks the young moult for the first time (top right) emerging as white insects as they did on hatching. The lower photographs show a second family born while the first is still being reared through successive moults.

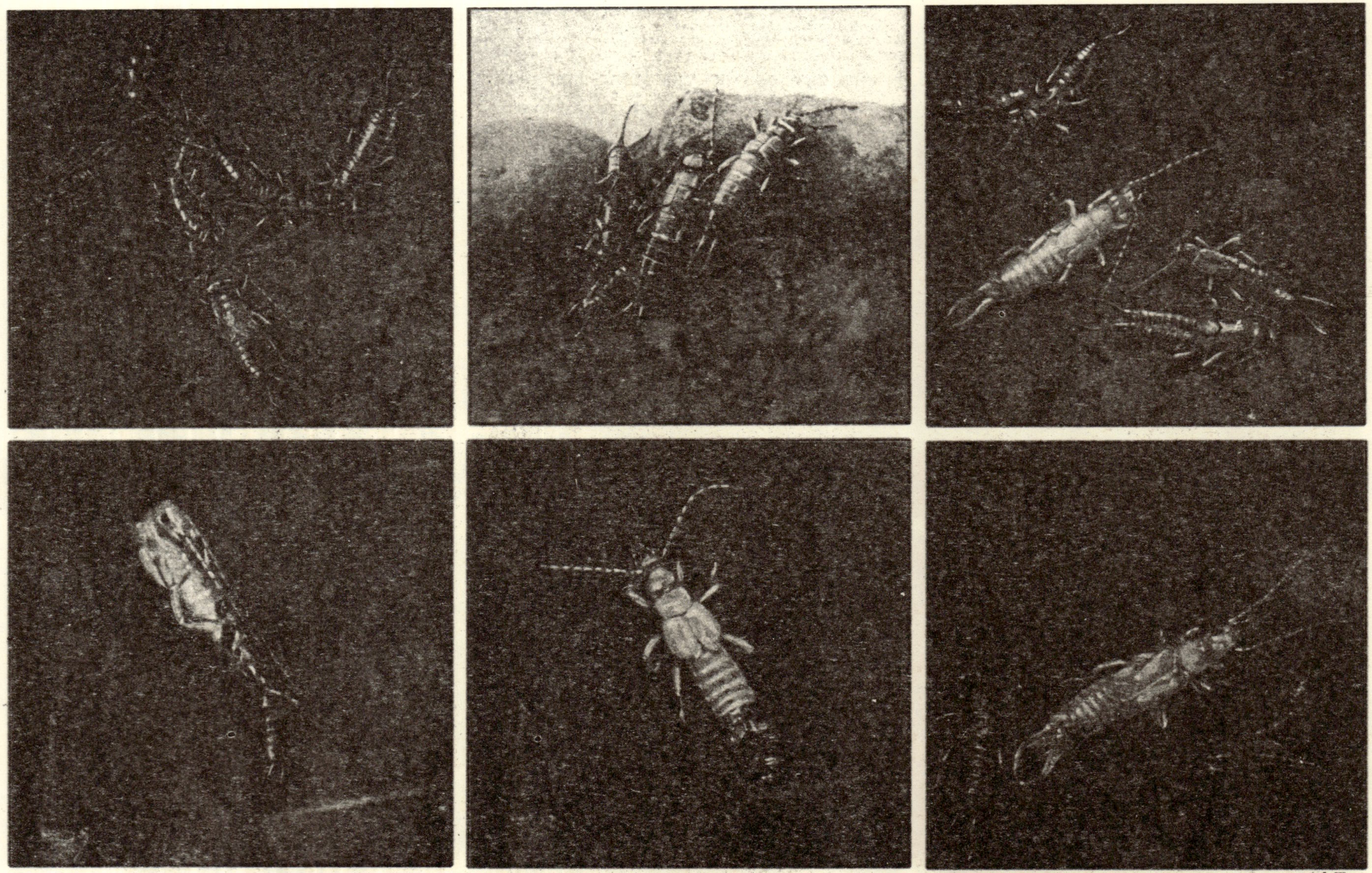

J. J. Ward

ELABORATE MOULTING PROCESS OF A YOUNG EARWIG AS IT GRADUALLY GROWS TO MATURITY

As the young earwigs grow they burst a succession of skins, each time emerging as silvery-white insects but rapidly becoming a neutral colour to harmonise with the soil. Here (top left) we have first a young earwig preparing for its third moult. The wing cases begin to appear at this stage and are present in the specimen nearest the lower edge of this photograph. Then the moult proceeds and the insect emerges from its old skin, and is larger than its brothers and sisters who have yet to moult. The bottom left-hand illustration shows the fourth moult being made on a dandelion leaf. Then we see the tail pincers being used to pull away the old skin until finally the insect appears, half as large again, in its new suit (bottom right).

The Wonderful Little Earwig

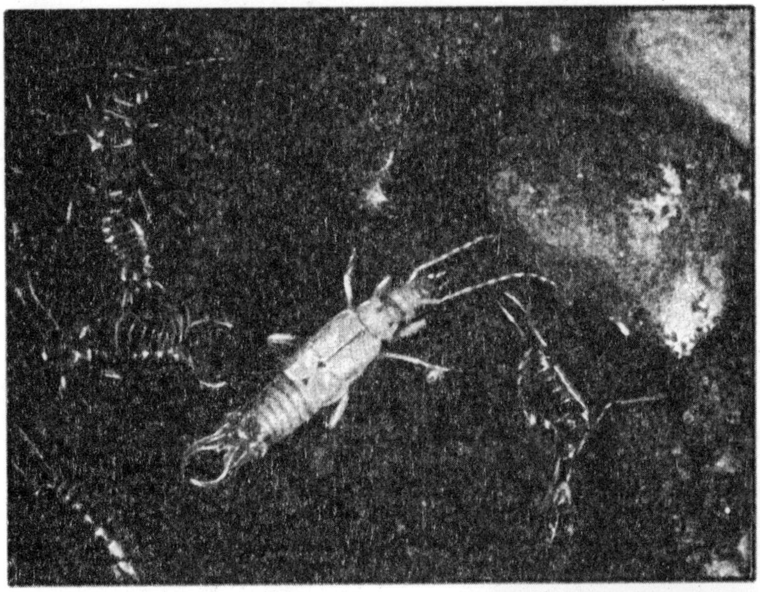

which are provided with more formidable tail pincers than those of the common earwig, that can scarcely be regarded as their true function. If, however, we observe the common earwig guarding its eggs just when the young are hatching out, we are able then, I think, to discover the import of these organs.

One earwig I had under observation with young appearing from her eggs, I gently touched with a quill toothpick. Instantly the tail pincers were turned towards the toothpick like a pair of fearsome jaws about to make a grip. A touch on the opposite side quickly brought them in that direction. Then, however, came a surprise. From out of the soil she suddenly jerked one of her hind legs with a savage side thrust,

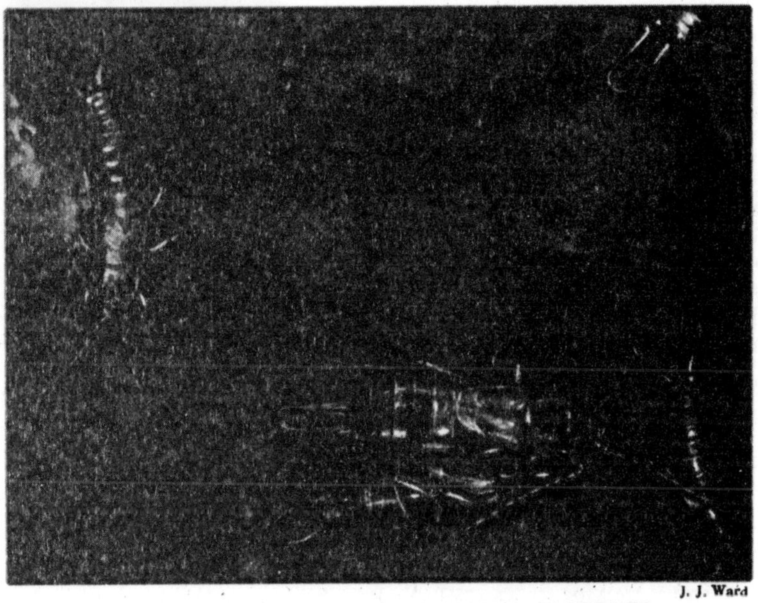

J. J. Ward

AN EARWIG FAMILY THAT KEEPS TOGETHER

The top photograph shows the final scene in the moulting process of the earwig we considered in the opposite page. Having finished with its old skin it hurries back to join the family. The formation of the pincers proves it to be a male. The lower photograph shows some of the family hiding in the soil till night time comes.

awaiting their first opportunity to lay their first batch of eggs. Until early spring they hide beneath stones, and below ground; but at the end of April the mother earwig comes to the surface of the soil, and in a sheltered spot rakes out a hole in which she places some fifty or sixty eggs.

The large, pearly-hued eggs are broadly oval in form, and when seen under a magnifying lens are iridescent with rainbow colours. They occupy the whole attention of the mother earwig; and that is an extremely interesting point, for it is few insects indeed that give any attention to their eggs other than providing a store of food with them for their developing offspring, or depositing them on a particular food plant suitable to them.

Altogether different is the behaviour of the mother earwig with her eggs, for she never leaves them except when she has to seek food, and even then she constantly returns to see that they are safe. She does not sit on her eggs to hatch them, as we are told in many natural history works she does. What she really does is to place them well in the soil and cover them with her foreparts and first pair of legs; her body and second and third pairs of legs, and her tail pincers, projecting upwards and effectually blocking the entrance to the hole.

The function of the tail pincers has always been a natural history puzzle, their only suggested use appearing to be that of assisting in replacing the earwig's wings under their covers (for it has a wonderful pair of wings, of which more anon); but in view of the fact that there are wingless earwig species

and the foot of that leg I found was encased in a hardened mass of dry mud—a kind of sledge-hammer "boxing-glove." The foot of the other hind leg was similarly covered.

Those actions surely suggest that the tail pincers, and the mud-covered hind feet, are means of protection for the eggs and young. That the hardened mud was purposely accumulated is certain, for two days later I noticed that she had lost one of the mud clumps, but the following day it had been replaced. Only the hind legs are so covered; the first and second pairs are needed for walking and raking up the soil. When she leaves her nest her mud-covered legs simply drag behind. When the young are about a week old, these mud clumps are completely disposed of.

The eggs hatch in fifteen or sixteen days, and during the incubation period the mother earwig is very active, continually re-arranging the order of the eggs, and not infrequently removing the whole batch to an entirely new burrow, which she first constructs for them. It is interesting to see her carry the eggs. They are slightly adhesive, and by taking hold of one in her mandibles she can often lift a dozen or more at a time, carrying them while held well up from the ground; when they look like a bunch of glistening, pearly balloons. Afterwards she returns and collects the scattered ones. This changing of their position is apparently to obtain the correct conditions of moisture and warmth for their incubation.

When the young are hatching out the mother earwig becomes very agitated, continually pushing her head and feelers in amongst them, and rendering every assistance for her babies to emerge. In about one hour she is surrounded by a crowd of fifty or more silvery white youngsters with jet-black eyes, all as active as a swarm of bees; for their mother is raking out a hole in the soil into which they run and commence to feed. What is the nature of their food at this stage is difficult to understand. It is probably bacteria and micro-organism, or particles of broken-down animal and vegetable matter. An hour after commencing to feed there is not a white baby earwig to be seen, every one has changed to the colour of the soil. It may be that earwigs serve some function in the soil like that of the earthworm, in reducing it to a friable state; or even in assisting to keep a natural balance in the bacterial colonies working below ground.

There is probably no insect in the world that possesses the maternal instinct in so large a degree as the common earwig. She leads her family about just as a hen does her chicks. At the slightest sign of danger, by means of a touch with her feelers, she brings her crowded family instantly to order, so that not one is moving in the burrow; probably the alarm is conveyed from one to the other. In any case, the action is very prompt, and they remain still until the "all clear" signal is given.

At two weeks old, the baby earwigs moult their skins, when they are again silvery-white, but almost immediately change to a dirty-grey colour. Their mother is then still actively assisting them in foraging for food. How long she would remain with them was a problem that needed solving. She and her eggs had been under my observation from April 23, and her family appeared on May 9, and when the young were half-grown, on June 3, I was confronted with a considerable surprise.

The mother earwig had laid another batch of eggs, thirty-eight in number. She was trying to hide them in the soil, but was much harassed by the members of her first family crowding round her, though she did not make any effort to drive them away. Two days later she was still tending her eggs and managing her half-grown family, some of which had once again become silvery-white, for they were moulting their second skins. It was then that I decided to remove her with her eggs to new quarters. Until that time she had been enclosed in a metal box filled with soil and covered with a glass lid, and no male earwig could possibly have found access to her. I was, therefore, desirous of testing if this second batch of eggs would prove fertile.

When I had prepared her new home, I found that all the eggs had disappeared excepting a few bits of broken shells. My arrangements for rearing the earwig family had been so perfect that I had not lost one of them, but I had failed to provide the young with an important item in their menu—that of insects' eggs. The now thriving family had made good that item, and devoured the whole batch of eggs their mother was tending; and, since they were her own offspring, instinct had not guided her to drive them off.

Twenty-two days later, that is, on June 25, the mother earwig, then isolated from her first family, deposited a third batch of eggs—but this time only twenty-six. On July 9 she showed considerable excitement over this new batch. Was instinct guiding her correctly? Would those eggs prove fertile? The following day she was rearing her new family. There is nothing particularly wonderful in these apparently unfertilised eggs hatching out young, for this phenomenon of parthenogenesis is familiar in the case of many insect species. Probably the mother earwig was fertilised the previous autumn, before her hibernation, and that holds good for all her eggs—as in the case of a queen wasp.

There is probably no other insect known that rears three or four broods of young in one season, tending each family until its individuals are able to fend for themselves. Regarding the feeding of these families, I found that they consumed almost every kind of decaying matter likely to be found in the soil, both animal and vegetable, and preferably in a sodden state. Decaying, over-ripe apples, and other fruits, together with bits of injured earthworms and dead insects, were much favoured feasts; but dahlia blooms I provided them with were never touched, although dandelion leaves enclosed with them were eaten to shreds.

On the same day that the mother earwig's new family appeared, the offspring of her first family were making the fourth and final moulting of their skins, appearing as snowy-white mature earwigs with conspicuous black eyes; but changing within an hour to the glossy brown colour with which we are familiar. It should be noted that there is no complete metamorphosis of larva, dormant pupa, and adult stages; the young earwig remains active throughout its development, its wing-cases appearing just before its third moulting, and its wings with the final stage.

The earwig's wings are rarely seen, because not one earwig in a hundred thousand ever expands its wings throughout its life period.

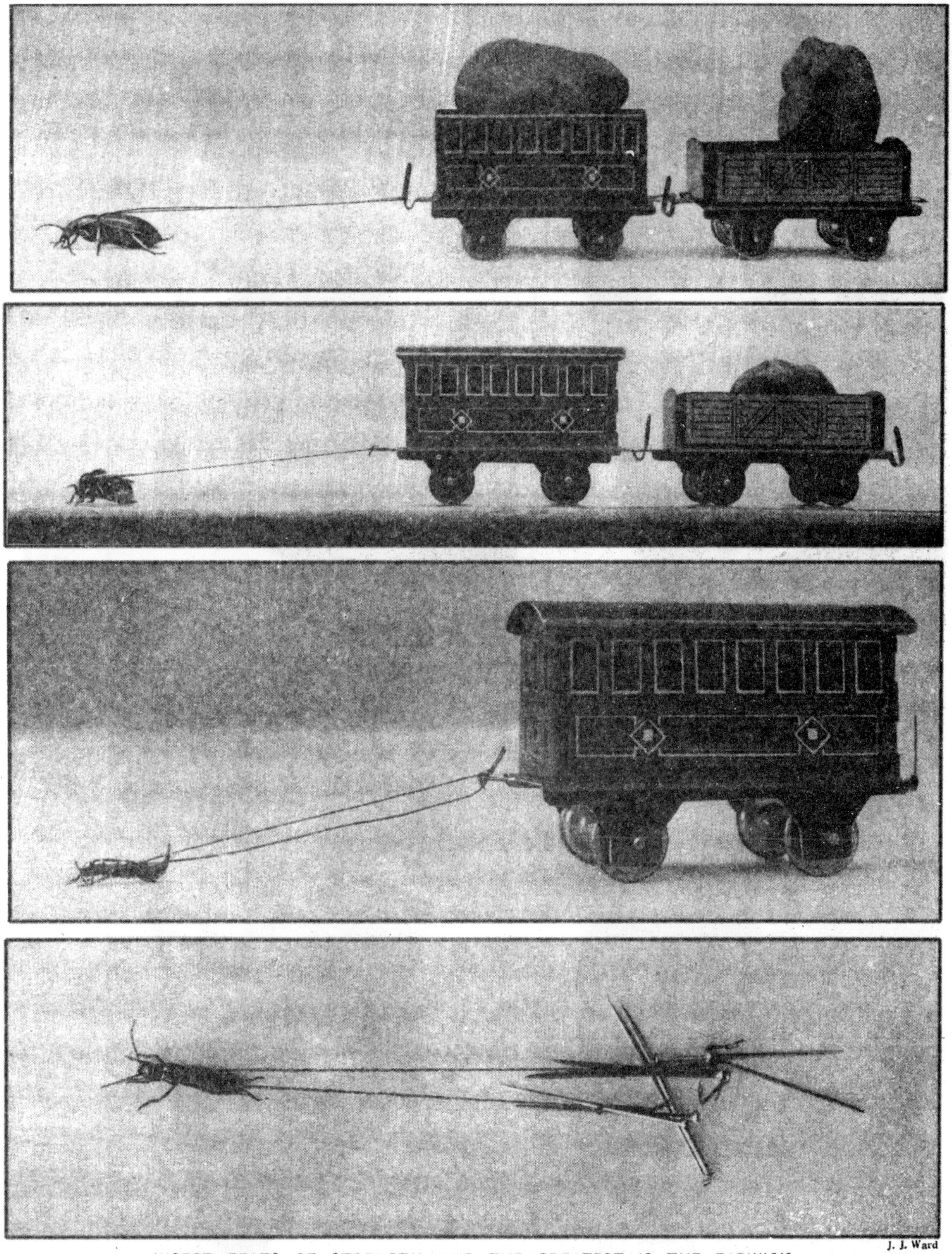

J. J. Ward

INSECT FEATS OF STRENGTH, AND THE GREATEST IS THE EARWIG'S

These astonishing photographs make wonderful revelations as to the strength of insects. The earwig is the Goliath of them all. From top to bottom the illustrations show: a ground beetle with a load of plasticene 182 times its own weight; a bumble bee with 300 times its weight; and an earwig (bottom but one) moving 530 times its own weight. In the last photograph we have our earwig dragging a dead weight of pins 27 times its own weight. In the other cases the load is on wheels and more easily moved than a dead weight dragged with much friction.

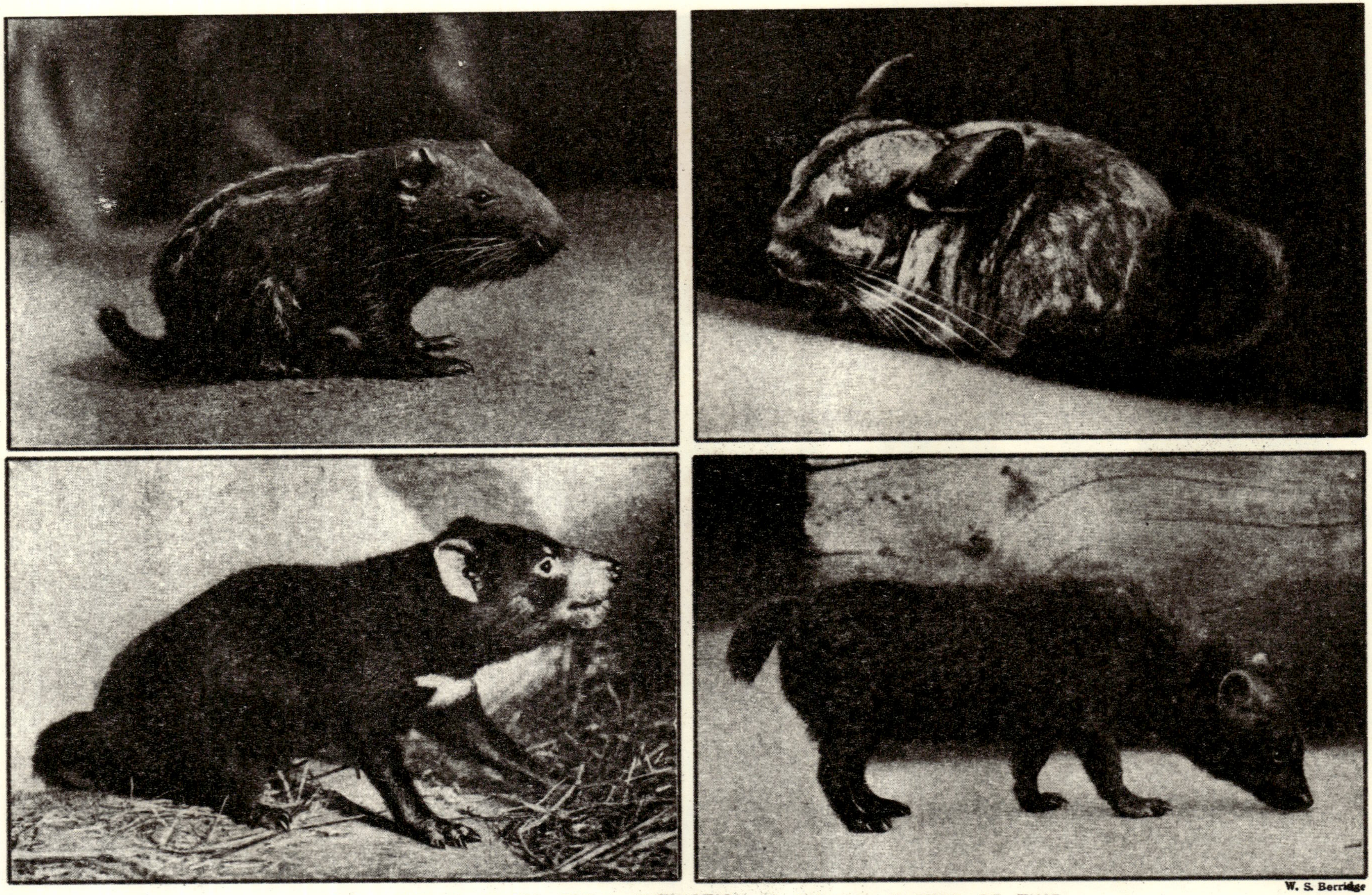

W. S. Berridge

FOUR ANIMALS WHOSE TOTAL EXTINCTION IS ONLY A MATTER OF TIME

So far as extinction is concerned, every race of animal, man included, has to fight against the danger of it and, in Nature, there is no mercy for the unfit. Many races of animals became extinct through one cause or another—change of climate, inroads of the sea, increase of old enemies or influx of new ones—long before man appeared on the earth. Since human beings became the dominant race of life, certain animals have, of necessity, come into conflict with them and been wiped out. The Tasmanian devil (bottom left) has been greatly reduced in numbers owing to its damage to flocks. The bush-dog (bottom right) of Brazil; the paca rana (top left) exhibited for the first time at the London Zoo in 1925, and the chinchilla (top right) are all disappearing.

Chapter CVI

Recently Extinct and Disappearing Animal Types

By W. T. Calman

Keeper of Zoology, British Museum

GEOLOGY has made us familiar with the fact that animals of innumerable kinds which once lived on the earth died out, leaving none to represent their race in the land of the living. It is a matter of common knowledge that the same sad story is being continued in our own time, and that many kinds of animals now living are doomed to early extinction. There is, however, a good deal of misconception as to the way in which this extermination has come about.

We commonly hear it said that a certain species has been " killed off " by man, or that it has disappeared before the advance of civilization. No doubt in very many cases one or other of these explanations is the right one, but there are many instances where man has been only indirectly and remotely responsible for the death of the species, and some in which savage man has been no less efficient in destruction than his civilized brother. There is evidence also that certain species, for the destruction of which man has been held responsible, were already on the down grade, and that human intervention has, at most, only hastened an end that was already in sight.

Most people, if asked to name an animal exterminated by man, would perhaps think first of the dodo. When the Portuguese discovered the island of Mauritius in 1507, they found on it numbers of this great, grotesquely clumsy ground-pigeon, unable to fly, and allowing itself to be knocked on the head with a facility which led them to call it " doudo," or " stupid." After the Dutch took possession of the island in 1598 we get more exact accounts of the bird and some individuals were brought alive to Europe. One at least was exhibited in London in 1638—to parody three lines of " Macbeth " by one word—

> . . . as our rarer monsters are,
> Painted upon a pole and underwrit,
> 'Here you may see the *dodo*.'

PERHAPS this was the specimen that afterwards came into the possession of John Tradescant, and so to the Ashmolean Museum at Oxford. The art of taxidermy, however, was little advanced in those days and in 1755 the specimen was in such bad condition that it was ordered to be destroyed, only the head and one foot being kept. Long before this, however, the last dodo had died. In 1681 we learn that none were to be found in Mauritius. It does not appear that they were intentionally killed in large numbers. The flesh was very hard and almost uneatable, only that of the breast being at all palatable. The Dutch called dodos *walgvögels*, " nasty birds." Their extermination was due chiefly to other animals introduced by man, pigs, rats and monkeys, which were quick to take advantage of such easy prey and devoured eggs and young.

The story of the great auk, or garefowl, is very different. Here, also, we have a flightless and defenceless bird, but one with a wider distribution, for these giant razorbills ranged over a great part of the North Atlantic, congregating to breed on certain rocky islets off the coasts of Newfoundland, Iceland, the Faroes, the Orkneys, and St. Kilda. When first we hear of it at the end of the sixteenth century, French fishermen on the Newfoundland coast were provisioning their boats with barrels of salted " penguins." Later, its eggs, skin, and feathers were sought after, and the birds were slaughtered in vast numbers and sometimes in circumstances of incredible brutality. Early in the nineteenth century the only remaining haunts of the species were two or three isolated rocks off the coast of Iceland. One of these, known as Geirfuglasker, " Garefowl Skerry," disappeared into the sea as the result of a volcanic convulsion, and, deplorably enough, about 1844 " the latest survivors were killed to supply caterers for the museums of Europe." In this instance, then, the evidence is conclusive that extermination has resulted directly from the ruthless persecution to which the garefowl was subjected.

BOTH the dodo and the great auk were exterminated, directly or indirectly, by civilized, or, at any rate, by European man, but there is no trustworthy evidence that the moas of New Zealand were ever seen alive by white men. They were gigantic birds of the ostrich tribe, some of them standing 12 ft. in height. When the Maoris reached the North Island of New Zealand, probably about 500 years ago, several kinds of moas seem to have been abundant and the Maoris hunted them for food. Within a century or so they were completely exterminated in the North Island, although in the South Island they seem to have lingered later, perhaps till the eighteenth or early in the nineteenth century.

As the story is commonly told, the moas are said to have been " killed off " by the Maoris, but there is reason for doubting whether this is actually what took place. It is certain from Maori tradition, and from the remains found at ancient native cooking-places, that the moa was a favourite article of food and in a country devoid of other large game the destruction may have been very great. It has been pointed out, however, that great quantities of moa bones have been found in very inaccessible localities on the

guess at. The passenger pigeons were certainly killed in large numbers for food, but one gets the impression that the toll taken by man would not, of itself, have sufficed to make much impression on the multitudes, any more than the persecution which they suffered from predatory birds and other animals attracted by the migrating flocks.

In all parts of the globe the arrival of man has been followed by the retreat or extermination of the larger mammals. What share our prehistoric ancestors had in the extermination of the mammoth we cannot now determine, but in more recent times the continuance of the process can be clearly traced. In 1914 the last survivors of the bison, the largest wild animal remaining in Europe, were to be found in two localities, the forest of Bialowicz in Lithuania, and the forests of the Caucasus. As it happened these two regions were traversed and re-traversed by rival armies during the Great War, and at its close the European bison had ceased to exist in the wild state. Some two score individuals are still alive in zoological gardens and parks in various parts of Europe, but it is doubtful whether it will be possible to maintain or increase their number.

The history of the American bison (called the buffalo in America) is still more disastrous. The vast herds which covered the prairies of the Wild West are familiar to us from countless stories of adventure, but fact has not

South Island, where there is no reason to believe that the Maoris ever penetrated. What caused the death of such large numbers we can only guess. It may have been epidemic disease or some climatic change ; it can hardly have been the Maoris.

The three examples discussed above were birds whose inability to fly rendered them an easy prey. It is less easy to understand the extermination of a powerful flier like the passenger pigeon of North America. The bird was formerly plentiful over a great part of North America, ranging from Canada to the Southern States. Audubon and other naturalists of the early nineteenth century have given memorable accounts of the vast flocks in which it migrated. In 1874 it was still common, but a rapid decline set in and twenty years later it was only to be found near the northern border of the United States and in Canada. At the beginning of the present century it was extinct in the wild state and though a few individuals lived for a few years longer in captivity they have left no descendants to carry on the race. The causes of this sudden decline are very hard to

OKAPI, A DISAPPEARING RELATIVE OF THE GIRAFFE

Related to the giraffe and the only near relative that animal now possesses, the okapi was discovered in 1901 although Stanley is said to have seen it previously. Only a few small herds are still left to-day in the very densest forests of Africa.

been outstripped by romance. As late as 1871 a traveller in Arkansas rode for 25 miles from east to west through a great herd of these animals on migration. "The whole country,' the record says, " appeared one mass of buffalo moving slowly to the northward." From other accounts we know that this same herd extended some fifty miles from north to south and at a very moderate estimate it must have comprised some four million head. How many herds like this the continent held we have no means of guessing, but even at that time buffalo hunting was a trade and buffalo skins were important articles of commerce.

The completion of the transcontinental railway and the introduction of the breech-loading rifle inaugurated a period of great prosperity for the industry. No one seems to have recalled the fable of the goose with the golden eggs, and when bison began to be less plentiful there were complaints that this result was due to shooting expeditions of " English sportsmen."

W. S. Ber.idge

W S Berridge

MANED WOLF AND BROWN HYAENA THAT ARE VANISHING

Very few specimens of this strange-looking, long-legged wolf (bottom) are believed to be now left in the wilds of Brazil, which are its home. It is called the red or maned wolf. The brown hyaena of Africa is also almost, if not quite, extinct. It was found south of the Zambesi, especially in coastal districts where it prowled on the beaches for crabs and dead fish.

The startling suddenness of the decline is illustrated by the records of buffalo hides consigned by a single railway, the Northern Pacific. In 1882 there were 200,000 hides; in 1883, 40,000; in 1884, 300, and in 1885 not one. By this time the chief industrial use made of the bison was the manufacture of fertiliser from the bleached skeletons which littered the prairies and which were collected in hundreds of tons to be ground up for this purpose. The last wild bison is said to have been killed in 1897, but a few small herds are preserved in the Yellowstone Park and other game preserves. A northern race of the bison, differing slightly from that of the great plains, still exists in Canada in the region of the Great Slave Lake and the Mackenzie River.

E.N.A.

REMNANTS OF THE ONCE ENORMOUS HERDS OF AMERICAN BISON

Most astonishing of all the stories of extinction is that of the American bison, which in U.S.A. is called the buffalo. Up till the 'seventies herds of almost incredible size wandered the prairies. In about twenty years these vast numbers were virtually wiped out. When we consider that a herd was observed on the move in Arkansas as late as 1871, and that it formed a mass of moving beasts, fifty miles long, and that this was just one company among many, the sheer immensity of the extirpation can be realized.

H J Shepstone

H. J. Shepstone

HANDLING BUFFALOES FOR TRANSPORT ACROSS THE UNITED STATES

So extraordinary was the speed with which buffaloes disappeared that it has been suggested that some kind of epidemic helped to carry them off. But contemporary accounts leave little doubt that the work was done by crack shots. "Buffalo Bill," subsequently proprietor of the celebrated "Wild West" show, undertook to supply the workmen on the Kansas Pacific railway with buffalo meat, and in eighteen months shot nearly 5,000 beasts. These photographs show the descendants of the old herds being handled for transport.

H. J. Shepstone

BISON CAREFULLY PRESERVED IN THE UNITED STATES AND CANADA

The building of the trans-continental railway greatly helped in wiping out the bison herds, and the trade in hides was carried on with imbecile fury. By 1885 the chief industry to do with the animals was the collection, and manufacture into fertiliser, of the skeletons which strewed the prairies in hundreds of tons. There still survives a race of bison in Canada, in the Mackenzie Valley, where the lower photograph was taken. It shows a boat used for transporting the beasts. Above is a scene in Buffalo National Park, U.S.A.

H J Shepstone

COWPUNCHERS NOW ATTEND TO THE CAREFULLY PRESERVED BISON

It is a far cry from " Buffalo Bill " and his crack shot associates to the cowpunchers of to-day, who are told off, not to destroy, but to tend the bison or buffaloes. These are preserved in various National parks, and when it becomes necessary to transport individuals from one part of the country to another the same methods are used as for ordinary stock. The lower photograph shows bison coming into a stock pen for branding, while above is a corral at Wainwright, with cowboys watching the great beasts.

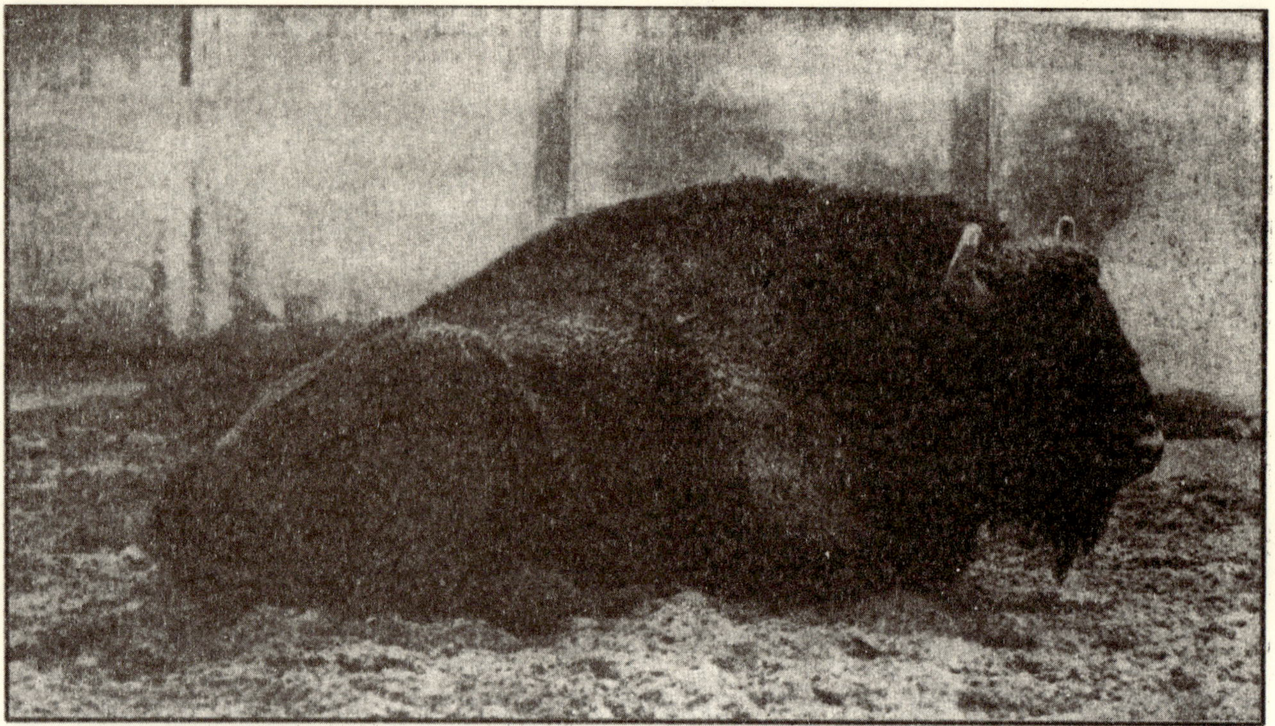

F. W Bond

Max Steckel

SOME OF THE LAST SURVIVORS OF THE EUROPEAN BISON

Taken in the great forests of Upper Silesia these photographs show some of the last of the wild European bison. These particular animals were the survivors of a herd on the vast estate of the Prince of Pless, to whom, in 1864, Tsar Alexander II had given a bull and three cows. In 1918 the herd numbered about 60, but the war and the revolution in Russia sealed its fate. Notice that the hump on the withers is much less pronounced than in the American bison, and that the European animals are more evenly proportioned.

James

The suddenness of the collapse of the American bison has led some to doubt whether it should be attributed solely to the rifle of the hunter. It has been suggested that it may have been due in some part to the spread of epidemic diseases introduced by domesticated cattle. In reading the accounts of the wild and reckless slaughter, however, one gets the impression that no further explanation is needed.

The fauna of Africa affords many instances of animals that are threatened with extermination and some that have become extinct within recent times. In view of the enormous size of the continent and the small area that has yet been settled by Europeans, this may appear surprising, but it has to be remembered that many kinds of big game, particularly antelopes, have only a very limited range of distribution. Further, the universal diffusion of modern fire-arms among the natives has had disastrous results upon the fauna all over the continent.

W. S. Berridge

TAKIN, A NOW RARE RUMINANT OF CENTRAL ASIA

Living on the remote mountain-sides of Bhutan—where the lower photograph was taken—and in the north of Assam, the takin seems to be dwindling away towards extinction. Its road to oblivion is helped by the fact that its very rarity has led people to expend a great deal of time and trouble in shooting it. The takin stands about three feet six inches at the shoulder.

W. S. Berridge

REPRESENTATIVES OF EXTINCT DEER FAMILIES IN THE LONDON ZOO

Père David's deer belong to a race of the Chinese water deer which were formerly kept in the park of the Imperial Palace at Pekin. The only specimens of Père David's deer known to be living are kept by the Duke of Bedford in the park at Woburn Abbey, and this solitary one (bottom) exhibited in the London Zoo. This kind of deer is fond of lying concealed in reeds. Above is of an example of Wallich's deer in the London Zoo where, at the time of the photograph, it was one of only two known survivors of its kind.

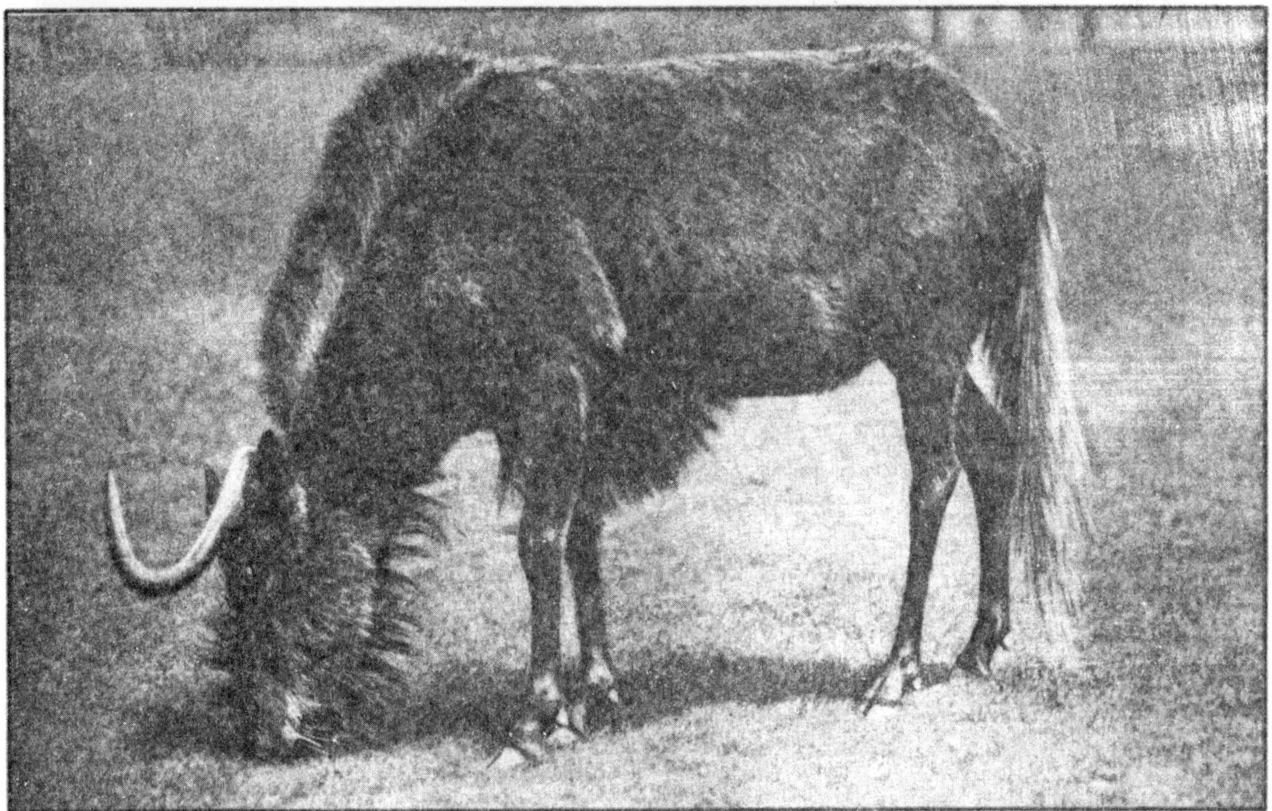

W. S. Berridge

WHITE-TAILED GNU OF AFRICA AND MONGOLIAN WILD HORSE

Africa, in spite of its enormous area and the comparatively sparse distribution of population save in a very few districts, has suffered losses in its fauna owing, partly at least, to man's intervention in the natural order of things. The range of certain animals, particularly of the antelope type, was very restricted and the possession of fire-arms by the natives has helped certain animals along the road to extinction. The white-tailed gnu (bottom) is now very rare. Mongolia is the last refuge of the wild horse (top).

Autotype

York & Sons

EXTINCT QUAGGA AND DISAPPEARING MOUNTAIN ZEBRA

Zebras have suffered greatly in various parts of Africa from the activities of hunters and natives armed with rifles. Several kinds are now much reduced in numbers and one, at least, the quagga (bottom) is now no more. The last survivor is believed to have been one that died in the London Zoo in 1864. Above is a specimen of the mountain zebra, now very scarce.

The African elephant has been hunted for the sake of its ivory from remote antiquity and has now disappeared from many regions where it was formerly common. Some local races or varieties of the species have certainly become extinct in this way. The Cape elephant, of which a small herd survives in the Addo Bush near Port Elizabeth, was almost exterminated some years ago by Government orders owing to the great damage it caused on neighbouring farms.

There is some evidence that a race of elephant formerly lived north of the Sahara and it may possibly have been this kind that was trained for war by the Carthaginians. In most of the British possessions in Africa elephants are now protected and in some districts they are stated to be increasing in numbers. It may be, however, that this is merely due to immigration from regions where they are more persecuted.

W. S. Berridge

BONTEBOK OF THE CAPE, NOW SURVIVING ONLY IN CAPTIVITY

Extinct as a wild animal, but still preserved in a few privately owned herds, the bontebok is a relative of the hartebeest. Its range was very restricted, having been confined to the sandy bush country round Cape Agulhas, which is the extreme south point of the continent of Africa. Possibly the bonteboks were cut off in this region by the drying up of the land immediately to the north, a process which has been going on for centuries. They would thus have evolved a distinctiveness of their own.

Several kinds of zebra have been greatly reduced in numbers in various parts of Africa owing to the activities of native and other hunters, and one at least is known to be quite extinct. This was the quagga, a zebra striped only on the head and forequarters, which was once plentiful on the plains south of the Orange River. The last survivor of this species is believed to have been one which died in the London Zoological Gardens in 1864.

THE inhabitants of the sea are much less accessible to man's destructive powers than are those of the land, but they provide one instance of extermination which is surely the most expeditious on record. When Bering discovered, in 1741, the sea which bears his name, the great sea cow was abundant round the shores of Copper Island and Bering Island. Before forty years had elapsed, perhaps even in twenty-five years, not one was left alive. It was a near relative of the manatee and the dugong, but grew to a length of more than twenty feet. Steller, the naturalist, who accompanied Bering's expedition, has given us the only account of the living animal, but its bones are still to be found embedded in the sand of the islands which it formerly haunted.

It was easily killed, its flesh was good to eat, and the fur traders and sealers who followed in Bering's wake used to feed their crews on it, with the result that it was speedily exterminated. Kipling, in his entertaining story of "The White Seal," which gives a vivid picture of the life on and around the seal islands in Bering Sea, makes a little slip in regard to the sea cow. It will be remembered that Kotick found that sea cow could not talk "because he has only six bones in his neck where he ought to have seven." Whatever be the fact as to his taciturnity, the sea cow had seven neck-vertebrae, like nearly all other mammals but unlike his cousin the manatee, which has only six.

The only mammals, other than the sea cow and its relatives, which are completely aquatic and unable to come on land, are the whales. All the larger kinds of whales are, or have been, pursued by man in different parts of the globe for the sake of their oil and, formerly, of their whalebone. While no species is known to have been completely exterminated as yet, several have been brought perilously near to that limit and the present scale of the whaling industry threatens the very existence of all. Even with the simple methods of the old whalers,

British Museum

W. S. Berridge

BIRDS EXTERMINATED BY MAN'S INFLUENCE

In 1507 the Portuguese landed on the island of Mauritius and found the dodo, a clumsy kind of flightless pigeon, in great numbers. About the end of the 17th century it became extinct owing to the persecution of rats and dogs introduced by man.

British Museum

GREAT AUK WANTONLY KILLED OFF

Owing to its helplessness on land, the great auk was soon killed off when it was found to have a commercial value. The last survivor in Europe was slain about 1844. This strange bird was flightless and rather resembled a penguin.

when the whales were attacked with hand harpoons from rowing boats, several kinds of whales were so reduced in numbers that the industry died out in the regions where it first flourished. The right whale of the North Atlantic, hunted by the Basques in the Middle Ages off the coasts of the Bay of Biscay, has long since disappeared from there, although it lingers elsewhere in small numbers. The Greenland whale was the chief object of pursuit of British whalers in the 18th and 19th centuries at Spitsbergen and Davis Strait and was later hunted by the Americans to the north of Bering Strait, but the fishery has now ceased in all these regions on account of the lack of whales.

The introduction of the harpoon gun, with the explosive harpoon, in the sixties of last century turned the attention of whalers to the large rorquals, which it was impossible to hunt by the older methods. Particularly the great blue whale, the largest animal, so far as we know, that has ever existed, was extensively pursued in various parts of the Northern Hemisphere. Here, again, history repeated itself and the industry languished as whales became scarce. In the early years of the twentieth century, however, the rich whaling grounds of the Antarctic were attacked, and since then, especially at South Georgia and the islands to the south of it, whaling has been developed on a scale previously undreamed of. In the season 1925–26 some 13,000 whales were killed in this region. It can hardly be doubted that this wholesale destruction is a serious menace to the very existence of some of the species.

In all the cases that have been mentioned and in many others of a similar kind the part that man has

RECONSTRUCTION OF A MOA COMPARED WITH TWO MAORIS

There is a mystery about the moas, the giant ostrich-like birds of New Zealand which stood twelve feet high. It is impossible to say why they suddenly died out, for it does not appear that the Maoris can have harassed them, especially in South Island, sufficiently to wipe them out. Possibly some epidemic or climatic influence killed them off. They seem to have lingered on till the eighteenth or early nineteenth century. No white man is known to have seen one. The photograph is by the New Zealand Government.

Neville Kingston

J. J. Ward

EXTINCT BUTTERFLY AND THE TUATERA

This handsome English butterfly, the large copper, seems to have disappeared about 1865 owing to the draining of the Fens where it lived. The tuatera (top) is a lizard whose relatives are now fossils. It is only found in some islands north of New Zealand

played is only too plainly that of a destroyer. Nevertheless it may fairly be questioned whether the blame for the extermination of some animals rests entirely with mankind. We know that countless species of animals that once flourished on the earth died out ages before man appeared. Whatever the causes of their extinction may have been, there is every reason to think that the same causes are operating to-day. It is quite conceivable that even if Mauritius had remained undiscovered, the dodo would still have died out. The sea cows, when Bering first saw them, were already the decadent and dwindling remnant of a once numerous and widely distributed family. Their extinction was hastened by man, but was probably inevitable.

The day has long gone by when the "state of nature" could be regarded as a kind of golden age in which, secure from man's interference, the lower creation would "live happy ever after." Darwin has shown us that the state of nature is a state of war, ceaseless for all and ruthless to the vanquished. The continued existence of mankind may necessitate the disappearance of yet more of the types of life that still share the earth with us. But it is not mere sentimentalism that will deplore the necessity and will demand that we diminish as little as we can the variety and the wonder of the living world that our successors will see. A motor car is a wonderful thing, but it is not so wonderful as an elephant. It would be a poorer world if the last African elephant had been killed to supply us with billiard balls, even if Africa were as full of motors as Piccadilly.

W. S. Berridge

THE LAST OF MAYER'S PIGEONS AND THE TRUMPETER SWAN

Man has been blamed for the fact that various animals have become extinct. But it should be remembered that, in a number of cases, the animal in question would have shortly become extinct in any case, and man only hastened the process. The dodo, for instance, could not be regarded as being in a very flourishing state if it could only populate one island. From the same place, Mauritius, came Mayer's pigeon, of which the last (below) was shown at the London Zoo in 1907. Above is a trumpeter swan, now extinct as a wild bird.

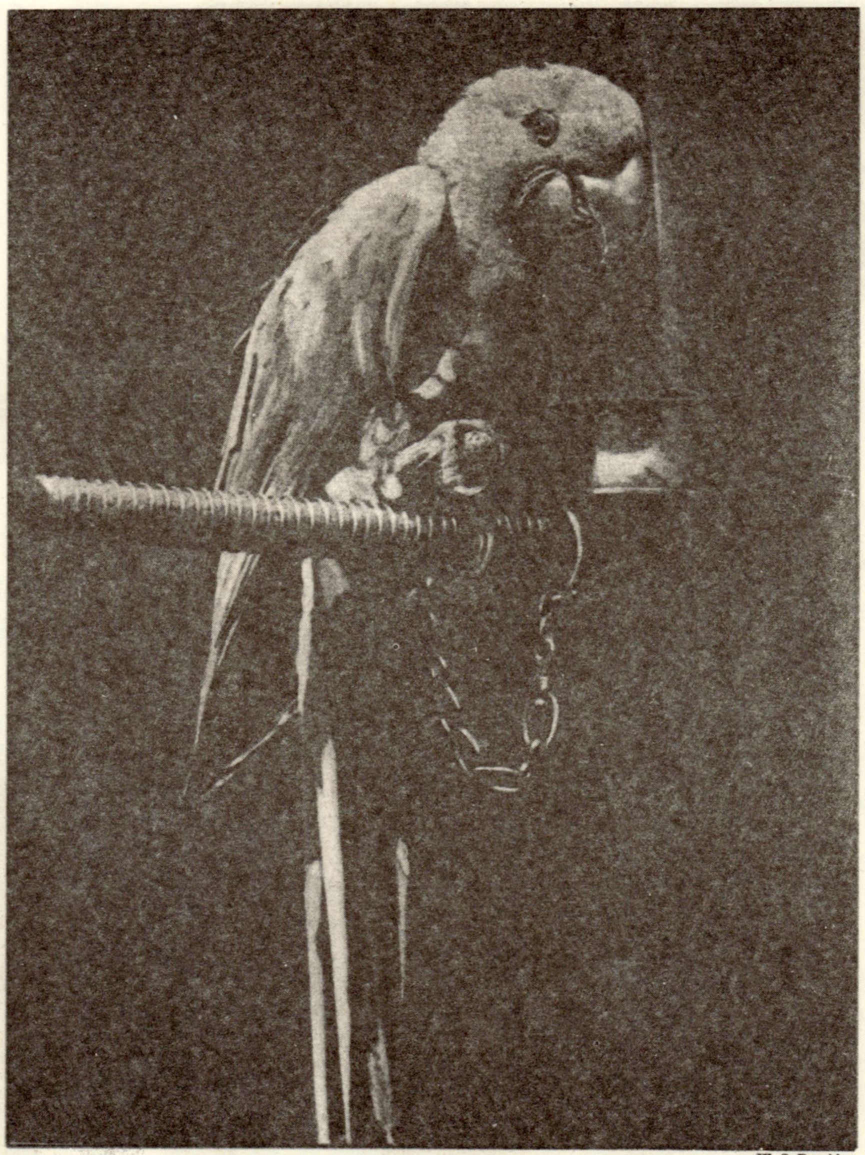

W. S. Berridge

TALKING BIRDS: INDIAN HOUSE MYNAH AND THE BRILLIANT HYACINTHINE MACAW

Perhaps the most magnificent of the talking birds, from the spectacular point of view, is the hyacinthine macaw (right) *Psittacus hyacinthinus*. It is not often seen in captivity for the simple reason that it is rather difficult to obtain. Instead of occurring in flocks, as other of the parrot tribe so often do, it is usually only found in pairs or else in single families. It haunts the dense forests of Central Brazil up to the latitudes of the Amazon. Its prevailing colour is a mauve blue, relieved by pale blue and a yellow band round the eye. The plumage is not only striking but brilliant in its colour. Our left hand photograph is of an Indian house mynah, a very entertaining bird and a great favourite in Indian homes.

Chapter CVII

The Talking Birds

By Oliver G. Pike

Author of "Bird Biographies"

SOME birds are very clever mimics. Among the British birds the members of the crow tribe are the most proficient, and a few of these become quite clever talkers. But in every case this is simply mimicry, and there can certainly be no intelligence connected with it.

I have known a raven ask for food, but he had learnt that if he uttered certain sounds, food would be given to him. This raven was one of the very best bird-talkers I have ever listened to. While he was alone in his large outdoor aviary, he would talk to himself for an hour at a time; when I heard him I thought it was the gardener speaking to a friend. He spoke in a low, guttural voice, but the words that his owner had taught him were uttered very perfectly. These words really meant nothing to the bird, they were just certain sounds that interested him, and he picked them up in the same way that a canary will learn certain notes from the nightingale if it happens to be placed near one of these singers.

I once possessed a wonderful jackdaw. This bird never learnt to talk properly, but he did make the most ludicrous efforts to repeat some of the things said to him. He was very good friends with most people that he met, but he had a very strong objection to one of my small boys, and he would chase him round the garden pecking at his legs as he ran behind him, all the time calling "Jaack, Jaack." He would sit on my typewriter and go to sleep on the carriage as it jerked along, and when he had had enough he would open his eyes and hurl the funniest imitations of words at me. Once, and once only, he was so annoyed that he ripped the paper I was typing into shreds, and flung the pieces to right and left.

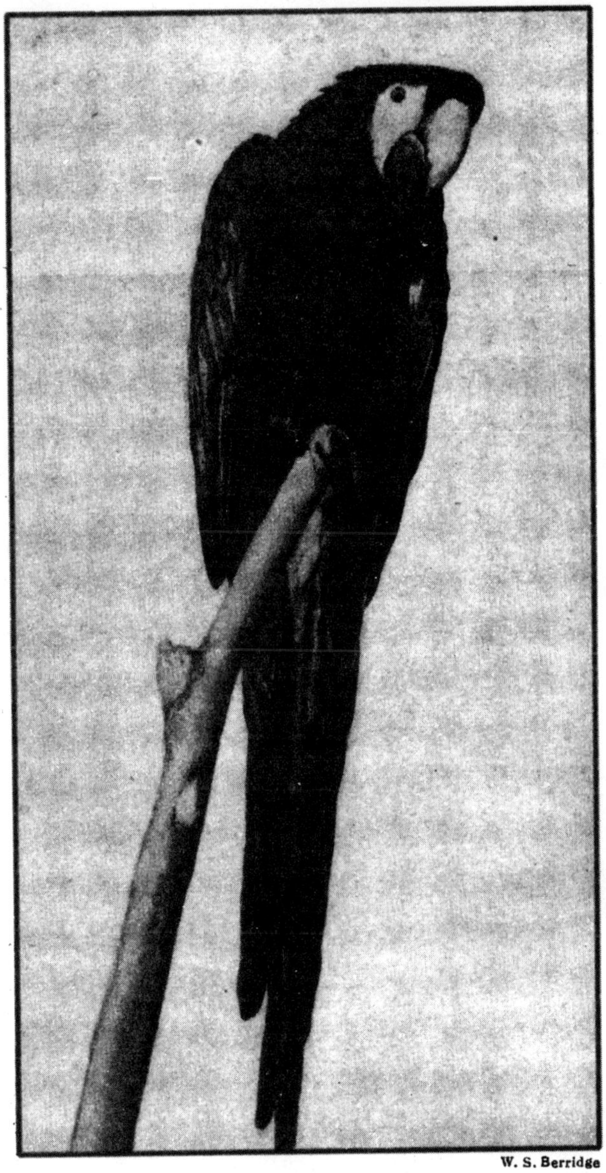

W. S. Berridge

RED AND YELLOW MACAW

Ability to talk among the macaws varies considerably with the individual bird, but care and patience are usually rewarded in time. This particular macaw, the red and yellow, is to be admired as well for its ornamental qualities as for its talkativeness.

At one time there was a very cruel practice prevalent in England. It consisted of splitting the tongues of starlings and other birds, and it was thought that by so doing they were helped to talk. The result was that the birds found it impossible to utter their own notes, and the strange sounds they made were considered by some to be an attempt at talking. In some remote country districts this ridiculous custom is still carried on. I have never known a starling to talk, but it is nevertheless a very clever mimic. I once heard a duck quacking loudly at the top of a tree, and as this seemed such a strange place for a duck to settle, I looked carefully among the higher branches, and found the culprit to be a facetious starling!

Parrots have the reputation of being very clever talkers; I have heard stories of them which seemed almost to prove parrot intelligence, but investigation has shown that the birds had been taught certain sentences, and when they spoke them correctly a special tit-bit was given to them. In time these birds discovered that they could obtain a definite prize if these words were uttered, and the fact that they had learnt this showed a certain amount of reasoning powers, but they certainly did not understand the meaning of the words.

One very clever talking parrot was the means of frightening a burglar. The man entered the house, and was preparing to look

W. S. Berridge

FAMOUS TALKING BIRDS OF INDIA AND AMERICA: MYNAH AND MOCKING-BIRD

One of the best " talkers " among the birds is the hill-mynah (bottom). This is a species found over almost the whole of India, where it nests in hollow trees and holes in the sides of banks. It is black with brown underparts, and is a near relative of the British starling. This hill-mynah is often captured and made a pet of on account of its fine whistling powers and its ability to talk. The upper photograph is of a northern mocking-bird, which has a peculiarly long, flat tail. This bird is a very fine mimic.

W. S. Berridge

CHAMPIONS OF THE TALKERS : BLUE-FRONTED AMAZON AND GREY PARROTS

So called because of the azure band above the beak, the blue-fronted Amazon (bottom) is found in Paraguay and Brazil in great numbers, and is considered the most teachable of the Amazon parrots. Although individuals occur which will hardly talk at all, the majority are extremely teachable and are regarded as the easiest to train of all the South American parrots. Some are even said to have been taught to sing whole songs. The grey parrots of Africa are the most gifted of all the talking birds. Here we have (top) a specimen from West Africa.

W. S. Berridge

SUBTLY COLOURED BUDGERIGAR OR AUSTRALIAN LOVE-BIRD

A species of parrakeet very widely domesticated is the little budgerigar or Australian love-bird. The notes these birds utter, a kind of rich warble, give the impression of great affection, and since the birds are always caged in pairs the happy spectacle of domestic bliss has made this bird very popular. Though it is very rare for a budgerigar to talk it is on recored that a certain English actress possessed one which learned the name of successful plays and would recite them much to the delectation of all who heard it.

round when a guttural voice said: "Who goes there?" This parrot, which knew quite a number of sentences, by a stroke of luck, said the one most likely to scare the unwelcome visitor away. It must have been very startling for the intruder.

Rooks, crows and magpies have all been known to learn words which greatly pleased their owners, and although I have had birds shown to me which were supposed to be intelligent pupils and understood what they were saying, careful investigation has shown that these pets were just uttering blind words that to them had no real meaning. It is always difficult to say where instinct ends and reasoning begins. There can be no doubt that intelligent dogs, such as well-trained sheep-dogs, understand many things said to them, and I see no reason why they should not understand slow conversation spoken by their masters, but we cannot say the same about birds which have learned to speak a few words of our language. A friend of mine had a rook which he had reared from a nestling, and it was a very clever bird, and could say a few words, but these were simply repeated "parrot-like," and meant to him that he received a reward if he gave out certain definite sounds.

Although the smaller birds, such as the warblers, never learn words, they very soon pick up the notes of other birds, and the little sedge-warbler has been mistaken for the nightingale because he sings at night, and is a clever mimic, including in his song notes of

TALKING BIRD OF GORGEOUS COLOUR: BLUE AND YELLOW MACAW

Especially prized for their highly ornamental effect and for their large size—some of the birds are three feet long—the macaws can be trained to talk in a very entertaining fashion. In a wild state they are famous for the noise that the great flocks of them make. In captivity, the blue and yellow macaw, seen above, is a hardy bird and considered to be the best talker among the macaws.

W. S. Berridge

TWO BRITISH WILD BIRDS THAT CAN BE TRAINED TO TALK

Although the raven (bottom) is usually associated only with a croak it can utter many other sorts of sounds and some ravens will even learn to talk. These birds make most amusing pets, provided there is a garden for them to get about in; but, of course, amusement must be paid for and a raven is full of mischief and cunning. The starling (top) easily learns to talk, and is not assisted in its lesson by having its tongue slit as has been the cruel and ridiculous custom in the past. The only effect of this mutilation was to stop the bird's natural notes.

W. S. Berridge

EXCELLENT MIMICS AMONG THE BIRDS THAT CAN BE TAUGHT TO COPY THE HUMAN VOICE

To many people the only noise the jay (left) is known to make is a harsh screech, but often, when one supposes that a certain bird is calling it is really some mischievous jay using its great power of mimicry. This bird can also make very good imitations of mechanical sounds, and it can occasionally be trained to utter a few words. There are obviously possibilities in the jay, but they have been little explored owing to the fact that the bird is seldom seen in captivity and is not at all easy to catch as it haunts the densest thickets and the closest parts of spinneys and woods, and is moreover exceedingly shy and wary. As for the jackdaw (right), it can certainly be taught to speak if caught young and properly trained.

W. S. Berridge

WHITE-BACKED AND BLACK-BACKED PIPING CROWS OF AUSTRALIA THAT CAN SING AND TALK

In Australia the piping crows are known as magpies. There are four species generally recognized of which we have two here: (left) the white-backed, and (right) the black-backed varieties. The latter is easily persuaded to become friendly and it is a favourite cage bird owing to its excellent powers of voice. Nevertheless, once caged, individuals vary considerably, some piping in proper full-throated manner, others in very subdued tones. In its wild state the bird is found in territory that has been mostly cleared of timber, or in open plains where there is a fringe of trees. It will readily come to human habitations if given the least encouragement, and painstaking people can teach it to say odd words.

COCKATOO BROADCASTING ON THE HUNDREDTH BIRTHDAY OF "THE ZOO"

During the celebration of the hundredth birthday of the London Zoological Gardens broadcasting was used in order to make the most of the occasion. One of the cockatoos was brought to the microphone for the entertainment of listeners. The bird deigned to imitate the sounds of kissing, but the performance had to end when the "artiste" tried to eat the microphone.

several other birds. I remember waiting in a "hide" to photograph a little grebe at its nest, and during the several hours I spent there, a thrush above me kept on calling "stick-to-it, stick-to-it." The notes were almost human, and it seemed as if he was encouraging me to continue. Many times I have been told by various people that a thrush in their garden had learned several human words. Thrushes vary very much in their singing, and many of their notes can easily be interpreted into words used by us.

There are birds at the London Zoo which will imitate sounds made by the spectators, but it does not follow that these birds have learned to talk.

An excellent talker is the Indian mynah, a ground bird related to the British starling. It nests in hollow trees, hedges and holes in banks and is insectivorous. Often its articulation is exceedingly good, and visitors to aviaries and zoos are often startled by hearing what is apparently a human voice when no people are visible who could have uttered it.

Chapter CVIII

Weapons and Warfare in the Animal World

By R. I. Pocock, F.R.S.

Of the Zoological Department, British Museum

In the generally accepted meaning of the word weapons are instruments of attack, and in that sense are contrasted with armour of which the function is essentially defensive. But in the animal kingdom it is not possible to draw a hard and fast line between the two. The spines, for instance, of sea-urchins, thorn-back crabs, globe-fish, hedgehogs and porcupines are in a sense weapons, although, since their function is passively protective, they are in that respect comparable to the "shells" of the snail, mussel, lobster, tortoise or armadillo which come into the category of armour. Weapons for attack are also equally useful for defence; and it is not always easy to decide for which of the two purposes they were primarily developed.

A similar difficulty presents itself in the interpretation of the word warfare. Organized warfare, in the sense of concerted raids carried out by castes of "soldiers," are restricted to such social insects as the ants, and the termites or "white ants." But the meaning of warfare must here be extended to the predatory persecution by carnivorous animals of those upon which they prey; and this conception involves the application of the word weapon to teeth, claws, stings and other appliances used for killing, of which there is such an infinite variety that it is only possible to enumerate the most important. Under warfare must also be included the fierce combats in which the males of some of the more highly organized animals engage for the possession of the females at the breeding season. For these duels the rivals are often provided with special weapons and special armour.

In the most lowly organized animals, the jellyfish and sea-anemones, in which definite weapons exist they combine the double function of killing prey and protection from enemies. They consist of remarkable batteries of microscopical stinging capsules similar in many respects to the stinging organs of nettles. Each capsule contains a fine, pointed, poisonous thread coiled up like a spring which is released under the stimulus of contact with another body so that the thread shoots out, penetrates any soft spot it touches, and instils its poison into the puncture. By this means these otherwise inactive, helpless animals are enabled to paralyse and kill their prey. The human skin is in most cases too tough to be sensitive to the prick of these minute darts; but bathers who have unwittingly encountered big jellyfish in the sea have no wish to repeat the experience. It is well known, too, that very few fishes will eat sea-anemones because they dislike the irritation to the mouth and throat to which these stinging threads quickly give rise.

DANGEROUS WEAPONS OF THE BEAR

Contrary to popular belief, the bears use their fore limbs to strike with, and depend on the terrific blows they can give for defence. They do not use the hug for killing their prey or in self-defence. Here we see what dangerous weapons a bear possesses

Tentacles, or "arms," of various kinds for the capture of prey are found in many marine animals; but they reach their highest efficiency in the Mollusca known as cuttle-fishes in which the mouth is surrounded by eight or ten long, flexible but very muscular arms, each provided beneath with numerous suckers. Anchored securely to a rock by their suckers, cuttles lie in wait for passing prey, and woe betide the unwary fish that ventures within reach of one of the arms; and many are the stories of loss of human life from encounters with some of the larger kinds which may be colossal in size.

Very different from the prehensile tentacles of the anemones and cuttle-fish are the pincers or 'claws' with which the hard-

EFFECTIVE WEAPON USED BY AN ELEPHANT IN THE MELBOURNE ZOO

Elephants have what seem to be very formidable weapons in their huge tusks. Yet these are chiefly used for uprooting vegetable food. The usual weapons used by the angry elephant are its feet, the animal charging the object of its wrath and trying to trample it underfoot. The elephant seen here, however, could not defend itself in this way from a pestering of small children. Therefore it used its trunk in this highly effective way. Just so dangerous crowds are sometimes broken up with fire hoses instead of with more lethal weapons.

shelled crustaceans, like the crab and lobster, are provided. These powerful weapons are used for grasping prey and for fighting, and, as many of us know to our cost, are capable of pinching with surprising strength. The shell of crustaceans is also frequently armed with spines, more particularly the fore part of the head which, as in the prawn and others, is often produced into a long beak, perhaps especially useful in guarding the eyes from attack.

Pincers similar to those of the crab in structure and use are also found in the scorpions; but these terrestrial arachnids are further armed with a sharp spine carrying a pair of poison glands and jointed to the end of the body which is narrowed to form a flexible, muscular "tail." This tail is usually carried coiled over the back ready to strike in case of attack; but its main use appears to be the rapid killing of living prey seized by the pincers.

Poison glands are also found in another order of this class, namely, the spiders; but in this case they are lodged in the jaws and open at the tip of sharp fangs which are buried in the tissues of the prey. The action of the poison, as in the scorpions, is very rapid. Centipedes, too, have powerful poison jaws; but it is only the largest scorpions, spiders and centipedes which instil sufficient venom to be dangerous to man.

The whip scorpions, which are related to the spiders, have no poison glands, but they possess killing weapons in the form of a pair of powerful limbs armed with strong sharp spines which, when the limb is folded, impale and hold their prey exactly as a gin-trap holds a captured rabbit; and the strong grasping fore-legs of the mantis, a predatory insect akin to our cockroach, are instruments made on the same principle. The fore-legs of the large aquatic bug, called the water-scorpion, are somewhat similarly modified for the prehension of prey.

IN other predatory insects, like the dragon-flies and many beetles, the jaws are the weapons for killing; but the ants, wasps and bees have a poisonous sting at the end of the abdomen. This is restricted to the female, the probe being a modified ovipositor consisting of a pointed sheath which makes the puncture, the poison being instilled by means of a couple of toothed styles which slide down the sheath and penetrate deeply into the wound. This apparatus is defensive in the nectar-feeding bees; but as a

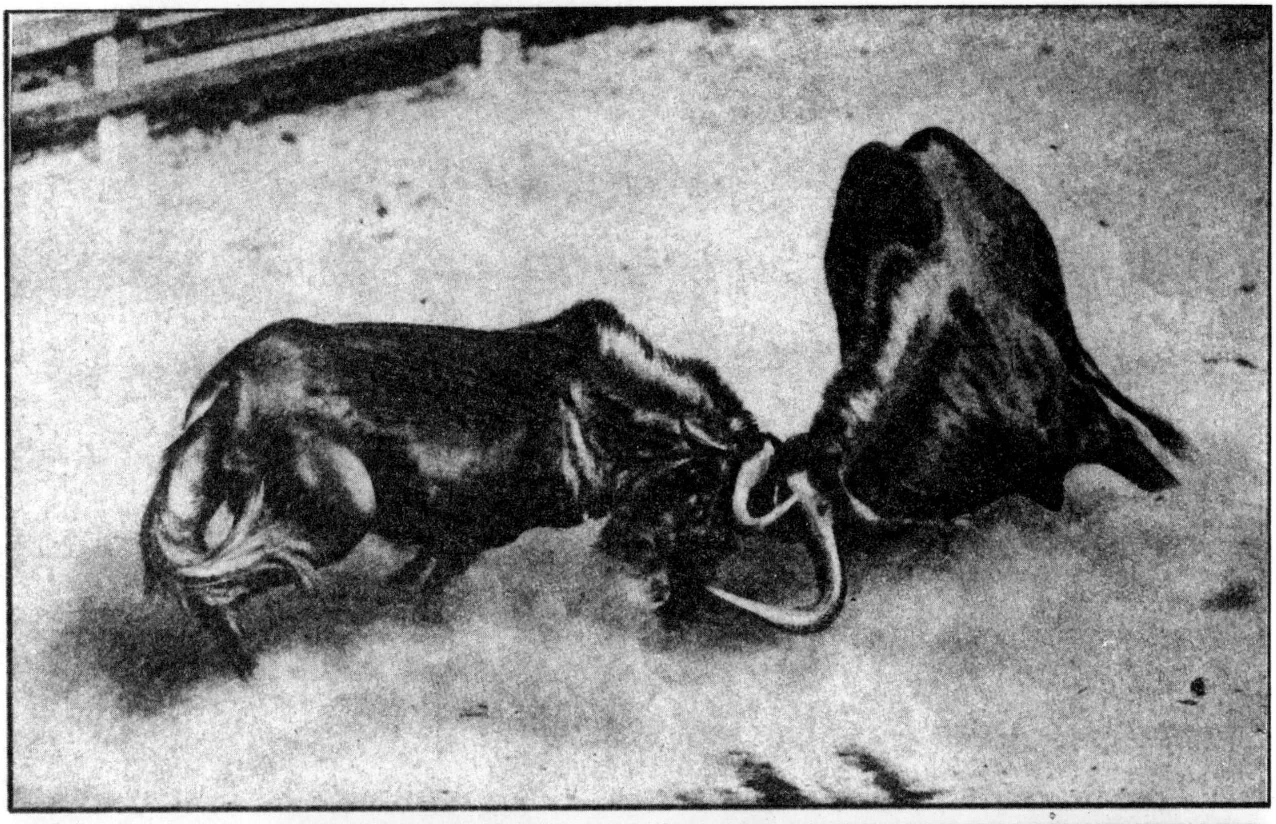

Mondiale

HORNS AS WEAPONS OF OFFENCE AND DEFENCE: COWS AND GNUS FIGHTING

These dramatic photographs show the defensive as well as the offensive use of horns. Below we see two domestic cows fighting for the leadership of their herd before going up to their mountain pastures in Switzerland. Above are two gnus. As the two animals meet in a charge, the bases of their horns serve to deaden the shock and ward off the dangerous points of their opponent's weapon. These gnus were obtained as specimens for the Melbourne Zoological Gardens but, on being turned loose in the same pen, took a violent dislike to each other.

Autotype

PROBABLY THE MOST EFFICIENT KILLING MACHINE IN NATURE: THE CROUCHING TIGER

Crouched and ready to spring, the tiger seems to be all weapon—a missile ready to be flung. The great retractile claws, cruelly curved and always kept sharp, are joined to paws so powerful that a blow from either of the front pair can break the neck of an ox or a tear from the hind pair disembowel a horse. Added to these weapons is the effect of the blow when the leaping animal's weight descends upon its prey at the end of the spring. The tiger also has very powerful jaws armed with big teeth which show to great advantage in the above photograph. This is almost certainly the deadliest killing machine in all Nature, combining, as the animal does, great agility with great strength.

weapon for attack, it reaches its highest development in the predatory mason wasps, which feed their young on spiders and soft-skinned insect grubs. Many of the ants have powerful jaws as well as stings, and some of them first bite their prey then squirt the poison into the wound. An acid fluid discharged from the end of the body is also a weapon used by the bombardier beetles; but in this case, it is solely defensive, the liquid volatilising on contact with the air to form a puff of acrid smoke behind which the beetles retreat from an enemy.

From the infinite variety of weapons for attack and defence, or both combined, in the vertebrated animals it is impossible to mention more than a few of the most important in each class. Taking first the fishes, we find astonishing modifications in the structure of the teeth for killing prey of

Autotype

CAT AND DOG WEAPONS PREPARED FOR USE

Special circumstances do wonders in the modification of animal weapons. The bulldog was bred for seizing the muzzle of the bull in the old sport of bull-baiting. Thus the jaws, like a steel trap, and the nose, compressed so as to let the animal breathe while its teeth were fast in the bull, have been produced by breeding. Above is a Scottish wild cat.

C les Reid

Autotype

DEER WEAPONS DEVELOPED FOR THE MATING SEASON'S FIGHTS

Wapiti stags are celebrated for the enormous antlers they grow, and this fine specimen from California admirably upholds his family traditions in this respect. The upper photograph shows a group of red deer on the island of Arran. In the distance is Brodick. These great horns are not so damaging as might be expected, since the various branches catch in each other when the animals are fighting and the battle becomes a sort of pushing match. The vanquished can usually "live to fight another day."

GRECIAN IBEX IN DEFIANT POSTURE UPON A CRAG

The long backward curving horns of this Grecian ibex are well designed for inflicting dangerous wounds. The way they are curved gives an extra thrust to the upstroke of the head when the animal is butting, the mode of attack adopted by the ibex and all the other goats. Why this particular beast is standing with one foreleg raised is not clear. Perhaps he is challenging some rival male on the next crag. Those cloven hoofs are amazingly sure among the slippery rocks where the animal has its home.

SHOWING THEIR TEETH: DENTAL ORNAMENTS OF A LIONESS AND A DOMESTIC DOG

There is nothing like a good yawn for showing the full extent of an animal's dental equipment and its possibilities as a weapon. The yawning lioness (left) has a gape that could span a man's thigh, and the two murderous-looking canines in each jaw are nicely opposed and come together with dreadful force like the shutting of a mantrap. Both teeth and claws are actuated by steel-like muscles, and these, backed by an almost invincible ferocity, make the lioness a terrible combatant. The terrier's mouth is built on the same lines, and it, too, has its four canines at the ends of its jaws. It is these teeth that do the damage to clothes and limbs when a dog bites.

Francis Birtles

H. J. Shepstone

FIGHT BETWEEN SEALS IN THE ARCTIC: CAT'S CLAWS VERSUS DOG'S JAWS

Seals are equipped with very sharp teeth, and can inflict a bad bite, although, to compensate for this, these animals are so protected by blubber that it would not be easy for a rival to find a vital spot save at the throat. Furthermore, while they remain on land these two fighters are not very active, and would find it hard to damage each other. The upper photograph shows the different attitudes adopted by cat and dog whilst sparring for an opening. The dog takes the active part, jumping round in a circle of which the cat is the centre. While the dog spreads its forelegs, the cat keeps hers stiff. The dog will have the advantage if it is only active enough to knock its adversary over. Otherwise the cat will be on the dog's back scratching its eyes out.

CAMELS THAT POSSESS DANGEROUS JAWS

Camels are strange, fractious creatures, and their tempers and their behaviour can never be counted on. They can bite with fearful force, and as the attack in the case of, say, a camel driver is often not made at the time of injury but some time after, it is all the more likely to be effective. These photographs show the dangerous looking jaws these animals possess.

different kinds, the most formidable in the way of wounding being those of the wolf fish, angler and some sharks. Of particular interest is a member of the shark tribe, the saw-fish, in which the snout is prolonged into a great blade with sharp teeth implanted on its two edges. With this weapon the saw-fish lacerates the bodies of its victims, tearing off great pieces of flesh to be swallowed.

A somewhat similar weapon, but pointed and without teeth, is found in the sword-fishes, large, swift, ocean fishes which use their weapons for transfixing prey. There are cases on record of their charging and piercing the bottoms of ships in mistake for whales. In their encounters with cetaceans, sword-fish are said by sailors to be helped by the thresher sharks which, leaping high in the air, lash the victims with their long tails as they descend.

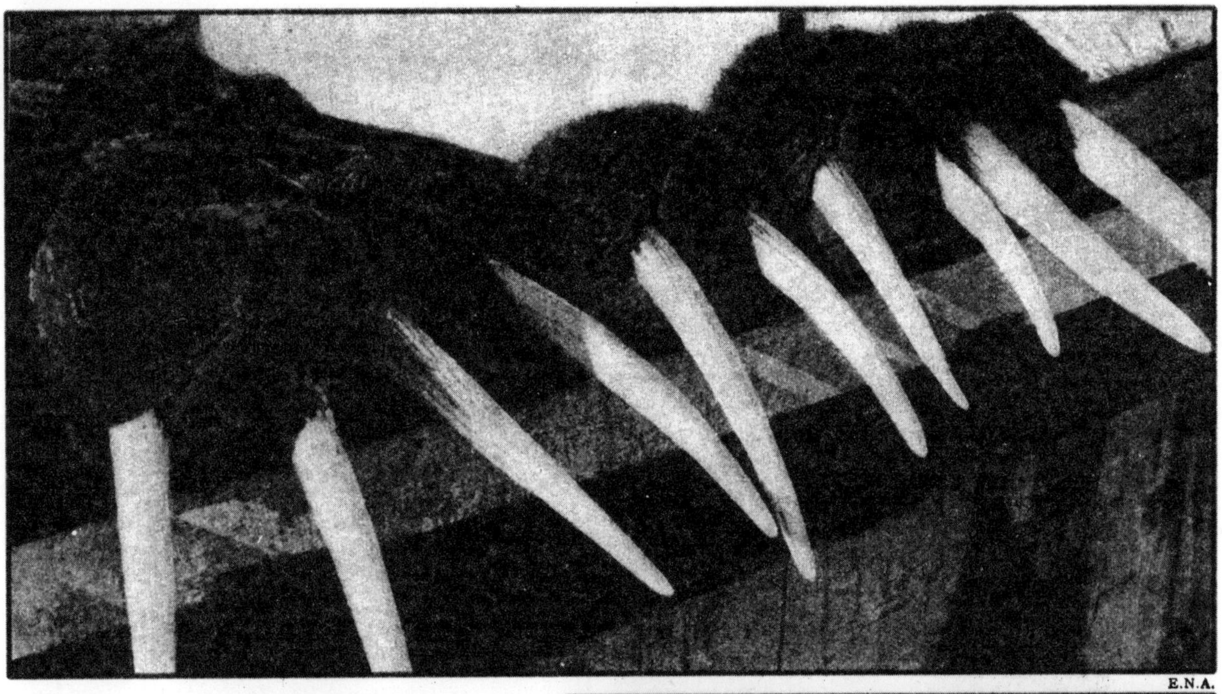

E.N.A.

But this use of the shark's tail as a weapon of attack has been denied by naturalists.

Not less varied than the teeth of fishes are the defensive weapons, in the form of spines with which many kinds are armed. The dorsal spikes of the common stickleback are a well-known instance. Somewhat similar spikes are developed on the back in the spiny dog-fish, the trigger-fish, and others; and the sharp barbed spike wielded by the long, lash-like tail of the eagle ray and sting ray is capable of inflicting a deep wound. It is in connection with such spines that we find poison glands developed in fishes. The British weaver-fishes, for example, have a poisonous spine on the plate that covers the gills and also on the back; and bathers who have stepped on them buried in the sand can testify to the acute pain that follows the puncture. But perhaps the most remarkable weapons possessed by fishes are the electric batteries found in several fishes of which the marine torpedo, one of the rays, and the South American fresh-water electric eel are the best known types. In the torpedo the batteries are placed on each side of the head, in the eel in the upper part of the tail. The shocks from these batteries are used for killing or stunning fishes which are then devoured; and their defensive properties will be appreciated by anyone who has had the temerity or the misfortune to touch one of these living electric machines.

W. S. Berridge

DEFENCES OF SKUNK AND WALRUS

While the skunk (bottom) relies for defending itself not upon strength but upon the power to discharge a squirt of the most foul-smelling liquid from special glands the walrus (top) goes in for heavy tusks, of which even the polar bear knows well that it must take care.

The amphibia, or frogs, toads and newts, are singularly devoid of weapons unless distasteful glands in the skin come under that category. But many reptiles are well armed. The sharp interlocking teeth, embedded in vice-like jaws, of the crocodiles and alligators are capable of holding under water and drowning even large land animals that come to the riverside to drink; and many of the larger lizards and non-poisonous snakes, like pythons, can inflict very painful bites. The tail, too, is an important weapon in this class. Crocodiles, when on land, use it with great precision to knock over any unwary animal suitable for eating that comes within reach; the blows of the long tails of monitor lizards sting like a whip, and in the case of other lizards, like the mastigures, the strokes of the tail are rendered doubly disconcerting by the rows of sharp spines that encircle

Otho Webb

THREE EXCITING STAGES IN A KANGAROO HUNT

In kangaroo hunting the odds are not quite so heavy against the quarry as in some other forms of the chase. Here we see three stages in the pursuit—first (top left) a kangaroo beating off the hounds by using its tail as a seat and kicking with its hind legs; second (top right), the quarry driven into a water hole, and third (bottom), preparing to seize and drown the dogs.

them. In other lizards, the "horned toad" of North America and the moloch of Australia, for instance, sharp spines on the head and body play the part of passively defensive weapons.

But the deadliest weapons known in reptiles are the poison fangs which are comparable to those of spiders and centipedes and are similarly useful for killing prey and protection from enemies. They are restricted to lizards and snakes; but only one family of lizards possesses them, namely, the heloderms or 'gila monsters' of North America, which are said to be very dangerous to handle. Of poisonous snakes there are many kinds, the adders and vipers, the cobras, and kraits being familiar examples, all about equally deadly even to animals much larger than themselves. Poisonous

PLAYING AT THE "REAL THING." HOW KANGAROOS FIGHT WITH ALL FOUR LEGS

Kangaroos box rather after the French style of "La Savate," that is, with the use of an occasional kick to aid the "fists." The animal supports itself on its tail while delivering the kick, as we see in the lower photograph. The long claws with which the hind legs are provided can inflict terrible wounds when the kangaroo is in earnest, for the blows are delivered with tremendous force from these very powerful limbs. The upper photograph shows the kangaroo delivering a good "straight right."

W. S. Berridge

PIERCING WEAPONS OF VARIED SHAPE: BEAKS OF EAGLES, VULTURE AND A COCKATOO

An assortment of medieval arms shows hardly more variety than the weapons of the birds. They have piercing implements of every sort of shape and the five photographs above give us a few examples from among the many. First, we have the vociferous sea eagle (bottom left), with its cruelly curved beak; then comes the tremendously hooked bill of the monkey-eating eagle (bottom centre). The fishing eagle is fierce of both beak and claw (bottom right), while the vulture adds a repulsive hood of horribly wrinkled skin to the threat of its curved beak. The great black cockatoo has an amazing-looking beak which curves back almost as though it would grow through its owner's throat.

E.N.A.

snakes, however, like wasps, scorpions, and other venomous animals, are for the most part not aggressive, unless interfered with, and use their poison mainly for killing prey; but the hamadryad or king cobra has been known to attack man without intentional provocation.

Some of the African cobras have learnt to use their poison in another way, namely, by spitting it in showers in the face of an adversary. The fluid is very irritating to the eyes and probably the habit is a useful defence against enemies like mongooses and secretary birds. Possibly in the category of weapons of defence in reptiles should be included the rattle of the rattlesnake. This is a sounding organ at the end of the tail which is useful to the protectively coloured viper, which does not wish to be stepped upon, by warning passing animals to be careful where they tread. Some other poisonous animals, the big scorpions and spiders, for instance, have analogous organs emitting sounds which, although inaudible to the animals themselves, are audible to their enemies.

In connexion with the weapons of birds, the first point to note is the absence of teeth and the modification of the jaws into a bony beak encased in a horny sheath. Since beaks have already been dealt with in a chapter by Mr. Frank Finn (pages 59–64), they require only brief consideration here. The beak is the weapon commonly used by birds for killing prey and also for self-defence, as those who have handled

James

HARPY EAGLE AND OSTRICH

Staring threateningly at the photographer the harpy eagle (bottom) grips its perch with its strong sharp talons and shows us a beak that is a weapon indeed. Above are two ostriches whose weapons are their powerful quick-kicking legs.

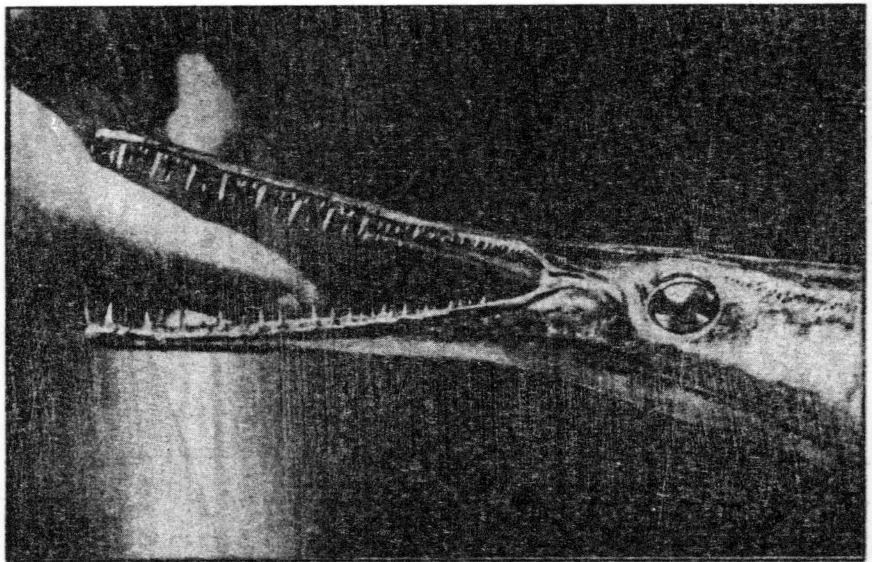

E.N.A.

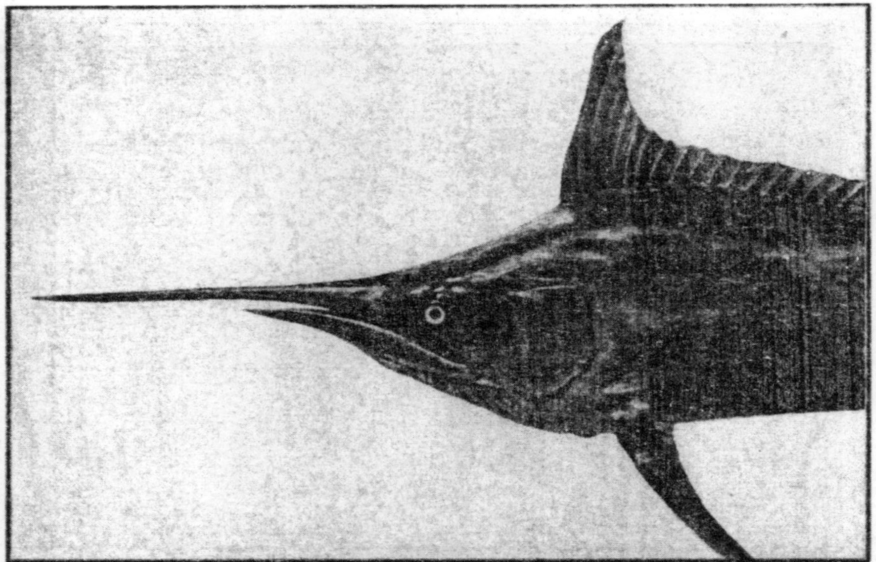

W. S. Berridge

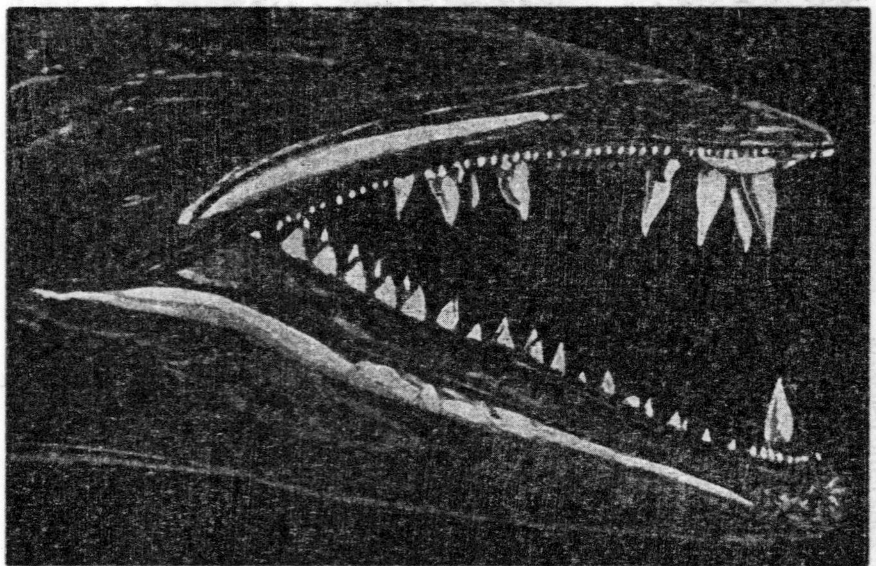

E.N.A.

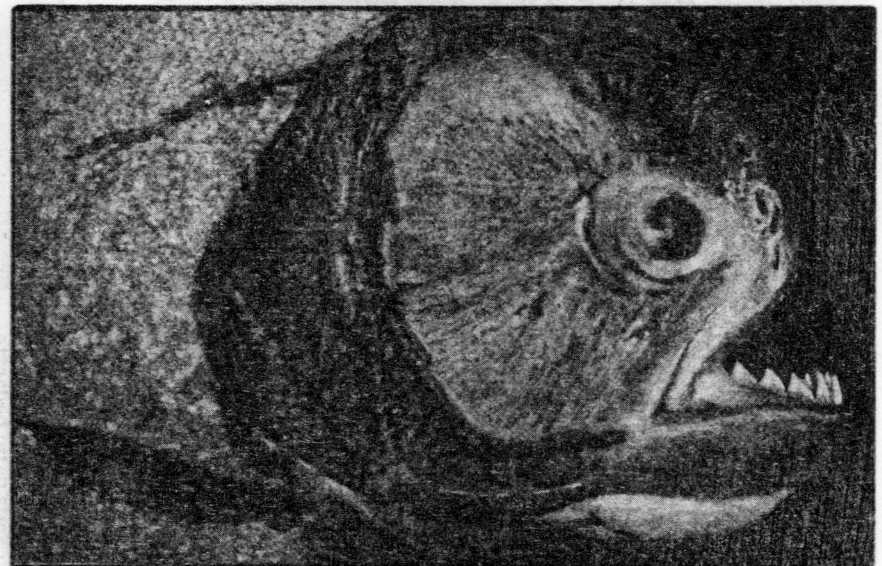

E.N.A.

SAWS OF SOME OF THE PREDATORY FISHES AND THE CRUEL TEETH WHICH LINE THEM

Famous as a sporting fish for which hundreds of anglers visit the Bahamas every year, the barracuda (bottom left) has a vicious, pike-like head and teeth which make it as much, or even more feared by bathers than the sharks. The fish in the bottom right-hand photograph is a piranha and was caught on one of the islands at the mouth of the Amazon It was captured with a piece of meat tied to a hook, its grip on the bait with its terrible teeth being so tight that the fish allowed itself to be hauled from the water rather than let go. Above we have (top left) a garfish with its extraordinarily prolonged jaws and (top right) a sail fish.

Otho Webb

even small birds, like robins and sparrows, are aware. Its efficiency depends upon its shape and size and the strength of the jaws. Even in grazers, like geese, it is a powerful, pinching instrument, and in parrots it is capable of inflicting a very painful wound. In the storks and herons perhaps, it reaches its highest development for offensive and defensive purposes. In the birds of prey, like owls, hawks and eagles, it is short and hooked and modified mainly for tearing prey already killed by the strong, sharp talons; and in these birds we find the feet, with their muscular clutch and long, penetrating claws, are the principal weapons. Other strong legged birds also use their feet. Ostriches and cassowaries, for instance, deal powerful blows with them, and in the case of the cassowary the efficacy of the stroke is increased by a great lacerating claw on the inner toe. Game birds also use their feet to great purpose when fighting.

MANY birds, like the pigeons and swans, which have feeble beak and legs, employ their wings as weapons, striking hard with the carpal angle or the edge of the wing below it; and in a few species this area of the wing is specially armed with sharp spurs, there being one such spur on each wing in the jacanas, spur-winged plover and spur-winged goose, and two in the screamers, the last being South American birds with powerful flight and as big as turkeys. Birds, however, as a class are comparatively poorly equipped with weapons because their flight gives them a ready means of escaping from enemies not so gifted.

Otho Webb

STING-RAY AND TIGER SHARK

Much broader than a man and one of the most deadly fish that swims is the sting-ray (bottom). It and the thirteen-foot tiger shark seen in the upper photograph were caught off the Barrier Reef of Australia.

W. S. Pitt

CARNIVOROUS TORTOISE WITH BEAK-LIKE JAWS

Although no tortoise has any teeth every individual has its jaws covered with horn so as to form a cutting beak. These beaks can inflict dangerous bites. Our photographs show a carnivorous tortoise that lives on worms. Below we see the under side of the animal with its hinged shell which protects the head and tail. Above is the tortoise on a worm hunt.

exceedingly sharp and loosely attached often stick in the flesh of an incautious carnivore that attempts to prey on these animals, causing dangerous wounds. In the tree porcupines of America the spines, although short and slender, are barbed in such a way that, once detached, they work into the lips, tongue or paws of an enemy, sometimes with fatal results even to such large beasts as pumas. Tigers, too, have been killed by the long quills of the Indian ground porcupine penetrating to vital organs. The erectile horny plates of the scaly ant-eaters or pangolins come rather into the category of armour; but in some species where they carry marginal thorny points capable of pricking sharply they may be regarded as protective weapons. Purely protective also are the scent glands of the skunks and other members of the weasel tribe which discharge a volatile, suffocating fluid in the face of an attacking enemy—a method of defence like that of the spitting cobra and bombardier beetle.

The Mammalia offer a great contrast to birds in this, as in other respects. Weapons of a purely defensive nature in the form of spines are found in the toothless spiny ant-eater or echidna of Australia, in the hedgehogs and some of their relatives in Madagascar, in some mice and in the porcupines where they attain their highest efficiency, and being

The use of teeth as weapons for attack and defence is so general in mammals that it is exceptional for them not to be so employed. Occasionally it is the

W. Saville-Kent

CREATURES THAT KILL WITH THE HELP OF POISON AND SUCTION

One of the lowliest animals possessing weapons is this Australian sea anemone (bottom) which has numbers of stinging capsules, each containing a poisonous thread which is coiled up within and released by the stimulus of contact. With the poison the anemone can paralyse and kill the organisms on which it lives. Above is a squid, whose weapons are its huge sucking tentacles

chisel-like gnawing teeth, as in the rats, squirrels and other rodents, but usually it is the canines, as in the dogs, cats, weasels and other predatory carnivores, as well as in the monkeys. Teeth when enlarged and projecting beyond the lips are called tusks. They are associated with other teeth which are useless for fighting. A case in point is supplied by the huge upper canine tusks of the walrus which are primarily for digging up mussels and other shell-fish upon which this great seal mostly feeds, but also serve for killing larger prey, like other seals, and for self-defence as many a hunter has testified. The tusks of elephants are also uprooting instruments which act as weapons of attack and defence as well. Very efficient weapons, too, are the wild boars' tusks, formed by the upper and lower canines on each side, the lower being kept sharp by rubbing against the upper, which in the wild swine of the old world turn outwards and upwards. So deadly is the ripping power of these tusks that even tigers, it is said by hunters and naturalists, fear to attack a wild boar at bay.

The elephant and wild boar, with their specialised tusks, introduce us to a great group of vegetable feeding, mainly ungulate or hoofed mammals in which the teeth, modified for grazing or browsing, are in most cases functionless for fighting and are replaced for that purpose by horns or hoofs, sometimes both combined. But the camels and llamas still use their teeth for fighting. So also do horses,

F. Martin Duncan

DEADLY SCORPION WITH ITS POISONED DAGGER

Though very rarely causing death to an adult human being who is in good health, the scorpion's sting can inflict a serious wound. In the lower photograph we have the sting in detail, and greatly magnified. Above is a scorpion ready to sting.

although their most efficient weapons are their solid-hoofed legs, fore and hind. The Asiatic rhinoceroses, too, despite their armature of nasal horns, always charge with the mouth, attempting to wound an opponent with the pair of small sharp tusks set in the fore part of the lower jaw. But the African rhinos, which have lost these tusks. are dependent upon their horns as weapons.

HORNS of another kind are found under a great variety of forms in the cattle, antelopes, sheep and goats, which never use their teeth. The horns may be short and sharp, as in many antelopes and the Indian wild goat or tahr; or long, straight and spear-like, as in the gemsbok, which can transfix a charging lion; or curved backwards, as in the sable antelope, so that the point inflicts a deep wound with a backward or upward sweep of the head. They are generally strengthened with ridges and often bent or twisted to lessen the shock to the skull from a direct blow; and very frequently the use of the point is supplemented by the expansion of the base of the horn over the forehead to form a boss or casque which acts like a battering ram, as in the musk-ox and the big African buffalo, one of the most formidable animals in existence. The use of the horns as a battering ram is perfected in wild sheep which fight by charging head-on and striking an opponent with tremendous impact.

Almost as important as teeth and horns for attack and defence are the feet of mammals, whether terminated by claws, big nails or hoofs. In some hornless species, which cannot or do not bite, they are the only available weapons. Doe rabbits, with young, have been known to rout even stoats by leaping in the air and kicking them with their sharp clawed hind legs; and hinds and hornless stags use their feet with great effect. A female prong-buck, indeed, has been known to lacerate a prairie wolf so severely with her hoofs that he abandoned the pursuit of the fawn he was after. Kangaroos when fighting raise themselves up and by using the tail and one leg as a support deliver rapid kicks with the other; and the toothless great ant-eater, with his back to a tree and his defenceless snout tucked down against his breast, can beat off dogs and is said to be able to repel even a puma with the blows of his powerful fore-legs, armed with lacerating claws.

But commonly the feet are accessory weapons to horns or teeth. Elephants and buffaloes use them for trampling or kneeling on a prostrate foe; and in carnivorous animals the paws are generally armed with claws of the greatest service in killing and fighting. The claws may be long and stout, as in the bears, which employ their fore-legs for striking an opponent, not for hugging as has often been said. But the most perfect claws for laceration are the sharp, hooked retractile claws of lions, tigers and others members of the cat tribe. Even the hands of monkeys must come into the category of weapons because they are used for holding an enemy before the teeth come into action. Baboons have been known to grip dogs by the head and rip the throat open with their great canine teeth, and gorillas are said to fell hunters with a blow of the hand.

The weapons hitherto considered are mainly those employed for the destruction of prey by predatory animals and for self-defence by the animals preyed upon, for warfare, that is to say, mostly between different species. But weapons sometimes serve more particularly the purpose of warfare between individuals of the same species, for the combats of the males for the possession of females. Some of these are alluded to in the chapter of this work dealing with Courtship Display Among the Animals. The subject, therefore, requires only brief notice here.

The tusks of elephants and wild boars, the canine teeth of monkeys and apes, and the horns of wild cattle, sheep, goats and many antelopes are larger in the males than the females. In some other antelopes horns are restricted to the males. Finally, in the deer which breed only once a year the horns or antlers are grown in readiness for that season, and are shed at the end of it. But a particularly significant point about antlers is that although stags engage in fierce combats for the hinds, these combats seldom end fatally, because the supernumerary branches act as guards against mutual injury and the fight resolves itself into a pushing contest from which the weaker individual disengages and makes his escape as soon as he realizes his inferiority.

Chapter CIX

The Teeming Life of a Quiet Country Lane

By Frances Pitt

Author of "Wild Creatures of Garden and Hedgerow"

PASSING along a country lane, all seems so still and quiet that no one would dream its hedge-banks were full of life; yet down in the tangled jungle of the wayside ditch, among the hedgerow plants of the fence, and even in the grass that borders the lane, are a host of creatures that live a life of gay adventure in the shadowy world among the undergrowth, from fierce hustling, bustling shrews to slow-moving snails.

Varied indeed is the wayside life of a quiet lane, the hedge-bank teems with spiders, grass-hoppers and caterpillars, with beetles, bees and wasps, with mice and even rats, to say nothing of birds, from the smart chaffinch, the demure whitethroat, the fussy wren, and the handsome greenfinch, to portly blackbirds and thrushes. And these are but a fraction of the creatures that haunt the wayside, a mere hint as to the real population that fills the world of hedge-bank and roadside herbage. When you peep and peer, and look carefully, you find that ditch and bank are tunnelled by highroads better used than the one on which we tread, these being the paths of the little people, who live in the shadowy depths of this miniature jungle, where existence runs fast and furious, where creatures more fierce than lion or tiger chase their prey, and adventure both gay and deadly lurks beneath the primrose leaves.

Now who and what are the inhabitants of the wayside jungle? First there are the mice; the sleek, smooth-coated, elegant long-tailed field-mouse, with great dark eyes, glistening like wet boot-buttons, its fawn coat, hand-like paws and dainty person; the bank vole, in red-brown, with a neat white waistcoat, and keen little face; and lastly the meadow vole, a rough-coated, short-tailed, plebeian-looking mouse; all of which haunt the hedge-bottom and ditch.

J. J. Ward

DRAGON-FLIES, AS THEY ASSUME THEIR WINGS

Hedgerows bordering a country lane are favourite hunting places of the dragon-fly. Here we see how the insects drag themselves out of their pupa skins (top) and dry themselves (bottom left). On the right (bottom) is an adult slender-bodied dragon-fly.

In the autumn you may find token of the long-tailed mouse in old birds' nests, for this mouse is no mean acrobat, and thinks nothing of going aloft, up into the thorn bushes and the briers, to raid the scarlet hips and haws, carrying each berry to some convenient dining-table, and there eating it at its leisure. Hence, as you walk along the road, you will see old birds' nests in the hedge filled to the brim with scarlet bits—this is where the long-tailed mouse feasted royally over night!

The two voles do not leave such obvious evidence of their presence, but now and again one may see a small brown shape dart across what, to it, must be the fearful arid expanse of the road. What nerves a bank, or meadow, vole to leave its home among the wayside grass, and face such a crossing? Probably the signal "danger!" has passed through the hedge-bank world. Considering their size, lions and tigers are timid beasts compared with the desperate hunters that haunt the seemingly peaceful ditch.

H. Bastin

WILD BEES THAT LIVE BY THE LANE SIDE

Many kinds of wild bees may be seen along the lane in summer. In the lower left hand photograph is a longhorn bee, a male above and a female below. Then we have (bottom right) a male and female of the *Halictus* family which live in burrows in the earth. The upper photograph is of a queen (left), drone (right) and worker (below) of a species of humble bee.

There is the weasel, a mighty Nimrod indeed, that is for ever hunting mice, voles and young rats, and races through their tunnels with relentless zeal. Slender, no bigger in girth than the mice it hunts, it passes like a fawn-coloured snake along their highways, to emerge for a moment upon the wayside and give one a fleeting glimpse of its dapper form. For a brief instant it sits up in a begging attitude, its little forepaws hanging folded in front of it, and its cream underparts exposed to the view, ere disappearing like the passing of a shadow into the tangled herbage.

Then there is its bigger relative the stoat, which is not only larger, but may always be known by its black-tipped tail (the weasel has *not* got a black " pencil ") that comes to the lane after the rabbits which dwell in the hedgebanks. Here and there are rabbit burrows, where their owners live peaceably save when the dreaded stoat carries out a lightning raid.

But hunt and be hunted is the lot of many of the inhabitants of the lane. Take the tiny shrews as an example, that live in the grassy jungle and hunt the small things such as worms, insects and spiders with a fierce eagerness greater even than that of the weasel.

Shrews, though often spoken of as mice, are not rodents at all, but belong to the Insectivora, or insect-eating mammals, and live, as hinted above, upon quite different fare from that of real mice. They are hunters, though their game is small, but then so are they, and for their size they are wonderfully plucky. I have seen a pygmy shrew, not so big in girth as my little finger, spring upon an earth-worm, which to it must have been a squirming monster, larger than the legendary dragons of old, grab it and fairly worry it to death.

The pygmy, or lesser shrew, is one of the smallest of mammals, and is so wee that it is often overlooked and mistaken for a young common shrew.

The common shrew, which is the little creature frequently found lying dead in the roadway, is not a big beast either, but again it is indomitably plucky. I kept one in a cage once to study its habits, and the " mighty atom " knew no fear. If it did not get what it wanted, it would fly at my fingers and bite them like a fiend—luckily its teeth were very tiny.

THE common shrew is one of the most numerous of the inhabitants of the wayside jungle, and as already mentioned, may often be found lying dead in the roadway. One reason for this is that it is an unpleasant-smelling little creature, and if a fox, dog, or cat, chances to kill one, it seldom eats it, but usually throws it away. Secondly, in the autumn shrews suffer from a mysterious mortality, dying off and being found lying dead on lanes and paths. In the days gone by it was thought that they were incapable of crossing a highway, but the modern

G. Hearn

G. Hearn

H. Bastin

J. J. Ward

W. S. Berridge

W. S. Berridge

SOME OF THE SMALL MAMMALS THAT LIVE IN THE HEDGE-BANKS

For those who have eyes to see it, the quiet country lane is busy with life and death, escape and capture. A soft progress down the lane will afford the best chance of seeing these larger inhabitants of the bank under the hedge. The mole (bottom left) is more often seen dead than alive, its appearance as a corpse before the wanderer's feet being not uncommon in the roadways in these days of fast-moving vehicles on rubber tyres. The rat, hedgehog, squirrel, and rabbit are all among the members of the lane's wild population.

Arthur Brook

S. Crook

WILD CREATURES CAUGHT BY THE CAMERA BESIDE A COUNTRY LANE

The country lane is, from the wild creature's point of view, merely an interruption in the countryside bordered by convenient cover in the shape of hedge or ditch, or fence or bank. Our left-hand illustration shows something that a cautious observer might see through a gap in the hedge, one fine evening. It is a vixen at the mouth of her earth, situated in the hedgebank, looking cautiously round before deciding to start on her night's prowl for food. The short-tailed field-mouse (right) is another of the dwellers in the bank beneath the hedge. In this case the mother of a family has had her nest disturbed and is removing her progeny, one by one in her mouth, to new and undiscovered quarters.

Mondiale

WHERE THE BROOK COMES NEAR THE LANE: FAMILY OF YOUNG KINGFISHERS

Easiest to see of all the lane's inhabitants are the many birds that have their homes and hunt for food there. Thrush, yellow-hammer and hedge sparrow catch our eye as we walk on summer mornings along some country way which still knows more of horse's hoofs than the wheels of motor cars. Where the lane goes through the brook by a watersplash, or over it by some old bridge, we may chance to get the dazzling, bright blue glint of a kingfisher's feathers as the bird flashes up stream to its fishing. Here we see a family of young kingfishers, sunning themselves on a rock. The young birds are always paler and less brilliant than their parents and their bills are all black, whereas those of the older birds have orange at the base.

M. H. Crawford

M. H. Crawford

M. H. Crawford

A. H. Wilford

BIRDS OF THE WAYSIDE: WILLOW WARBLER, WREN, THRUSH AND GREAT TIT

Life in the lane is as intricate and interwoven as the grasses and the boughs that grow beside the way. Below (bottom left) we have a male willow warbler which has just caught sight of a grub on a branch below and is deciding whether or no it is good eating. Another lane side bird is the brown wren (bottom right). Sometimes a flint, kicked up by a passing cart horse, serves as a convenient anvil on which a thrush can smash the shells of snails to which it is very partial (top left). The upper right-hand photograph is of a great tit.

Oliver G. Pike

T. T. Roberts

M. H. Crawford

M. H. Crawford

THREE WINGED PIRATES OF THE EVENING AND A WINTER SINGER

Discrepancies in size between some of the hunters and their prey which play hide and seek for dear life—on both sides—among the hedges are enormous. The big barn owl (bottom left), coming like an ill omen over the meadow at dusk, feeds largely on field mice, among the smallest of the lane's creatures. The brown owl (top left) and the little owl (top right) are two other hunters of the hedgeside and the latter, an imported species, is on the increase. By contrast to all this, the robin (bottom right) sings us a cheerful song on a winter's day.

G. Hearn

G. Hearn

G. Hearn

M. H. Crawford

HEDGE SPARROW, GOLDFINCH, BUTCHER BIRD AND WILLOW WREN, COMPANIONS ON A COUNTRY WALK

Soberly clad but pretty to watch is the hedge sparrow (bottom left) which does not belong to the same avian family as the common house sparrow and can be readily distinguished from the latter by its smaller size, neater appearance and the absence of a white bar on the wing. This one is just going to its nest in a tree in the hedge. The goldfinch (bottom right) is a little smaller than the hedge sparrow and may be seen where the lane goes past a copse or through woods. It is a great eater of the seeds of weeds and in this respect a friend of the gardener. The red-backed shrike (top left) or butcher bird makes the hedge into a larder, spitting its prey on thorns near its nest. It is shown with a stolen egg in its beak. On the right (top) is a willow wren.

P Webster

HOUSE MARTINS ON THE BEAM OF A BARN ROOF

As we pass a barn or a farm house there may fly out two or three birds which a townsman might mistake for swallows. But their glossy black heads and the white patches on their backs at the base of their tails show them to be house martins. The swallow's head is chestnut brown, and there is no white patch on the back. The house martin lives exclusively on insects and is therefore a great boon to cultivation. Unfortunately it is often driven from its nest by the house sparrow which, when adult, is almost entirely a seed eater in rural districts

theory is that they are like annual plants, the old ones dying off in the autumn after rearing their young ones.

Other inhabitants of the wayside ditch are the toad and the frog, who during the day keep to its dampest recesses, but come hopping forth at dusk, even into the roadway, on hunting and adventure bent, for even these quiet, unobtrusive creatures are hunters, their quarry being likewise insects

The fact of the matter is that the wild life of a quiet English lane is an epitome of Nature in the outer wilds, every creature being part of an interwoven net of life, one dependent on another, each complementary to its fellows, the frogs and toads, shrews and weasels, and the hundred and one other creatures, having their part in the Balance of Nature, and so keeping each species in its place and preventing its increasing unduly.

The frog eats insects and grubs, but gliding along the mouse runs comes the grass snake, which has a liking for frogs. In some parts of Great Britain the adder may also be found on the wayside, but in my experience " vipers " are usually nothing of the sort! It is the harmless blindworm that more often than not gets the credit of being a " dangerous snake." The blindworm is not only quite inoffensive to everything bigger than small earthworms and such lesser fry, but is not really a snake at all, being a legless lizard. As a rule it lurks in the green depths of the wayside tangle, under the shade of hedge parsley, " lords and ladies," and the scores of competing plants, but when the sun shines it comes out to enjoy the warmth, and it will perhaps be found sunning itself in the lane.

Apropos of shrews, frogs and blindworms, what of the tiny things on which they live? These indeed throng the wayside, and what a varied horde they are. There are the tiny scarlet black-spotted froghoppers that disport themselves each summer day on the wayside herbage, while active green tiger beetles dash about on the dusty road; there are ladybird beetles in their well-known uniform, the dingy click-beetle, parent of the destructive wireworm, and many another.

At dusk, when the " flittermouse " (the country folk use this term indifferently for the pipistrelle and whiskered bats) comes fluttering up the lane, to wheel, turn and twist on rustling skinny wings about the wayside bushes, certain mysterious fairy lamps are lit down among the grass. Little phosphorescent greenish lights appear, the night lights of the glow-worm, that little female beetle's equivalent of the dazzling signs that flash advertisements into our great towns' darkness, which are likewise an advertisement, and a matrimonial one at that. The female glow-worm, though a beetle, is unable to fly, but her mate has retained his wings, and uses them to seek his lady-love, flying through the summer night in search of her beckoning light.

We may divide the population of a country lane into the day world and the night world, for a host of hidden creatures come forth as the twilight descends. Not only are there the fluttering bats, but dor beetles hum past like heavy engined aeroplanes winging their way into the night, and moths appear as if by magic. The pallid ghost moth dances over the wayside grass, other soft-winged insects brush against one's face, mice scuttle with rustling steps in the hedge-banks, and a ponderous toad adventures forth upon the dangerous roadway.

The lane at night is full of life; if the creatures of the day have gone to rest, the creatures of the night are up and about, and they hold high revels until the sun rises once more, when rabbits seek their burrows, the toad its retreat in the ditch, the mice their holes in the bank, and the fluttering moths sink into the herbage or alight on palings, tree trunks or posts, where they draw their cloak of invisibility about them and vanish from sight.

Take the buff-tip moth (*Phalera bucephala*) as an example, which when it closes its wings loses all

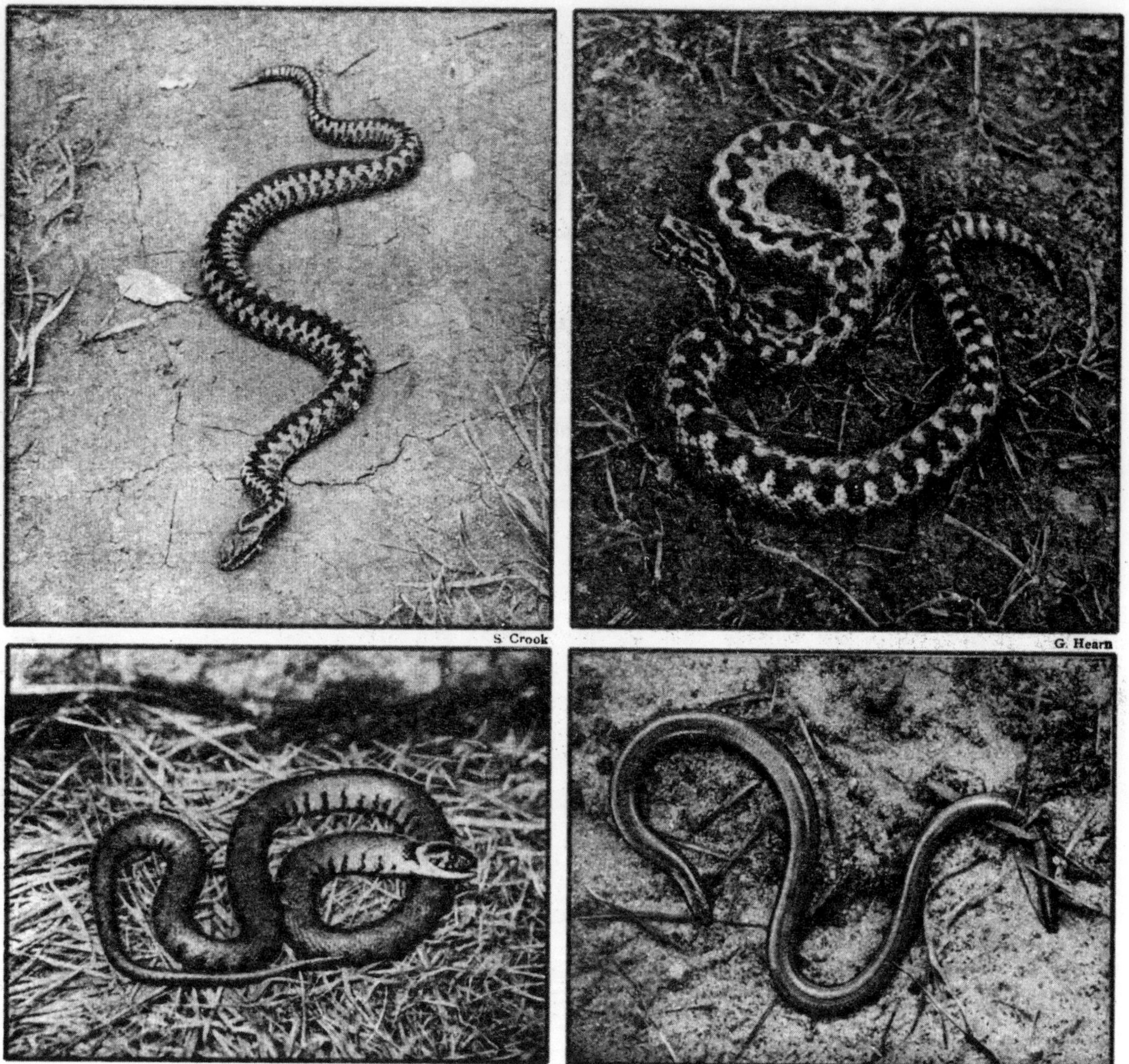

S. Crook G. Hearn G. Hearn J. J. Ward

TWO SNAKES AND A LIZARD THAT HAS LOST ITS LEGS

In the byeways of English counties snakes are not often seen, though they often hunt the ditches and the tall grass for their food. The grass snake (bottom left) and the slow worm (bottom right) the last not a snake but a legless lizard, are often killed on sight, though they are entirely harmless. The viper or adder (top), distinguished by the " V " mark on its head and the zig-zag line down its back, is venomous, though seldom fatally so. It sometimes comes on to the road for a sun bath, but will always rather flee than fight a human being.

resemblance to an insect and takes on the appearance of a bit of broken stick ; or the angle shades (*Phlogophora meticulosa*), that as it rests among the wayside plants becomes nothing but a dry, crumpled leaf.

But the boldest camouflage is that of the clouded magpie moth (*Abraxa ssylvata*), which does not try to hide, merely taking the first resting-place that it meets with and seating itself there with outspread wings, that make a white patch slightly specked with grey and amber, so that the moth loses all semblance of an insect and looks just like the casual dropping of some bird.

Then in considering the insect life of the lane, there are the caterpillars, from the slender stick-like larvae of the Geometridae to the fine, furry caterpillars of the tiger moth, the drinker and others. Not one is more conspicuous than the social larva of the buff-tip moth, which in company with some scores of its fellows, strips the leaves mercilessly from the nut bushes.

The fact of the matter is that the lane with its fences is an entomologist's paradise, where everything that creeps, crawls and flies may be met with. It is here that the earliest of the spring butterflies appear, orange-tips, brimstones and cabbage whites, and where later in the summer gauzy dragon-flies wheel, turn and dart, in company with gorgeous peacock butterflies, red admirals and painted ladies ; while bees, from the ponderous bumble bee to the various tiny solitary bees, buzz about their business. There are lacewing flies, hover-flies, and countless others, there are wasps, with a paper nest hanging in the fence (*Vespa sylvestris*), and the common wasps with their nest in the roadside bank ; while of spiders there are great numbers—wolf spiders racing through and over the grass, carrying their family cares behind them, bearing their cocoon of eggs attached to their spinnerets, and great fat orb-weavers sitting motionless but alert near their snares spun on the fence.

A BOOK could be written upon the spiders of a country lane, on the orb-weavers, sheet-weavers and others, but the reader will have to go and discover the many kinds for himself, because one of the most important sections of the population of the wayside has been neglected, and space is running short. I mean the birds. Bird-life looms large in our country lane. Partridges and larks come from the nearby fields to enjoy the luxury of a sand bath at its dusty side, and other birds seize the opportunity afforded by a shower to wash in the rain puddles. I have often seen chaffinches and blackbirds splashing water far and wide, bathing in the middle of the track in a manner they could not have done on a well-used highway, where roaring motors would speedily have sent them about their business. Our quiet lane, however, is but little worried by noisy traffic, and birds nest happily in its straggling fences. The aforesaid chaffinch commonly makes its neat cup of moss and lichen in the thorn hedge, lays its purple-streaked eggs therein, and broods there in happy indifference to passers-by.

S. Crook

S. Crook

NATTERJACK AND COMMON TOADS BY THE WAY

Natterjacks are rare toads, but are occasionally to be found among the grass at the side of the road. Here we have a fine specimen (bottom). The common toad is a familiar discovery, especially in damp surroundings. Sometimes a dead one may be found crushed in the road. This one (top) is thinking over the next meal beside a clump of rushes by a pond.

The yellow-hammer is another bird that loves the lane, and, what is more, is one of its most noticeable inhabitants. This is not because it is a noisy or conspicuous bird, but it has the habit of sitting on the topmost twig of a bush, or the telegraph wires if there are any, and from this vantage spot saying persistently " little bit of bread and *no* cheese ! " Even if the smart yellow

S. Crook

S. Crook

J. J. Ward

LIZARD, NEWT AND FROG BY THE ROADSIDE POND

A pause by the roadside pond will reveal another little world of absorbingly interesting life. By the stones on the margin of the pond we may find a lizard (bottom) stalking some new hatched fly that has just left the water on its first flight. Or some newts may put in an appearance (top left) if the watcher keeps quiet enough, or a frog in its bright uniform (top right).

waistcoat of the yellow-hammer (otherwise yellow bunting) was not sufficient to identify it, that oft-repeated phrase is unmistakeable. Wires are a favourite perch with many of the birds of the lane, and one may see birds of all sorts and descriptions taking the air upon them.

One morning I had a splendid view of a cock butcher bird (red-backed shrike) sitting aloft, the sun shining on his grey head, reddish back and the dark markings on either side of his beak which looked just like a black moustache. A very smart fellow he was, but I looked in vain for his larder, yet it was probably somewhere near. The butcher bird is a creature of catholic tastes, ready to pounce on anything from small insects up to the callow nestlings of its fellow hedgerow birds, but it is also of a provident nature, and acts on the principle of "waste not, want not," hence somewhere near its headquarters, somewhere in the neighbourhood of its nest, it has a larder, a thorn bush with spikes, whereon it hangs its provisions. Here you will find bumble bees, beetles, mice and even, as said above, nestling birds, impaled on the thorns, being hung there until required by their owner. No wonder this shrike is usually known as the "butcher bird."

To return to the yellow-hammer, its nest must be sought in the low-growing tangle of the hedgebank, where the dainty white-throat, or as the children call it, the nettle-creeper, also weaves its fragile cradle, often as its country name denotes in a protective bed of nettles.

Then what of the familiar robin? It, of course, is to be found down the lane, and in the spring time each pair appropriate a certain length of it to their own use, no other robins being allowed to

S Crook

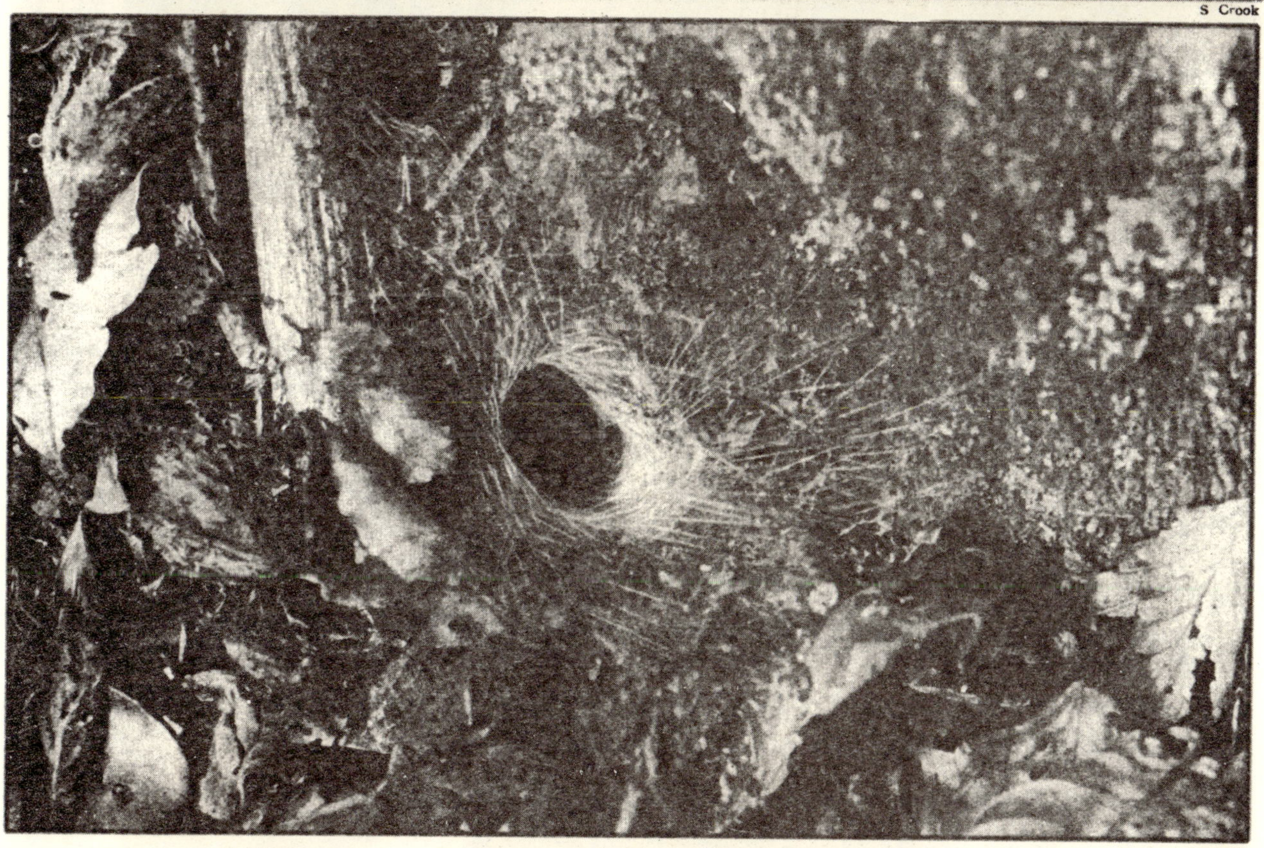

H Bastin

CLEVER THREAD SPINNERS THAT LIE IN WAIT FOR PASSING PREY

So many different creatures live in the lane that we cannot hope to see more than a tithe of them at any one time. The large inhabitants—stoats, rabbits, and weasels—are usually more hidden from our eyes than the smaller, and, of course, are not so numerous. One may find ten spiders before seeing a single hedgehog. The wolf spider (bottom) makes a gossamer house as we see, and lurks inside waiting to rush out upon any passing insect it may care to tackle. Above is the familiar wheel-like trap of a web-spinning spider.

H Bastin

H. Bastin

AN ANT COLONY BENEATH A STONE; SIGNS THE ELM BARK BEETLE MAKES ON WOOD

If we sit down incautiously on a bank under the hedge we may find, to our cost, that we have intruded upon an ants' nest. Our photograph shows part of a community of brown garden ants upon the stone under which they have chosen to construct their city. A peep under the stone will reveal a continuous and apparently aimless running to and fro of hundreds of tiny citizens. Yet each has his task and is doing it. On the right we see the marks made by a family of elm bark beetles. The mother makes a central burrow, lays a row of eggs in it and, when the grubs hatch they bore tunnels outwards feeding as they go, marking the wood with these strange patterns as we see.

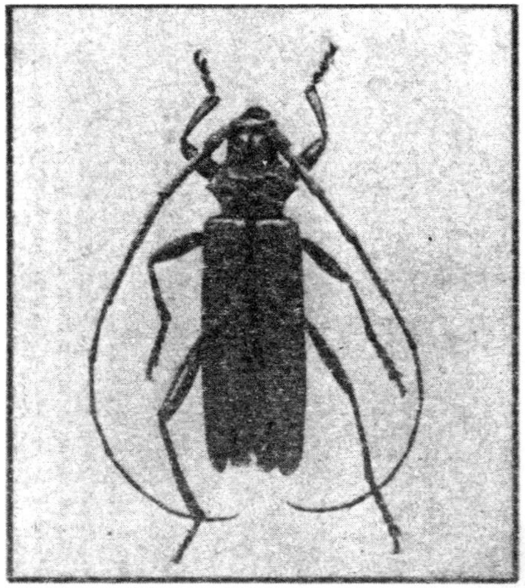
Musk beetle

Male stag beetles fighting

Common dor beetle

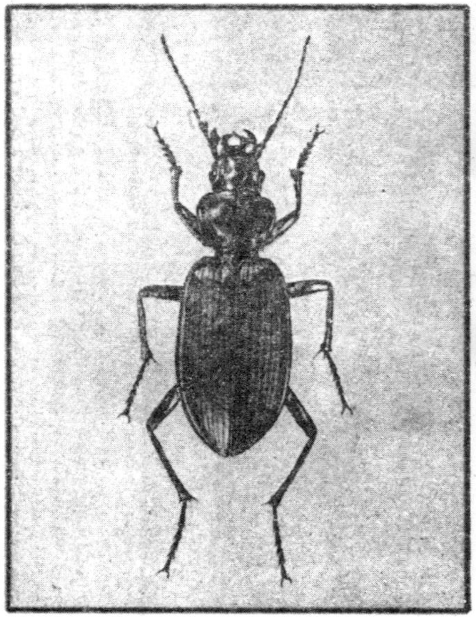
Violet ground beetle

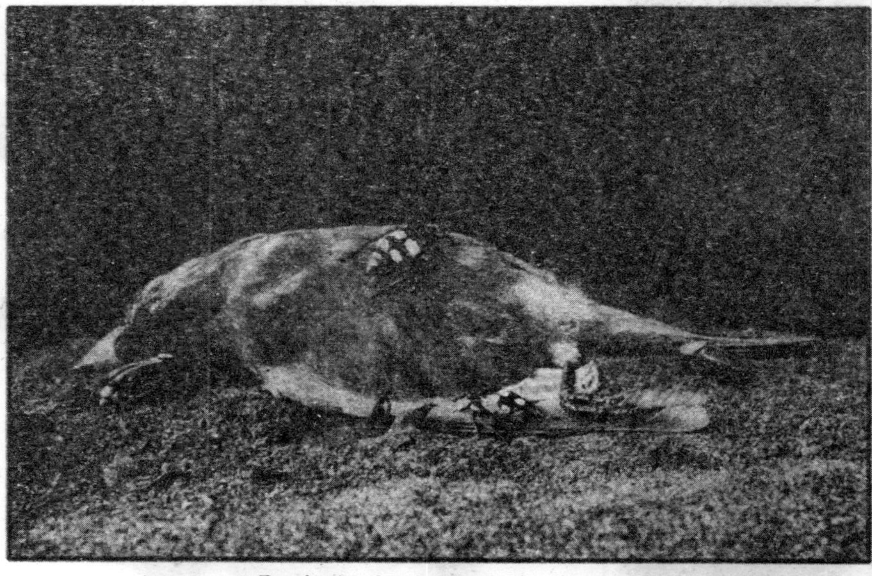
Burying beetles about to bury a linnet

Ground beetle

GROUND BEETLES THAT ATTACK ROOT EATING GRUBS, AND THE ANTLERED STAG BEETLE

Scuttling off among the grass-stems or perhaps hurrying apprehensively across the roadway before our feet we may chance to see one of the numerous ground beetles of which there are over three hundred species in Great Britain. For the most part these beetles are the friends of the farmer, for they spend most of their life underground hunting for the grubs which destroy the roots of plants. The violet ground beetle (bottom left) is one of these. It is shiny black in colour but has a violet sheen upon it. Burying beetles (bottom centre) act as sanitary officers in removing decaying bodies and the male stag beetles (top centre) may entertain us in their mating season by a battle with their formidable looking antlers. Photos by H. Bastin and J. F. Corrigan.

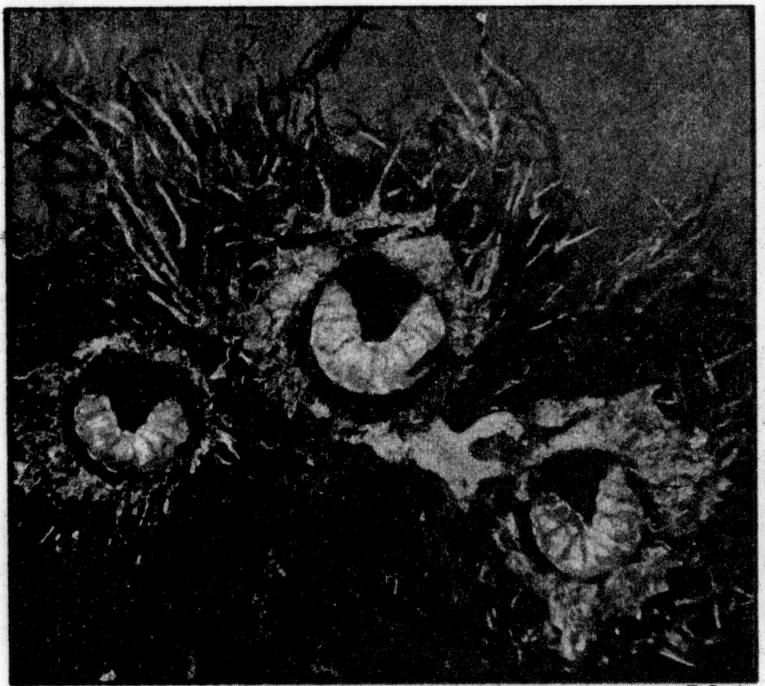

H. Bastin

H. Bastin

Henry Irving

H. Bastin

STRANGE WORK OF THE GALLS ON TREE AND PLANT

Here we have some of the minute life to be found in our country lane. It does not force itself upon the attention as the larger and active forms of life do. Galls on plants are formed by the action of various grubs. The oak leaf is liable to suffer from cherry galls (bottom left), while it may also be attacked (bottom right) by the silk button (left) and spangle (right) as well as suffering from marble galls on the twig between the leaves. Above are (top left) the inside of a bedeguar gall magnified, and (top right) the same gall on a rose.

Crimson underwing larvae

Poplar hawk moth caterpillars

Lackey moth larvae

Death's-head moth larva, the largest British caterpillar

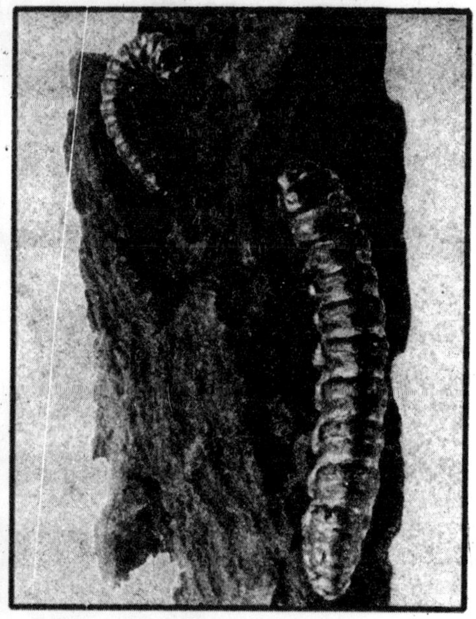

Goat moth caterpillars

MOTH CATERPILLARS FOUND IN THEIR HIDING PLACES

If we come across a large caterpillar about five inches long, with transverse bars of purple brown, we know we have found the largest British caterpillar (bottom left), that of the death's-head moth. The general colour is usually green or greenish yellow, but some specimens are brown or nearly black. An odour as of a he-goat may assault our noses and betray the presence of the caterpillar of a goat moth Above are caterpillars of the crimson underwing (top left), poplar hawk moth (centre) and lackey moth (top right). Photos by H. Bastin and J. J. Ward.

J. J. Ward

BRIGHT BUTTERFLIES THAT SPEND THEIR LIVES IN SUMMER SUNSHINE

Rivalling the flowers in brilliance the butterflies will attract the attention of the most casual observer. A common and very beautiful butterfly is the red admiral (lower illustrations), whose caterpillars live on stinging nettle plants. The mottling of white above the crimson bands helps to make this brilliance less conspicuous. The silver washed fritillary (top left) has the typical fritillary spots on the upper sides of its wings but the under sides are relieved with a silvery tint. The chalk hill blue (top right) is usually to be seen in downland districts.

Plume moth

Common tiger moth

Scarlet tiger moths

Mottled umber moth

Eyed hawk moth

Eyed hawk moth

Poplar hawk moth

Purple thorn moth

Swallow-tail moth

MOTHS OF THE GLOAMING AND THE DARK HOURS OF NIGHT

Between moths and butterflies in Great Britain it is easier to draw distinctions than between those of other parts where, in some cases, the one sort copies the habits of the other. Most butterflies appear by day, have clubbed antennae and all four wings working separately, while the moths usually prefer the evening and the night, have unclubbed antennae and have fore and hind wings joined. The number of moths about will soon be realized by a slow drive down a country lane in a motor car at night. The head lights attract dozens. Photos: H. Bastin & J. J. Ward.

J. J. Ward

VORACIOUS CATERPILLARS OF CINNABAR, BUFF TIP, LOBSTER AND PUSS MOTHS

On a ragwort plant beside the way is the place to look for the black and yellow caterpillars of the beautiful cinnabar moths. They are to be found in July and August especially on hillsides. Here (bottom left) is one on a flower head of its food plant. Next (bottom right) we have some full-fed larvae of the buff tip moth, while above are two larvae of the lobster moth (top left). The resting one on the left and the feeding one on the right both look like shrivelled leaves. In the upper right hand photograph are three puss moth caterpillars.

trespass on that territory, and all intruders of their own species being warned off with the utmost rigour.

The robin is indeed a pugnacious bird, for even when all the excitement of the breeding season is past, and the pairs have parted company, each robin, whether cock or hen, still likes to have its own little bit of country, its estate which it keeps to itself and to which it does *not* invite visitors of its own kind. This is the reason that we hear the robin's song in the chill days of winter, when most birds are far too busily engaged in food hunting to think of singing. That cheery little song is a warning to its friends and neighbours, telling them that this stretch of wayside has an owner and that all other robins must keep away—when they do not take the hint the fun begins! And many a merry duel is fought during the frosty days of winter.

WRITING of winter reminds me of that frequent sight on a winter day, a song thrush searching the hedge-banks for snails, and bringing its victims to an "anvil" on the road. Thrushes are very fond of snails, and when food gets scarce, when fieldfares and redwings are stripping the crimson "haws" from the thorn bushes, and the wood-pigeon flocks wing their way overhead, the search becomes a keen one. Each thrush prys and peeps, glancing under the ivy leaves, beneath the tufts of grass, into every secret nook and cranny, to drag forth the hidden snails, yellow ones, striped ones and brown ones, and bear them to their doom. Now a snail in its strong shell is not an easy morsel for a delicate-beaked bird like a thrush, but the thrush has a simple method of extracting that dainty morsel, the snail, from its sheltering house. The bird merely carries it to an "anvil" and beats it thereon until the shell is broken into fragments, when it has nought to do but pick out the snail and eat it!

By an "anvil" I mean a convenient stone of just the right size and shape for the thrush to beat the snail upon. When a thrush finds a good stone it uses it again and again, until the ground around is littered with snail shells. I once made a series of experiments with a young and inexperienced thrush to find out if the bird would know instinctively how to deal with snails. It did not; it had an instinctive aptitude to beat unmanageable food, but it took it some time to discover that snails were edible, and then had to find out how to deal with them. It had to learn how to use an anvil.

Another common sight in the lane, or rather from the lane, on a winter day, is the flocks of winter migrants feeding in the fields, the redwings in large numbers on the meadows, and the white-rumped bramblings, together with chaffinches and other finches, on the arable ground. The fields are full of life; here you see a stately cock pheasant stalking along, and there a covey of spruce partridges. By the way, we might speak of the partridge as one of the birds of the lane, for when spring returns, and the question of nesting-places comes to the fore, it is a common thing for the hen partridge to creep into the wayside ditch, scrape a slight hollow, and lay her nine or ten olive eggs beneath the meadow-sweet.

Chapter CX

Morals and Manners in the Animal World

By Frank Finn

Author of "Birds of the Countryside"

If the old saying "manners makyth man" be correct, a good many of the lower animals are more human than a large proportion of humanity, and if the expression "living like the beasts" be taken to mean living in a turmoil of strife and sensuality, this also is misleading in many cases, though it must be admitted that the morality of beasts is as a whole far below that of birds.

The beautiful emotion of love—the exclusive preference for an individual of the opposite sex of the species—may, however, occur in beasts as well as in birds, and a very touching instance of this is recorded by Dr. Anderson, the first superintendent of the Indian Museum. The Calcutta Zoo in his time had three orang-utans, a male, a female, and a young one. As the narrator speaks of the female as the constant but distant companion of the male, they were evidently not mated; yet his love for her was such that when she died, he persistently remained on the roof of the shelter, gazing in the direction in which her body had been carried away, and unmindful of the fierce tropical sun, which a forest animal like this would in its right state of mind avoid. This naturally resulted in sunstroke, and the poor "man of the woods" came down, dizzy and staggering, to die. The youthful member of the party had also displayed much grief, if in a less dignified way; it had to be prevented by force from following the corpse, and when so treated screamed and rolled on the ground in passion, a very common trick in orang-utan children.

It must be admitted that Marcus, the late great orang at the Zoo, and the grandest animal I ever saw, did not show by any difference in behaviour, that he grieved when his female companion died; but naturally one cannot expect to find equal intensity of emotion in all individuals of a species. A very charming monkey family that lived long at the Zoo was a pair of capped langurs and their successive children. The male was separated as a precautionary measure when there was a young baby, but he tore a hole in the canvas hung over the netting in order to peep at the family, and when he was re-admitted all one could say was that the children did not pull his tail as they did their mother's.

I have seen the flapper monkey cuff her junior's head for doing this, but the mother was so sweet-natured a creature that on one occasion when a very tiny infant was reaching out its minute hands for something to play with, she actually turned up her tail and held the tip of it convenient to the little creature's clutch.

Moreoever, she was not, as female monkeys so often are when in charge of young, shy, touchy and jealous, but would bring the baby up to the bars, when lady visitors would say to her, "Oh, don't drop it," not noticing that the infant did not need to be held carefully, as it was clinging quite tightly to her fur with hands and feet on its own account.

Topical

THE MORAL OF GOOD MANNERS

Such natural enemies as dog and cat can overcome even the old-established antipathy if the acquaintanceship is begun at a sufficiently early age. There is also a noticeable tolerance of young things on the part of adult animals, while good behaviour begets kindly treatment.

A pigtail monkey, at the Zoo in 1929, and the mother of the quaintest of little imps, was also a very reasonable animal, and let the little creature play about the cage as it liked, evidently realizing that no possible danger threatened, as the two had the cage to themselves. When, however, the big Gibraltar monkey next door started on a wordy war with the Japanese pair in the cage on the further side, it was amusing to see how she caught up the child and sprang to the bars on Gibraltar's side, evidently anxious not to miss any of the fun, but at the same time to be quite sure that she knew exactly where baby was all the time.

When a previous Japanese pair had a baby the mother was indeed very jealous,

LEARNING THE RULE OF GIVE AND TAKE: LIONS AT PEACEFUL PLAY IN THEIR CAGE

When two lions are shut up together in a cage the authorities have a pretty good idea beforehand if they are the sort that are likely to make friends. But nothing is certain about the behaviour of these big cats and they may take an instant and unhesitating dislike to each other. A lion's dislike is apt to be dangerous. On the other hand the pair may live in amity for years such as these companions here which are seen performing, in fun, the evolution they might well go through in deadly earnest if they were annoyed with each other. Even a lion can learn the law of give and take, especially when the lesson is backed by tooth and claw.

and her husband loyally joined in whenever her nerves exploded against her neighbours or the public, though he took good care to see he got the lion's share of all the cakes and sweets that were bestowed on the family—the most spoilt monkeys the Zoo ever had. The patience of this grim-looking beldame, however, was admirable; time and again she would clutch her straggling imp by a leg or by its little bob-tail, brush the sawdust out of its fur, and re-arrange it in her arms when it had turned upside down to grab her eyebrows with its hind hands, only to go through the whole performance again a few minutes afterwards.

ROBBERY COMMITTED BY CURLEW AND LIZARD

There always seems to be some excuse for thieving when that crime is committed under the stimulus of sheer hunger. In the case of the curlew, on the left, this cannot quite palliate the offence since curlews have many other things at hand to eat. Laziness may have been the cause of this robbery. As for the lizard (right) it is an inveterate egg stealer.

Some monkey mothers, however, are not so long-suffering; a late member of the Zoological Society once told me he had seen a monkey haul her baby across her knee by the tail and spank it, and Tickell very amusingly describes how wild crab-eating monkeys in Burma pull back truant youngsters by that convenient appendage and cuff their heads, though they soon make amends and appease the fractious outcries of the *enfant terrible* by cuddling it up to the breast.

I HAVE never heard women object to the insinuation of our simian affinities when a mother and child monkey are in question—the resemblance is too touchingly obvious.

There is, however, an ugly side to monkey nature, and Hughes, a late member of the Indian Geological survey, has described how he saw regular warfare, complete with atrocities, between two troops of the common langur or entellus of India. The leader of the smaller party, a fine fellow in every way, engaged two males on the opposite side, and had actually killed one, when two females from the other side forgot their neutrality and mortally injured him by a treacherous attack from behind. The winners then held the losers imprisoned on a tree, and shook down a nursing mother, causing her death in addition to his. Here the animals were living in a state of polygamy, but a polygamous animal may exhibit finer sentiments at times. There are few more inveterate polygamists than the beautiful Indian blackbuck, which will hold and rule half a hundred does; yet a pair have been found in company only with their fawn, which the buck, with rough tenderness, butted over again and again when it tried to follow them in retreat, till it understood that it should "keep dark and lie low."

An example of very opposite behaviour was told Darwin by a Gaucho in the Falklands; he saw a wild stallion brutally maltreating a mare by biting and kicking her, till she was at last forced to leave her foal, too young or weak to follow the herd, to its fate, which would be, no doubt, to be worried by the local fox-wolves which then existed, or to have its eyes pecked out by the "Johnny Rooks" or Falkland carrion-hawks. This was a case of real equine vice, yet Darwin elsewhere quotes a French authority to the effect that stud-stallions are capable of falling in love with a particular mare; and I was once told by her owner of a case in which a mare showed touching and unexpected attachment to him. This animal had a dislike, unusual in horses, though common in donkeys and mules, to entering water; yet, having on one occasion ridden her down to the sea-shore and picketed her there while he went into the sea to bathe, he found her swimming out to him, desire to rescue him from what she regarded as danger, or at any rate to be with him, having impelled her to pull up the peg and enter the element she hated.

The lion has long had a reputation for generosity and magnanimity; it certainly has some idea of what may be called justice, for ancient and modern writers have both noted that when hunted it will single out him who inflicted the first wound for attack. Anyone also may see at the Zoo that lions do spare mice, which are not to be seen disporting themselves in the cages of the other great cats as they do very freely in the lions' dens.

THE story of Androcles and the lion may be really true, for a female moose, an animal probably far less intelligent than a lion, has been known to approach a man under circumstances suggesting that it desired his help, it having been badly injured by the antler of an unchivalrous male.

The tiger has always had the reputation of being fiercer and more merciless than the lion, and it is certainly less social in the wild state and less depend-

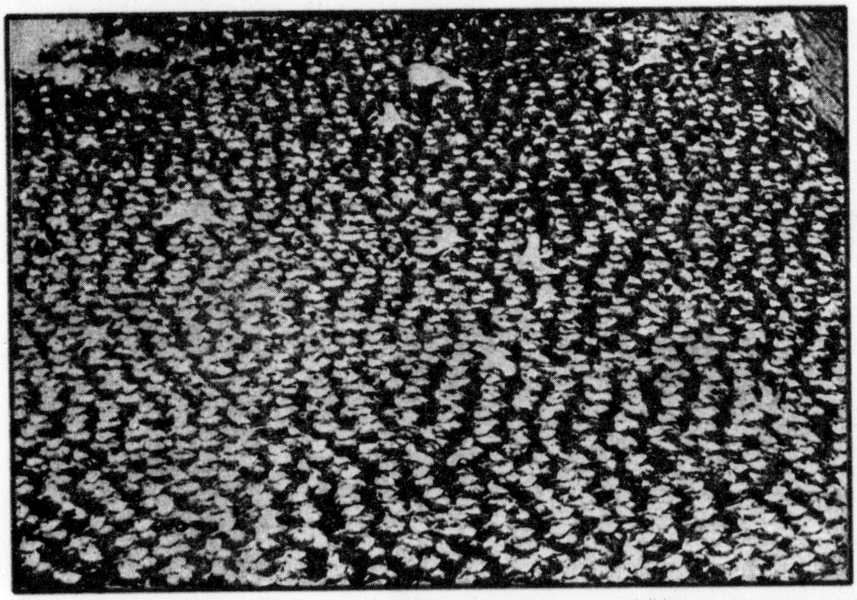

This may be from a desire to keep an eye on the movements of a foe, or they may look to him for protection against a far worse enemy to birds, the leopard.

The leopard itself has a particularly bad name for ferocity, and is very unreliable in captivity; yet a leopard in West Africa, where the reputation of its species as an enemy to man is worst, has been known to live as a domestic pet, so tame that he was harmless even with the children of the house, who actually pulled him down by the tail on one occasion when he was in their way at the window.

able in captivity. Yet, as Sterndale points out in his book on the mammalia of India, natives distinguish between the characters of tigers living in their neighbourhood, saying that some are morose and others mild; and another Anglo-Indian authority mentions a tiger which lived in the same neighbourhood for twenty years, preying on his human neighbours' cattle, and during that time only killed one man, and him by a curious accident. The peasants were netting for hares, and caught the tiger, which knocked over and incidentally killed one of them in clearing the way.

A casual death-blow on man inflicted by mistake has been known to make a harmless tiger into a man-eater, as he has thus learnt his power over what seemed to him uncanny creatures; that the tiger above mentioned went no further may be due to his having come to regard his neighbours with a friendly eye, for it is a curious fact that carnivores, solitary as they often are by the necessity of keeping a hunting-ground to themselves, may form friendships with weaker animals in captivity. This is well known with the lion, and a flock of wild guinea-fowls have been seen to run off with a troop of lions; while only recently a case was recorded at the Manchester Zoo, and photographed, in which a tigress made friends with a peacock. Peafowl are killed by tigers in India, and yet are often found in their neighbourhood.

H. Cottrell

GANNETS' SUCCESSFUL COLONISATION OF A NEW ZEALAND CAPE

At Cape Kidnappers, which is in North Island, New Zealand, at the southern extremity of Hawke's Bay and quite near Napier, a most interesting sight is to be witnessed where thousands upon thousands of gannets, or solan geese, nest together without trespassing on each other's preserves. In the nesting season the birds are very tame.

It is noticeable that the cats as a whole are far superior in manners to the dogs—less wantonly aggressive, and without the vile inclination to persecute the injured and obscenely to insult a defeated foe. Moreover, the wolf and jackal are habitual baby-stealers if they get the chance, and all the good qualities we find in the dog have been developed by the long selection of exceptional individuals which displayed an amenable disposition towards ourselves. Wolves, which when reared in

Otho Webb

BATTALIONS OF CRESTED TERNS BREEDING ON MASTHEAD ISLAND, AUSTRALIA

Crested terns breed and nest by the myriad on Masthead Island off the coast of Queensland, Australia. The lower illustration shows them as they look when undisturbed. Above thousands are flying and screaming overhead at the approach of possibly dangerous and in any case suspicious human beings. Despite the close proximity of these thousands—conditions under which human beings are often excused bad manners—these birds do their business of bringing up another generation in a spirit of mutual forbearance.

Arthur Brook

E.N.A.

WELL PRACTISED AND CUNNING EGG THIEVES: MONGOOSE AND JAY

As is well known, the mongoose has a certain skill in killing snakes. It is not so widely known that it often prefers birds' eggs to snakes and has as great a facility for stealing them. Our lower photograph shows a mongoose confronted by the eggs of an ostrich and a hen. Having failed to cope with the big shell it made off with the small one. Above is a jay, a bold bird bandit with a refuge in the thickest part of the woods, stealing an egg from the nest of an absent missel thrush.

AFFECTION AMONG THE ANTHROPOID APES: CHIMPANZEE AND ORANG

If apes and men branched off from their common stem of the genealogical tree at a comparatively late date, as some scientists assert, it is not so surprising to find the culture of affection carried to greater length among the apes than among any other animals. While comparisons of men and anthropoids should not be pressed too far, yet it is undeniable that, in their expression of emotion, apes are nearer to the human than the rest of the animal kingdom. Here we have two apes of different species whose manners are mutually kind.

Otho Webb

E.N.A

DARK AND BRIGHT SIDE OF COMMUNITY LIFE AMONG BIRDS

It is always the way of things that the peaceable community is eventually preyed upon by the irresponsible and much more active pirate. This frigate bird (bottom) swooping down on the nest of a helpless booby is a case in point. The booby is as defenceless as its name suggests, and it has to put up with having both the fish which it has caught and the nest materials it has laboriously collected being stolen. The upper photograph, taken on Pisonia Island in the Gulf of Carpentaria, Australia, shows a colony of noddies nesting happily together in a tree.

E.N.A.

FRIENDLY BEAR FIGHT AND A BULL SEAL AND HIS FAMILY

Bears at play are sure to draw a good audience at the London Zoo (bottom). The play consists mostly of a sort of mixed fight, half boxing, half wrestling, but conducted with a nice regard for the border line which separates the serious from the frivolous. It is rarely that a game develops into a quarrel. In the upper photograph we see an old bull seal inhabiting one of the lonely islands off the coast of Alaska with his wives and family. He will unhesitatingly risk his life in their defence.

H. J. Shepstone

A HERD OF WILD REINDEER QUIETLY SHARING THE WATER THAT ALL MUST HAVE

Animals that live in flocks behave according to the necessities of the flock and even in the most vital business of life, eating and drinking, take their turn without too much scrambling at the feast. Here we have a herd of reindeer which has come down to the water on which life itself depends. If all cannot drink at once the rule of first come first served is obeyed and each one gets served in due course. In other parts of the world herds of different animals obey the same code about drinking as between herd and herd. There is a considerable number of animals here, over a space of several acres. The majority have yet to come and drink. Notice the wide spread of the antlers, reflected in the water, of the animal nearest the camera.

I. J. Shepstone

TOLERANCE OF INDIVIDUAL BY INDIVIDUAL IN A BIG AUSTRALIAN SHEEP FLOCK

Sheep seem to be the most unintelligent of animals. Domestication is the sole cause of their apparent lack of brain, for they have been bred to a standard, either for wool or for meat, and standardised individuals are the reverse of intelligent, since intelligence breeds individuality. But when left to run more or less wild, as are the New South Wales sheep seen here, some intelligence is soon developed and each sheep seems to realize what is the code of manners for the flock and obeys it. There is no strife about feeding.

captivity displayed the fidelity of the dog, are on record, and the pariah dog of the east, which represents the next stage from the wolf and jackal, although he has been described as "a bully when he is full and a cur when he is empty," occasionally produces stock of a far better nature. I knew two at one time at Mombasa, a dog which had unusual courage and had even fought a hyena, and a bitch which, though not demonstrative, showed marked fidelity. Had these been paired, no doubt their offspring would have been as good as or better than themselves, and early dog-breeders would have seen to this when dogs were first tamed.

That there is a good deal of the wolf left in the dog is shown by the frequent cases of sheep-worrying that occur, though we can only regard this as a crime from a human point of view, for after all such beasts as sheep are the natural prey of the wolf, and raw mutton must taste to a dog much better than dog-biscuit, to say nothing of the pleasure of the sport.

The grizzly bear is an animal which used to have a great reputation for ferocity; according to the old tales, if "Old Ephraim" got a man's wind he dropped all other engagements to settle with him. Improved fire-arms did away with this inconvenient disposition, and grizzly bears, like other large animals which used to be more dangerous than they are now, have been reformed at the rifle's mouth.

But Richardson tells a tale of a grizzly of the good old stock which displayed something very like magnanimity, according to Reskarrah, an aged Redskin chief in the fur countries, who told how, confronted along with his old squaw by a big grizzly on the other side of a stream, he had induced the bear to go away and leave them in peace by assuring him of the respect he felt for the ursine family, none of whom, he told Ephraim, he had killed except under sheer necessity.

Animals, like young children, instinctively respect sincerity in many cases, and there can be no doubt that, for the time being at any rate, Reskarrah's respect for the bear was sincere enough of its kind. A shouting attempt to scare the brute off would very likely have led to trouble.

Of all beasts, except the dog, which is so artificial an animal psychologically that it must always be considered apart, the elephant has most engaged the kindly feelings of man—that is of civilized man, for the savage is not so enthusiastic about him, not being in an equally good position to teach him respect for human life and property. Making all allowances for ill-natured elephants, however, the beast is certainly remarkably harmless for its size, and compares very favourably with the hippopotamus and with at least the black African rhinoceros and with the Indian wild water-buffalo, all of which bear decidedly bad characters.

"ROGUES" or destructive and murderous Indian elephants seem always to be males, but that the gentler sex has its failings also is evidenced by the fact that unpleasant cow-elephants, not being able to bite off their rivals' noses to spite their faces, at any rate contrive to ruin the view of the rear elevation by biting off their tails. The African elephant is more peppery, though, in defence of the animal, it must be taken into consideration that a large proportion of the species have been themselves peppered with various scratch 'missiles by native hunters. However, when the film "Paul Rainey's African Hunt" was shown in London before the writer, a she-elephant which had come down with her baby and flapper daughter slapped the former with her trunk because it bothered her for milk while she was scraping for water in the river-bed, and when the sister came towards her apparently saying, "Oh, ma! don't be so rough with baby," fairly chased her off the screen.

While, also, one cannot blame Napier, an elephant which had been shipped to the Andamans for timber-work, for going on a one-elephant strike which lasted for fourteen years of roguery, it must be regarded as a blot on his character that an official record accuses him of visiting the tame-elephant lines at night and not only injuring a male elephant, but killing a female outright; picketing the picketed should have been peacefully performed, with due consideration for the gentler sex.

THERE is not much room left to discuss this subject in relation to birds, but anyone who can observe a poultry-yard can see how just is the estimate of the ancients of the cock as the knight among birds, and of M. Rogeron's characterisation of the duck as the jolly bourgeois; while he will find in the guinea-fowl an arrant hooligan, and in the gander and turkey-cock generally coarse bullies—though quite recently Sir W. Beach Thomas recorded a case in which bubbly-jock fought a rearguard action in defence of his family against a fox until they got too near the farmstead for Reynard's liking.

The eagle, credited, like the lion, with magnanimity, is more inclined to pacifism than are some of the less noble members of their respective families, and very possibly the small birds which make their homes in the interstices of his nest do so largely to avoid "the lesser tyrants of the air."

A chained eagle has been known to retire, as if conscience-stricken, from the body of a chained falcon it had killed, and this brings us to the important question as to whether animals know when they have done wrong—whether, in fact, they have a moral sense. In the case above given the eagle may previously have been corrected or threatened for aggressive behaviour to its neighbour, and obviously the signs of what look like conscience in dogs generally have relation to the man-made laws by which canine behaviour is regulated, and do not reflect actual canine opinion. Yet Romanes tells of a very sensitive terrier of his which not only interfered when other dogs were beaten, but even seized his master's sleeve when he touched the horse he was driving with the whip; this dog was evidently a born humanitarian. There is also a recent record of an Alsatian bitch which of her own accord would go the round of the farm and not only see that all the animals were in their proper place, but incidentally stop any cock-fights.

Cocks themselves, as is well known, will stop cockerels from fighting, and a wild boar has been seen to knock apart two porkers who were engaged in a duel. This may be an unconscious instinct to check what might develop into a menace to the over-lord, but such an explanation will not apply to this police instinct when applied to alien creatures, as in the case of the dog just mentioned and in the numerous cases whereon a stronger bird will stop the disputes of weaker alien species.

IN London, too, I have seen two cases, in birds of the same species, of reform under improved conditions of life, and of original and inexcusable sin defeated by heroism in the oppressed. An unmated male black-necked swan at the Zoo, confined for long in a small pen for bullying ducks, was at last put on a large pond with a mate. There he was the kindest of creatures, carrying the cygnets that were born to the pair more often than their mother did.

Yet a mated swan of the same kind, not even pinioned, but living with his mate, also full-winged, on the fine lake at Kew, not only never carried the cygnets as far as I saw, but bullied a family of Chinese geese until the gander, in spite of the fear he had previously shown of him, attacked him in desperation when a gosling was seriously threatened, with the result that the swan soon gave way.

It may be mentioned finally, however, that wanton mischievousness seems as a rule to be developed in mammals and birds in proportion to the vegetable element in their diet, the vegetarian species being the most quarrelsome and mischievous, and then the omnivorous; the ferocity of the carnivores is directed to the utilitarian purpose of killing prey, and the unsociability they often show is simply the need of the game preserver.

Chapter CXI

In the Grip of the Past

By Professor J. Arthur Thomson

Regius Professor of Natural History, Aberdeen University; Author of "The Study of Animal Life"

CHARLES DARWIN was interested in the way a dog turns round and round on the hearth-rug, as if to smooth down the herbage and make a comfortable bed for the night. This is a habit among wolves, from which the domesticated dogs were derived, and the habit has lasted for many thousands of years since Neolithic Man first succeeded in making the dog his partner. No doubt the habit of turning round and round would be useful in ancient days before there were houses in the modern sense, but it has long ceased to be necessary, and yet it persists. It illustrates the hand of the past on the present. Perhaps there is some significance in the fact that the past asserts itself in this case of the sleepy dog, when the unconscious has more chance to exert its influence than in waking hours.

The same survival of old habits is seen when the well-fed dog buries a bone or some remains of its meal, for this is a wild trait, seen, for instance, in the fox. Another thing we have all seen a dog do is scratching backwards with its hind feet, as if to throw earth over its excrement. It no longer succeeds in doing this; and there is obviously no sense in scratching, as it often does, on a bare pavement. The past lives on, and a habit may outlive its use.

Darwin gave a number of instances of habit-survival in his book on "The Variation of Animals and Plants under Domestication"; and there is an interesting book by Dr. Louis Robinson on "Wild Traits in Tame Animals." Let us bring together some striking examples.

Some cattle were transported from Aberdeenshire to a Californian ranch where they found themselves in relatively wild conditions. It was observed that when a cow calved away from the farm, which is not favoured in Britain, she hid her calf in a thicket when she went out to graze. This hiding of the calf is a wild habit, which has remained dormant for many generations of men and cattle, but has reasserted itself when there has been a change of surroundings in the direction of the ancient wildness.

Here it may be recalled that cattle, disturbed when at rest, rise on their hind legs first, while horses rise on their front legs first, part of the explanation being that the wild horses rest in the open plain and rise in front to see over the tall grass; while the wild cattle under the shelter of the forest or thicket rise on their hindquarters so as to keep their heads low to see under the branches of trees. More convincing, we think, is the persistence of the mare's habit of giving her foal many short drinks, while the cow gives her calf a very long drink at a time. There is a physiological reason for this, as also for the way an animal rises, but both have also to do with old habits and surroundings, for the difference becomes more intelligible when we recall the fact that the troop of wild horses shifts often from place to place, and that the foal has to stagger after its mother soon after birth, so that a big meal would be inappropriate. But it is different with the calf hidden away in the thicket, to which its mother returns to chew the cud. For our present purpose the interesting fact is the persistence of the difference in habit after it lost no small part of its significance in conditions of domestication.

W A. Rouch

W. Reid

GROWTH GOVERNED BY THE PAST

While a calf has short legs at birth we notice that the foal's legs are long. In the old wild state, the ancestors of our domestic cattle hid their young, but the wild horses kept their foals trotting with them.

Why does a horse shy? At a sudden rustle in the hedgerow, or before a wind-borne ball of paper, it suddenly swerves and may unseat the careless rider or upset the gig. There can be little doubt as to the meaning of this nervous trick. It is almost certainly a re-awakening of an ancient "reflex"—that is to say, an involuntary automatic jerk, which saved the wild horse from being bitten by a snake or by some lurking carnivore. The profitable reaction in ancient days was to make a

TWO WAYS OF GETTING UP

A horse rises on its forelegs first (bottom) and a cow on its hind legs (top) when disturbed. This is because the wild horse had to see over the long grass to make sure of safety, while the forest-dwelling cattle had to spy under the branches of the trees.

sudden swerve away from the rustle or movement. Sometimes, no doubt, the individual horse is very highly strung, and sometimes there has been an individually experienced scare; but for most cases the historical interpretation is sound. The hand of the past on the present is not dead but living.

We must not think of these re-awakenings as like our own recollections, where genuine memory is concerned. For true memory is the mental revival of a previous individual experience, such as an image, or an impression, or an idea of some sort. But the shying horse on the road and the sleepy dog on the hearth-rug illustrate an enregistration of their ancestors' experience, not a memory of their own. No clear-cut dividing line can be drawn in such cases between the bodily and the mental, but the grip of the past that we are illustrating has more to do with inborn nerve-and-muscle linkages than with the revival of mental images. Let us take more examples.

The donkey is the domesticated descendant of the wild ass of North Africa, and its unwillingness to cross the smallest stream of water is probably a persistent outcrop of prejudices and preferences established long ago in the dry desert. Perhaps its fondness for rolling in the dust has a similar historical origin; but there is no need to overwork the idea. Darwin wrote: "The same strong dislike to cross a stream is common to the camel, which has been domesticated from a very ancient period. Young pigs, though so tame, sometimes squat when frightened, and thus try to conceal themselves even on an open and bare place."

DOMESTICATED sheep are the descendants of several species of wild sheep, such as the mouflons of Cyprus, Corsica, and the East; but except when they are lambs they seldom show much of the adventurousness and intelligence of their ancestors. Man is largely to blame for this, as some exceptional breeds show, for he has usually bred for wool and for mutton, not for brains. When any of his sheep persisted in being enterprising and original, he removed them from his flock by the simple process of eating them, and thus he has succeeded in evolving an ultra-docile and very stupid race. Furthermore, as the playful lambs prove, there is a depressing and stupefying influence in an over-sheltered life. Domesticated sheep are protected from all enemies; even the wolf has become a protecting dog! There is no danger except from snow-storms, and where there is no danger there is apt to be degeneration.

Among domesticated sheep we see some interesting instances of the grip of the past. Everyone familiar with a varied countryside must have noticed how fond sheep are of chewing the cud under the shelter of a low rock or against a bank broken by rabbit burrows or the like. In short, they seek out a position where they cannot be easily disturbed from behind. We may be sure that they do not think this out, for they have no enemies nowadays to be afraid of in a country like England. Moreover, they often choose a place where there is no real protection from a rear-attack, only a suggestion of a protection. The interpretation is historical, and takes our thoughts back to the fear that the wild ancestors had of carnivores. For herbivores of relatively small size the profitable habit is to graze rapidly in the pasture, and then return to the shelter of the rocks where they cannot be surprised from behind, and where they can chew the cud in peace. This is why sheep persist in huddling against the steep bank of the bunker on the golf course.

When wild sheep are passing quickly in single file along the side of a mountain, the routine rule is that they must all do what the leader does. If he or she jumps over a narrow but deep fissure or the like, all the others must do the same without hesitation. This saves time and trouble, but it is a quaint survival when it is illustrated by sheep going along the street of a town. It is often possible to see the succession of little jumps travelling along a file of sheep. Another interesting re-awakening is seen when a ewe is going to give birth to a lamb, especially if it is for the first time. There is an instinctive prompting to get away from the flock, and the ewe will sometimes force herself through a difficult hedge to separate herself from her neighbours. This is characteristic of the wild sheep. Another piece of behaviour that we see at lambing time on a sheep-farm is that the ewe scrapes with her fore-feet as if to make a little bed or cradle for the lamb that is to be born. This was useful for her ancestors who lived in rough places, but it is not needed in the modern sheep-farm.

The two words "instinctive prompting" give us the clue to the whole matter. Think again of the "gimmer," that is to say, a ewe that is about to lamb for the first time. She does not know what is going to happen, but she obeys an inborn, hereditary prompting to a certain routine of behaviour. It is quite easy to prove that she does not understand what she is doing, for she is often very much startled at the appearance of the lamb and will even run away afraid. But if she once licks the lamb, there is an instantaneous release of a series of maternal instincts, and she allows it to suckle. But she does what she does not because she understands the situation, nor because of a recollection, but because part of her inheritance is a series of instinctive promptings. There are pre-established linkages between certain nerve-cells and certain muscle-cells, and once the trigger is pulled the behaviour follows.

No one is wise enough to say how soon the creature becomes aware of what it does, and how soon there are ripples of emotion as well as nerve-thrills and muscle-contractions. But we must try to understand that instinctive promptings are inborn or hereditary, ready-made inspirations, which do not require any learning or apprenticeship. They are as much part of the racial inheritance as the convolutions of the brain or the shape of the teeth, the strength of the heart or the crinkliness of the hair.

Darwin tells us of the musk-duck (*Dendrocygna viduata*), that in its native country and wild state it often perches and roosts on trees, a very unusual thing for a duck to do. Now it is very interesting that domesticated musk-ducks, though very sluggish birds, are fond of perching on the tops of barns and walls. If allowed to spend the night in the hen-house the female will generally go to roost up beside the hens, though this may mean leaving the drake who is too heavy to mount so high.

There is a significant old story of a race that was arranged between a flock of domesticated geese and a flock of domesticated turkeys, which were to be driven for miles along the highway. The farmer who arranged the race put his money on the geese, and knowing the habits of the two kinds of birds timed the contest so that the turkeys would be passing under an avenue of trees about nightfall. The turkeys were driven off at a great pace, and the geese lagged behind. But it was a foregone conclusion in favour of the geese. For when the turkeys reached the part of the road where there were trees they flew up and roosted among the branches whence they could not be driven. The European turkey is in great part at least derived from the American wild turkey (*Meleagris gallopavo*) which roosts in high trees. The wily farmer knew that the old instinctive prompting was sure to assert itself.

Why does a hen make such a fuss when she lays an egg? It sounds like a proud hysterical excitement, but it is obviously open to the criticism that if the laying is in the open the cackling advertises to possible enemies the whereabouts of the egg. The plausible interpretation is historical. The domestic fowl is derived from the wild jungle fowl (*Gallus bankiva*) of India, a gregarious bird of the forests. The

W.N.A.

THE GNU OF THE AFRICAN PLAINS GETS UP LIKE A HORSE

That strange animal the gnu, which seems half related to horses and half to cattle, proves its affinity with the former by getting up on its forelegs first. The gnu lives for the most part in quite open country where the cover consists of grass. In order to see over it the animal rises on its fore legs and peers about. There are also physiological reasons for the preference.

flock moves about after food and the cackling is probably useful in making it easier for the hen, that has been separated off during the egg-laying, to rejoin her companions till next time. Her call is answered and she hears where they are.

Beautiful instances of habit-survival are seen in the play of young domesticated mammals, for example kittens, puppies, lambs, kids, and calves. It has been shown by Groos and others that the play-period among animals is of value as an irresponsible apprenticeship to the serious business of life, and as an opportunity for testing variations in habit before consequences are too critical. Thus we understand why wild kittens and others should play at hunting and sham-fights, while wild sheep and goats play at "Follow My Leader" and sham-races. Play is in some measure the young form of work. But for many domesticated cats that have given up hunting, and for most domesticated sheep that have given up adventure, the playing activity has lost a great part of its meaning. Yet it illustrates how the living influence of the past may exert itself in youth, though weakening gradually as the animal reaches the age of discretion.

A FREQUENT cause of obscurity is the double use of the word habit. When intelligently controlled behaviour, such as playing an instrument or riding a bicycle, is repeated many times, it becomes easier and easier, it requires less and less attention and control, it illustrates habituation. The transmission of nervous impulses along certain lines becomes very easy, so easy that the whole succession of steps may follow almost automatically when the first one is taken. This is habit-forming in the strict sense; it is an individual acquisition—an automatisation of behaviour that required, to begin with, much attention and possibly much intelligent control. It is unfortunate that the same word "habit" is often used for acquired longings and cravings and desires which we call "bad habits"; and it is not less unfortunate that the same word is used for the customs and ways of animals, as when we say that Fabre devoted his life to studying the "habits" of insects. These customary ongoings, as they might be called, are sometimes very varied and plastic, controlled by intelligence at every turn, as is true of many of the ways of otters, foxes, and monkeys. Or they may be predominantly instinctive, as in the ways of ants, bees, and wasps. Or it may be that an animal's behaviour includes a good deal that is more or less intelligently learned, along with a good deal that is instinctive.

Whenever a customary activity has become so thoroughly engrained in the animal's constitution that its performance requires no apprenticeship or learning, then the animal may be more free to make experiments; and many birds and mammals show a happy mixture of instinctive behaviour (in the wide sense of inborn or enregistered) and of intelligent behaviour in the sense of profiting by experience and showing something in the way of judgment. This is an intricate subject which we must not pursue further, but the important point is that wild traits in tame animals are always of the enregistered or instinctive type, never of the intelligent type. This is why they sometimes last on in domestication after their original utility is past; they are part and parcel of the hereditary constitution.

IT is not that new habits acquired under the conditions of domestication oust old habits which were established in the wild life of ancestors, for this is using the word 'habit' in two different senses. The grip of the past on the behaviour of domesticated animals is illustrated in reference to little ways which were enregistered in the nervous system and formed part of the racial inheritance. The little ways, like the dog's turning round and round before it falls asleep, cannot suddenly disappear, though they may dwindle in the course of many generations.

In man's clothes there are not a few dwindling relics of structures that once were of use. At the wrist of a man's jacket there are buttons which are never used. They cannot be taken out of their buttonholes, and in many cases the holes have vanished. At the small of the back of the morning coat there are two buttons to which the tails of the coat used to be attached when the wearer was riding on muddy roads. The buttons are useless vestiges, and in our body there are much more striking illustrations of the same sort of thing.

In the inner upper corner of our eye there is a vestige of the third eyelid, which is well-developed in most mammals, where it is used to clean the front of the eyeball. In the trumpet or pinna of our ear there are small muscles, vestiges of those which move the ear in many mammals, such as the donkey. In occasional men these dwindled or vestigial muscles are still strong enough to enable the individual to flap his ear. Now these useless relics, which Darwin compared to the unsounded letters in words like leopard and doubt, are historically very interesting; they are vestiges of the dim and distant past, when they were well-developed and of use.

Similarly the persistent "little ways" that we have been illustrating are vestigial habits, which have no doubt their physical seat in some part of the central nervous system. They cannot disappear quickly for they are part and parcel of the constitution, enregistered and engrained long ago in such a way that they took a lasting grip. It is useful to remember that the whalebone whale has actually two sets of teeth which are entirely useless, since they never cut the gum. We suppose a million years must have passed since these teeth were used!

THE question rises why there are not more numerous instances of ancestral habits living on in domesticated animals. It is likely that there are more than we have as yet thought of; but there are deep reasons why the useless should dwindle. Most organs of the body are variable from generation to generation. But even if they vanish, the hand of the past lives on, holding firmly to that which is good.

Chapter CXII

Hunting Wild Animals with a Camera

By Angus Buchanan

Author of "Wild Life in Canada"

THE sweetness in our holiday pleasures, or treasured recreations, often gets its origin from childhood, and can be traced back to a source where the influence of parents or environment first prompted some strong inclination that is never afterwards entirely eradicated. But whether the bent of an early love gains or diminishes as the years advance rests largely with the character or the circumstances that develop afterwards.

Some of us are fortunate; others find their favourite pursuit too much for them to hold on to against the battering of life's serious worries, and they reluctantly let go. Wherefore we, who find pleasure in photography, ought to try to put all the beauty we can into the pictures we make, since the image may be for eyes other than our own that are eager and penetrating, and full of zeal to find a responsive and happy value in the things they love.

Nearly as serious as that should be all hobbies, for with the growing of hobbies goes the moulding of character, and with the growing of character goes the making of nations.

Many of us have a deep-rooted love for Nature, and, in all sorts of ways we try when we can to lay hold of the beauties we find in it in its rarest moods.

In this connexion the camera is a boon, an ingenious invention of man, constantly made use of to-day for the purpose of grasping and recording what the eye sees in flashes of inspired activity.

The popularity of the camera has grown by leaps and bounds, and the influence of photography, with the perfection of the kinema, is an influence to be reckoned with to-day. It is a new mode of making record—perhaps, I might even say, a new mode of education. And it is making revolutionary changes throughout the world, in Press work and entertainment and in our school curricula. It is no longer essential to read or write to learn what is going on, neither is it necessary to shoot a rare specimen to see its form or its colours. Photography, with care and patience, can show us very much of those things to-day.

The hunting of wild life with a camera is on the increase, and I venture to think that it is helping us to understand much more about Natural History than hitherto. We cannot photograph wild creatures before we become intimate with them and their habits, and intimacy leads to understanding.

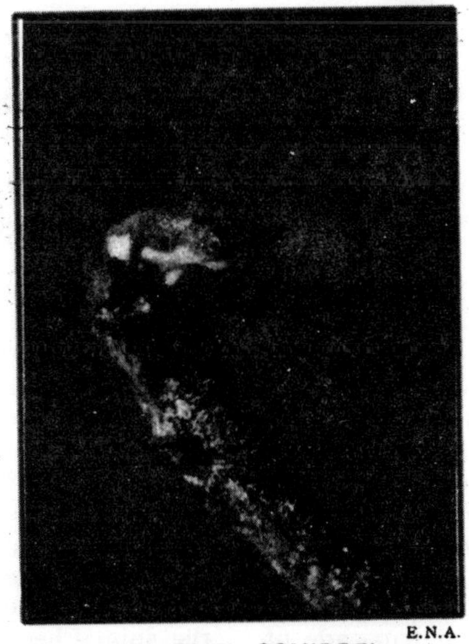

E.N.A.

CANADIAN SQUIRREL

Telephotography makes possible the "snapping" of the shyest animals. This Canadian squirrel is sitting on the stump of a tree felled by a beaver.

I began my studies of wild life as an invalid child. Right back as far as my memory goes I can just recall that a pair of willow warblers, reared from the nest as pets, and a pair of ordinary house sparrows, played an important part in my little life of that time and were my real first treasures. Later they were succeeded by sparrow-hawks, owls, and the like.

It is strange to look back. The thoughts I pen have probed the past back to the surface. I remember I photographed those pets—I see a significance hitherto unguessed. So I search for an old book and find it, and the warblers and the sparrows are before me now looking from an old album that has come to me from parents who are gone.

It is a brave step from then to the time when I was first able to photograph wild life abroad with the purpose of bringing home some pictorial record of the strange lands I visited and the creatures that inhabited them.

My first expedition was to the Arctic regions of Canada, north to the "Circle" and west of Hudson Bay. I was equipped with two hand cameras, for the kinema had yet to come in outdoor fields. Of all the Canadian birds and animals I photographed I feel I cannot do better than quote my diary description of hunting some of the Barren Ground caribou with a camera.

It was the depth of winter in the Great White North. We (two Indians and myself) were in good caribou country, and at the narrows on Sand Lake we planned to spend some time and prepare unobtrusively to influence the direction of caribou travel, so that they might come to pass right before the camera.

Our procedure was this—to cut from the forest on the shores armfuls of spruce boughs and lay them, at widely spaced intervals, on the white lake surface of the upper lake to form a thin boundary line. This fence was laid after the tracks on the forested shores had been examined and the wind considered, and Philip and Eaglefoot (the two Indians) had decided that caribou would possibly come from the west on the morrow. Where caribou were expected to come on to the lake from the forest a few boughs were placed very close to shore, so that when our quarry stepped on to the lake the strange objects would not be observed until the animals looked back or tried to return by the path they had come.

NIGHT PHOTOGRAPH OF ANTELOPE IN AN AFRICAN FOREST

Night is the best time to photograph most animals, for then they leave their retreats and the same darkness that shields them also covers the photographer. Taking photographs under such conditions is rather like setting a trap. One makes all arrangements and hopes the animal will pass by. Then the flash-light powder goes off and the likeness is on the plate.

As will be shown, caribou will not pass near any suspicious-looking object. Along both shores the fence was carried out, making short cuts across the bays; and after the shores were laid the slim enclosure was completed by running a line of boughs from shore to shore across the centre of the lake. There then remained open, to any animal that might enter the enclosure, only the narrows leading into Sand Lake, where I and the camera would be hidden.

It was night when we had finished and returned to camp. Camp was made snug against the keen wind and bitter frost by building the usual barricade of spruce boughs and snow in a half-circle, backing the wind, and within the circle, just beyond the length of an outstretched man, a great log-fire was built to blaze merrily, and to die out long after the fur-blanketed forms had gone to sleep. All the ten sled-dogs were tied up this night—an unusual proceeding — to keep them from wandering to the traps on Philip's line, and from chasing any caribou that they might scent in the night. They were then given the whole of a caribou that had been killed and twenty frozen fish—a repast intended to keep them quiet on the morrow.

THE following morning we were moving about camp before daylight, preparing in earnest for deer-stalking. Any of the dogs that showed inclination to howl or whimper was securely muzzled with rope; the morning fire burned low; the ordinary quiet voices of the Indians sank to hushed whisperings—those precautions even although our camp was well back from the shore and in the shelter of forest where there was but slight likelihood of smoke or sound reaching the senses of any animals that might approach.

A hide for the camera and myself was built of spruce boughs on the outskirts of the point of land, and commanding the lake at the entrance to the narrows where the caribou were expected to pass. The hide was built as small and insignificant as possible, and the outside, that which might be apparent from the lake, was sprayed with snow until it resembled the natural surroundings. The first two hours of daylight passed uneventfully, and it was not until about ten a.m. that two caribou were sighted. These animals came on to the ice south of the narrows—they had come off the shore past the camera—but the cunning Indians had foreseen the possibility of this, and a few spruce boughs barred the narrows some distance beyond my outlook. At this fence the two caribou were turned, and after a long wait they began to approach the hide. Of the leading buck I obtained one good exposure, and though slight was the click of the release the animal heard it, and swung round as if he had been shot at; there he paused for a second, proud head up and great eyes alarmed, while I remained motionless; but in a moment more he turned and retraced

British Instructional Films

UNREHEARSED INCIDENTS FROM CINEMATOGRAPH FILMS MADE IN THE WILD

While a film was being made in the Sudan a young giraffe came up to investigate a camera which had been left in the shade of a tree (bottom). The upper photograph was obtained during the making of a film in Africa when, in order to get within camera distance of the shyer animals, the skins and plumage of two ostriches, which had been especially shot for the purpose, were put on by two of the party, who were thus able to obtain some wonderful films. The camera can be seen protruding from the body of the nearer of these "birds."

E.N.A.

horns lying back over the shoulders. Without a halt he came right on, and I allowed him to pass unmolested—he was well ahead of the others—then made some exposures of the following line of does and fawns that filed past the hide. They were fine fat deer, Philip decided, after they were past—he had, in his keenness, come quietly beside me to watch also—and he ran back to camp for my rifle to shoot them, but luckily they were gone ere he returned and he couldn't spoil by the noise of shooting what chance there might be of other animals approaching. However, it was then getting late, and the light was failing, and we were on the point of leaving off for the day, when Philip, who had been moving around the shore

his steps, smelling the ground suspiciously, while his companion followed.

After this there was a long period of patient waiting—not an easy matter in the numbing zero cold—and it was noon when the next caribou were seen. It was then a small herd of a dozen came on to the lake, and within the enclosure, from the west shore. They were very nervous, probably because of the "fence," and they made one or two short rushes as if they meant to risk galloping through the barrier that lay across the lake, only to come to a halt in the end, and to look about wonderingly. The wind was from the north, hence their inclination was to get beyond the fence across the lake; but each time they "funked" crossing between those harmless bits of spruce.

Twice the buck that was the leader came half the distance forward to the narrows only to turn back again to the north-west, and mingle with the others in frightened bewilderment. Finally, the buck made up his mind, and came for the narrows at a long-reaching trot, neck outstretched, head up and

JUNGLE SNAPSHOTS: LIONESS AND ONZA

Whether the lioness or the photographer was the more surprised at the circumstances of this photograph (bottom) is not known, but the lioness seems to have been more effectually frightened since the camera-man lived to develop his photograph. The upper illustration is of a cat-like animal called the onza which is only found in Central and South America.

GIRAFFE "SHOT" BY THE CAMERA AT A WATER HOLE

Water holes, often made by elephants and used in turn by all the other animals of the district, are the best places at which to try to photograph wild animals. But the giraffe often lives in very arid country and seems to be able to exist for weeks together without water. This, then, is an especially remarkable piece of good hunting with a camera. The animal's forelegs are so long that they have to be splayed for drinking.

a little way, came to tell me that a single fawn was approaching. This animal walked all along the fence, smelling the ground where the others had previously passed, and uncertain where to go. Finally it got on the fresh track leading to the narrows and came ahead quickly. As the animal passed I made two exposures, though the light was by then very poor and the result uncertain.

It was now three p.m. and too dark for further camera work. It had been snowing lightly all day, and the light was not very good for making rapid exposures. However, what was really worrying me was the action of the intense frost on the focal-plane shutter. Twice it had absolutely stuck in the middle of an exposure, and twice, also, it had refused to act at all when beautiful caribou pictures were possible. I was beginning to fear the shutter was going to spoil everything, and that I wanted a very simple instrument to replace this complicated mechanism, to which tiny frost particles clung and jammed the finer workings. Over the evening camp-fire I spent an hour trying to prevent any recurrence of a hitch in the shutter-workings. Before the heat of the fire it worked perfectly, and I laid it aside in the end with renewed hopes for the morrow.

There you have most of the elements assembled that make up the quickening excitement in wild-life photography, the scheming to outwit wary game, the care and detail of preparation, the long waiting, the thrill in a real success (which is yours perhaps *once* after weeks of trying), and, above all, the pleasure of being very close to Mother Earth among shy creatures that are given to seek the silent nooks and hidden dens of solitudes furthest from man and nearest to the cleanliness of God.

F.N.A.

OSTRICH, ZEBRA AND ARMADILLO CAUGHT UNAWARES

From wonderful South Africa comes the lower photograph which seems to show some incongruous acquaintanceship between an ostrich and a zebra, which are both feeding together as though they enjoyed each other's society. Above we have an armadillo caught in the act as it came down to a pool to drink. Rarely are photographs obtained of this animal actually in the water.

GROUPS OF LIONS—BUT IN THE WILD NOT THE CIRCUS

While it is a pleasant thought that men can now go out and hunt wild animals with a camera and not a gun it is much more so from the point of view of the person who reads about it than the photographer. Because the lion, for instance, is just as well armed as usual and objects as much to a camera as a rifle. Even with a crack shot beside the camera it must be nervy work obtaining such photographs as these. In the upper photograph, taken by Col. Maxwell, there are two groups of lions, one in the foreground discussing a dead zebra.

Col. Maxwell

UNUSUAL SPECTACLE OF A LION THAT HAS CLIMBED UP INTO A TREE

This photograph is remarkable for showing a lion that has partially climbed up a tree and was taken by Col. Maxwell in Africa. In this connection it is interesting to learn that, at the London Zoological Gardens, an experiment was tried in the lion house. An arrangement of branches was fixed on a platform in one of the outdoor cages so that the lion had to climb for its meal and get the benefit of a little exercise. It was not realized till recently that lions did climb trees but every year courageous men extend our knowledge of natural history.

PROVING THAT A LION MAY SOMETIMES CLIMB A TREE: A LION GROUP ENJOYING A SIESTA

Contrary to the opinion of many hunters and naturalists, who supposed that lions never resorted to tree climbing, it is now proved that these great animals both can and do climb trees sometimes. Indeed it would seem strange if a member of the cat tribe were unable to climb. This and two of the preceding photographs, all by Col. Maxwell, show that the case is now beyond dispute. One of the lions in this interesting group at ease beneath a tree, has climbed on to one of the stronger branches and is enjoying the rest with the others, the tail hanging contentedly down without so much as a twitch. In fact all the group look as though they were enjoying a lazy afternoon, though some of them have been attracted towards the camera. This photograph and those on pages 1290, 1291 and the top photograph on page 1296 are by Colonel Maxwell and were published in "The Times."

There is one other element, not directly apparent in the above, the element of danger. In wild-life photography abroad it takes two forms: danger from climate, or danger from an infuriated beast. To my mind the danger of climate is the greater. When the weather goes wrong and storms break loose the strength of the man who, from necessity, sleeps out-of-doors on the bare earth can be very small against the fury of the blizzard or hurricane or intense set of temperature.

CONCEIVE the land where my caribou pictures were taken. Travel for months was necessary, through a vast white land of silent snow and piercing cold, to reach the place where the animals were to be found. Sometimes we were smothered by awful blizzards of snow and had to stop travelling altogether, to shelter round our sleds like waifs. The giant elements of heartless cold that was always with us, the dumb, boundless ice-locked, snow-smothered land appalled the stoutest heart. At times it seemed preposterous that against those forces such little things as we, mere dust-specks in such mighty company, should dare to go on, and go on. Indeed, within you you are almost sure the overpowering forces will get you in the end, some day when you go just a little too far and are contemptuous for an hour of its antagonism.

W. Lowther Kemp

SEVEN LIONS PHOTOGRAPHED IN INDIAN FILE

After a wait of an hour and a half, the photographer was rewarded by the marvellous sight of nine lions walking in single file. When within range, he operated the shutter but, at that moment only seven were actually in view. The one bringing up the rear may be seen in the distance. The next two in front of him had momentarily become hidden by the bush.

The danger of being attacked by an infuriated animal is, in my experience, a far less constant danger. It is a swift sensation of the moment, unlikely to happen more than once or twice in a lifetime. I would rather the quick blow and the quick settlement than the blow that hangs over one's head perpetually and demands that you shall endure.

I have only once been seriously charged by an animal, and that a wounded caribou, one of the least expected of beasts. I have been rushed by both elephants and rhinoceros in fairly thick bush country in Africa, yet I am convinced that in every case they were far more anxious to get away than to harm me, though they dived past within arm's length.

Generally speaking, wild animal sense has an inborn fear of the human smell or touch. I have myself seen the lion, in some situations the proud king of beasts, sneak off at my approach as shamefully as a guilty cat. At the same time, it is far from my mind to advocate that anyone can afford to take liberties in photographing our greater game. There is always a certain tense element of uncertainty and risk, and disasters of the past have proved to the world the full penalty the hunter may pay, even in face of long experience and calculated prudence.

With regard to nastiness in animal temperament I rate the cow elephant, with young, and the African buffalo by far the most dangerous of all wild animals for the hunter to interfere with if they show the slightest sign of being in a mood to be roused. Turning to another aspect of animal temperament;

Keystone

THE PUMA IN AMBUSH AND THE CROUCHING LYNX

While the rifle taught us, indirectly, a good deal about wild life, because big game hunters had to study the habits of their quarry and an examination of the dead animal, when shot, added new data to the scientist's note-book, yet the camera can carry on the lesson and supplement it without destroying the subject. Our lower photograph reveals a puma hiding behind a big boulder in the Colorado mountains in wait for passing game. Above is a lynx, fiercest of American carnivores, crouching in a thicket.

F. W. Champion

F. W. Champion

WONDERFUL FLASHLIGHT PHOTOGRAPHS OF TIGRESS AND LEOPARD

Taken in the Indian jungle by night, these two illustrations are fine examples of the result of many hours of preparation and careful watching—the reward of a first-rate photograph. The tigress (bottom) was stalking through a path in the forest during her night's hunting, while the leopard was coming up from the pool where it had been drinking. If the leopard gets a taste for human flesh it is considered even more dangerous than the tiger, although it is neither such a heavy nor such a powerful animal.

Herbert Lang

ALMOST EXTINCT WHITE RHINOCEROS AND A COW RHINO WITH A CALF

At the last hour, as it were, attempts are being made to save the white or square-lipped rhinoceros from extinction. Thousands used to live in the territory of the Union of South Africa, while now it is believed there are only about twenty individuals left. This photograph (bottom) was taken within fifteen feet of the animal, a bull. The territory in Zululand which is the last refuge of these great beasts has been abolished as a game reserve. Above is an ordinary rhino cow, with her three-parts grown calf, photographed by Col. Maxwell.

E.N.A.

HIPPOPOTAMI PHOTOGRAPHED IN TRANSVAAL AND BY THE BANKS OF THE ZAMBEZI

A hippopotamus does not look a war-like animal, but it is not, nevertheless, to be trifled with, for it can run at considerable speed and anyone who approaches near enough to obtain a photograph such as the lower of these two certainly runs a risk. But if the hippo is to be watched carefully on land, in the water (top) it is a much uglier antagonist since it can crunch a canoe in its enormous jaws and upset a much larger boat by coming to the surface underneath the keel. The group seen above is in the Zambezi.

E.N.A

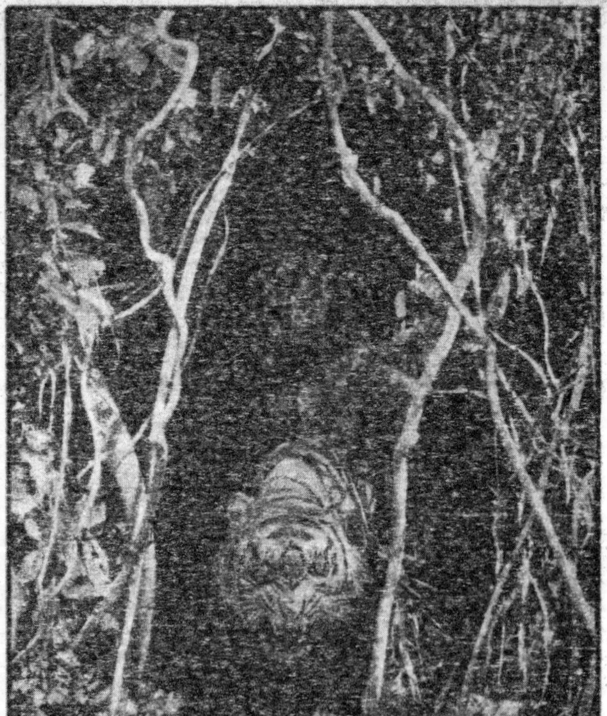

Chang

PUMA, TIGER AND BEAR CAUGHT BY THE CAMERA

In the lower left-hand illustration we see a puma. Its lair was discovered and the photographer lay in wait and succeeded in getting a picture of the animal just as it emerged. On the right (bottom) is a fine tiger regarding the camera with a dreadful hatred in its eyes. Notice how, as it stands in a sort of cavern in the thick jungle, the branches cast shadows upon its striped hide. This photograph is from the film "Chang." Above we have a bear and a puma "snapped" while climbing trees.

H. J. Shepstone

F. W. Champion

SLOTH BEAR, A HORRIBLE DANGER OF THE INDIAN JUNGLE: AN AMERICAN BEAR

Save for leopards and those few tigers that are man-eaters, the sloth bear (bottom) is considered the most dangerous animal in India. It is not vicious tempered but its sight and hearing are both poor, and some villager may approach one of these animals unknowingly. The bear does not become aware of the man's approach and move off, as most other animals would, but is suddenly surprised at a short distance, and, in its fright, may scalp or blind a man with a blow before it flees. Above is a bear in a forest in North America.

ZEBRA AND GAZELLE AS THEY COME TO THEIR DRINKING PLACE

In some parts of Africa where water is rare, every animal in the neighbourhood must visit a certain drinking place within a day or two. The water holes are therefore excellent places for the photographer's purpose. Below we see some zebra beside a dried-up stream. Here the term water hole is literally true and we can see two of the animals drinking at small holes in the ground in which some water has oozed up in the neighbourhood of the parched stream. Above is a nervous company of gazelles.

H. J. Shepstone

H. J. Shepstone

BIG DEER THAT ROAM NORTH AMERICA: MOOSE AND WAPITI

Naturally very shy and made more so by much hunting the moose (bottom)—sometimes called elk in America—is not an easy subject to obtain for the camera. It lives in the loneliest forests, usually on high ground, during the winter time but comes down to the swamps round lakes in the summer. A bull may stand seven feet or so at the shoulder, for the moose is very long in the leg. The wapiti (top) is a big and handsome deer allied to the red deer of Britain, and is now getting scarce outside the state reservations.

Autotype

HERD OF THE HANDSOME SABLE ANTELOPE THAT RANGES THE WILDS OF AFRICA FROM UGANDA TO RHODESIA

Between Uganda and Mashonaland is the range of the handsome sable antelope. It keeps to moderately wooded country avoiding both thick forests and open plains and never goes far from water. The herds are usually not large, twenty cows running with a single adult bull. It is very rarely that a herd is seen with more than one full grown male and it is thought that the supremacy of the herd is fought for very fiercely. However, the herd may be so small as to comprise only ten or a dozen other members, while, on the other hand, fifty may run together. The bulls are very dangerous when hunted and even if brought to the ground by a wound, continue to fight with vicious strokes of their long, pointed horns.

MOST DANGEROUS ANIMALS IN AFRICA: HERD OF BUFFALOES IN A SECLUDED FOREST GLADE NEAR NAIROBI

Seldom can a man approach as near as this to a herd of these animals. Hunters are agreed that the African buffalo is, when wounded, the most vengeful and the most cunning of wild beasts. It will even feign death if, by that means, it can lure its enemy within killing distance. Other animals can often be frightened away or stopped temporarily by a bullet, but it is only death that can stop the buffalo when once it has decided to charge. This remarkable photograph, taken in thick cover not far from Nairobi, by Colonel M. Maxwell (and published in the "Times") shows an unsuspecting herd browsing peacefully in a tropic glade. One animal is looking up in the direction of the photographer's "hide" as though it suspected something.

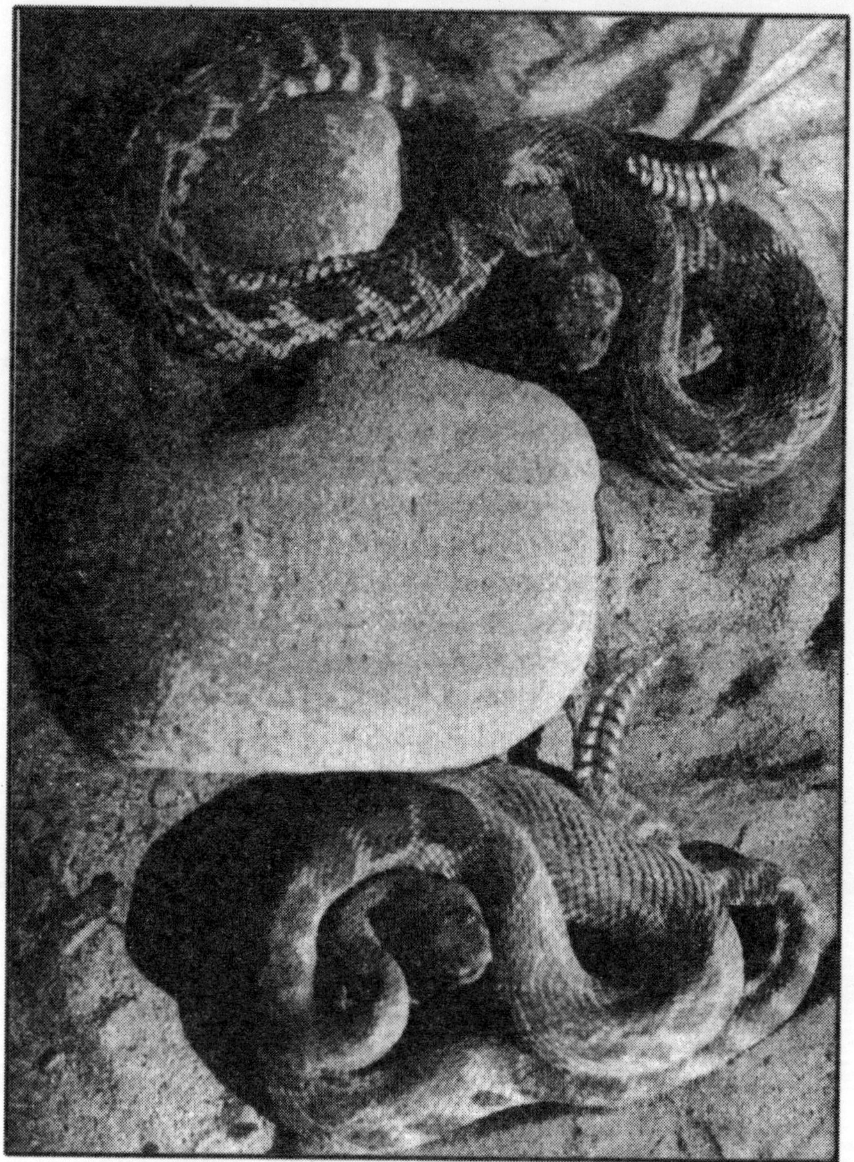

DANGEROUS TO PHOTOGRAPH! COILED RATTLESNAKES Shepstone

Rattlesnakes are found in North and South America, but especially in the dry desert districts of Arizona where they lie, concealed by their protective coloration, amid stones and dust. Their bite is extremely dangerous, and to get a camera within close range means taking a risk indeed. The snake in the foreground seems to be waving its rattle in a threatening manner.

as a rule animals that graze, such as giraffe, elephant, antelope, and so on, give the photographer his best opportunity to get results from his hunting, while the cunning carnivorous wolf-like or cat-like beasts have a knack of outwitting one at almost every turn. There is certain quiet confidence about undisturbed grazing big game which gives the stealthy camera-man a chance; but fox, or wolf, or the like, appear never at ease, and even when asleep keep half an eye open.

It is somewhat similar with the nature of birds. Those that flock to the ground, like plover or egrets, or are content on lakes, like ducks, or gather to grain, like pigeons or finches, are possible to photograph, but those that prey, like eagles and hawks, and roam widely, like ostriches and bustards, are tremendously difficult to get within reach of to catch with a steady focus.

Wherefore it is readily seen that wild-life photography has before it a very wide field and is an exacting undertaking. It is a study that no single man can complete in a lifetime; the best he may hope to do is to add some links of knowledge to the work of others before him. Weeks, months, even years may pass without one picture being obtained of a single subject fondly desired. It is a study that absorbs an unbelievable amount of time, when we live in a business age that puts a money value on every working hour of the day. I am sure I am safe in saying that no man ever brought home pictures and got from them profit in money, nor tangible return for his work. The reward lies in it being a labour of love—love of subject—love of surmounting difficulties and reaching out into new fields that we think must grow to bigness in time in the eyes of fellow men who are slow to grasp the majesty of that wonderful creation which has different lights at every boundary of the earth.

When you sit in the luxury of a theatre and see fast-speeding pictures of scenes in other lands, which adventurers only might see in the olden days, you, no doubt, often try to picture the actual conditions under which they were taken. On the screen you probably see the very brightest incidents and scenes; the result of long months of painstaking work. In editing a picture everything likely to be monotonous is left out, yet monotony is prevalent, in fact, throughout all long journeys in the wilderness. You read between the lines and guess so much.

If you picture so much you have a soul ready with sympathy for your fellows. That soul is a very valuable thing even though it is inarticulate.

Photographing wild life entails plenty of hardship and a great deal of patience, but it is an alluring quest, and surely the joy in it is in being privileged to bring a record of other lands for the entertainment of those who are office-tired at the close of an exacting day, and find relaxation and refreshment, even in reflection, of open winds upon the Plains.

Chapter CXIII

Little Animals that might Overwhelm the World

By Dr. J. G. Myers

of the Imperial Bureau of Entomology, London

One of the most engrossing of all the activities of animals is that which is concerned in carrying out the original command to multiply, to be fruitful and replenish the earth. So important does this need appear, and so much does all seem directed to this end, that it has been said that Nature cares nothing at all for the individual, and everything for the race.

Perhaps the most widespread of the ways by which the perpetuation of the species is ensured is the production of abundant offspring, so that however great be the adversity of circumstances and the activity of enemies, at least a few survivors may remain to breed in their turn. Chapman has proposed the term " environmental resistance " for the sum total of the adverse influences of the environment and, carrying the electrical analogy a little further, has given the name " biotic potential " to the inherent power of an organism to reproduce and survive, or to hold its own against the environmental resistance. One of the greatest factors in biotic potential is reproductive capacity. A summary view of the Animal Kingdom will afford us many striking examples of this capacity.

Woodruff kept one of the simple microscopic one-celled animals, a slipper animalcule (*Paramecium*), and observed carefully the rate at which reproduction—in this case by simple division—took place. He maintained this pure stock for five years, and recorded in that period no fewer than 3,029 generations, the average rate of reproduction being three divisions every 48 hours. Woodruff calculated that had all the offspring during the period been allowed to survive and reproduce at that rate in their turn, there would have been produced a mass of protoplasm ten thousand times bulkier than the earth. It was estimated further, according to Lull, that at the end of the nine thousandth generation the volume of living substance would have exceeded the confines of the known universe, and would be growing outwards at a rate equal to the speed of light.

H Bastin

CORN BORER MOTHS

Caterpillars of these moths bore into the stalks of maize and do immense damage. But it has been found that only a very small proportion of eggs laid ever produce insects that reach maturity.

Travellers are never tired of describing the beauties of phosphorescence when the sea looks like liquid fire for mile after mile. In many cases this light shines from the pin-head-like bodies of minute and simple animals (for example, *Noctiluca*), of which a single bucket of sea-water contains more individuals than there are people in London.

The common tape-worm (*Taenia solium*) of man periodically discharges segments of its body packed full of its ripe eggs. Raillet states that one worm may cast off as many as fourteen of these segments or proglottides every day, and each contains at least 8,800 eggs. Caullery believes the parasitic worm will produce eighty millions of eggs per year.

The queen bee is often considered very fecund, for she has been estimated to lay thirteen times her weight of eggs in a year. But these figures become insignificant before the performance of the common round-worm of man (*Ascaris*) which, as stated by Caullery, lays annually sixty-four millions of eggs, equal to 1,700 times the weight of its own body.

The oyster has been calculated to lay up to 60,000,000 eggs per year, though the average American yield (Lull) is considerably smaller—less than a third of this. Even on the latter basis, however, if all the progeny of one oyster survived and multiplied and so on, until there were great-great-grandchildren, their number would be 66,000,000,000,000,000,000,000,000,000,000,000,000, and if gourmands could be found to make away with such a feast, the heap of shells from the Olympian banquet would be eight times as large as the earth.

One of the mites or so-called " red spiders " (*Tetranychus bioculatus*) in India has been the subject of calculations by Misra, who states that the theoretically possible progeny of one female fertilised at the beginning of March might by the end of the month be 3,500,000 mites.

Coming to the insects, we find that the aphides, or plant-lice, which Erasmus Darwin compared to the " Vampire of Asia," have above all impressed observers with their

H. J. Shepstone

H. J. Shepstone

DEALING WITH THE PRAIRIE DOG

Every now and then the little prairie dogs or gophers of North America multiply more than usual. War has then to be waged on them as they are very destructive. Below is a gopher at its burrow and above a pile of 1,600 poisoned in one night in Arizona.

tremendous potential rate of increase. One of the first to calculate the possibilities—the great French naturalist, Réaumur—advanced the opinion that one parthenogenetic (that is, fertile without pairing) female aphis, if all her descendants survived and reproduced, might in one month have progeny numbering 5,904,900,000 millions.

Huxley's estimate is perhaps better known. He estimated that a single aphis, if environmental checks were removed, might produce in a year a mass of protoplasm which would outweigh all the inhabitants of China. Buckton, from his observations, believed this to be underestimated, and showed that if each aphis produced only 20 young, the progeny at the end of 300 days would number 17,000,000,000,000,000,000,000,000,000,000,000.

There is in Kenya Colony a distant relative of the aphides—the coffee mealy-bug (*Pseudococcus lilacinus*)—which is a very serious pest. So high is its reproductive capacity that Kirkpatrick has calculated that were it not for checks the offspring of one mealy-bug by the end of one year would weigh 40,000 millions of tons.

The vinegar-fly, *Drosophila*, was chosen as a good subject for studies in heredity, partly on account of its rapidity of increase. Maxwell Lefroy, investigating it in India, estimated that, under the most favourable conditions, a single pair of these little flies would produce in one year progeny sufficient to cover the whole of India 50,000,000 miles deep with their bodies when packed a thousand to the cubic inch.

H. J. Shepstone

J. J. Ward

RABBIT WHOSE FECUNDITY IS A MENACE TO MAN

Rabbits may have four or even five litters in one year and the young become capable of reproducing their kind at the age of six months. In ordinary conditions natural checks are present, but in Australia and New Zealand these animals are a menace. In England the wild rabbit (bottom) is often a nuisance locally. Above is the result of a rabbit drive in California.

The house-fly is another rapid breeder. Lull states that the progeny of a single fertilised female without checks, would theoretically, in six generations of three weeks each, occupy a quarter of a million cubic feet, allowing 200,000 flies to the cubic foot. Howard believed that under Washington conditions, beginning on the 15th April with a single over-wintered female fly, and supposing all the offspring survived, we should have by September 10th no fewer than 5,598,720,000,000 flies.

Even the little cheese-skipper (*Piophila casei*) has a potential annual increase from one female of 240 multiplied by itself 30 times (Chapman).

The queen of one of the large African termites, or so-called "white ants" (*Termes bellicosus*), according to the observations of Smeathman and of Escherich, lays at least 30,000 eggs per day. She is reduced practically to an egg-laying machine, assiduously attended by the workers, and thus enabled to keep up this amazing output day after day and year after year, so that she may produce as many as 10 millions of eggs per year or 100 millions in her lifetime. *Termes natalensis* is said to lay only about a tenth of this total.

H. Bastin

J. J. Ward

H. Bastin

H. Bastin

INSATIABLE APHIDES THAT SUCK THE LIFE JUICES OUT OF PLANTS

Aphides, or green-fly, debilitate plants by sucking their juices. As their bodies become full the excess is secreted as " honey dew " and, this falling on the skin of the plant, chokes the pores by which it breathes. Below (bottom left) is a plum leaf infected with green-fly, and (bottom right) a portion of the same photograph enlarged to show young and old green-fly swarming on the underside of the leaf. Above are (top left) leaves affected by the currant-blister aphis, and (top right) an aphis reproducing its kind by budding off young.

H. Bastin

H. Bastin

MAGNIFYING LENS REVEALS COLONIES OF APHIDES BREEDING AND FEEDING

These photographs, taken with the aid of magnification, show some green-fly communities, each a little plague in itself, clustering thick on the underside of leaves where they are less conspicuous and where rain will not dislodge them. In the lower view the objects looking like white insects are really the skins of the aphides cast as the individuals grow. Above are a number of newly hatched insects. So fast is the rate of reproduction, that if natural checks were temporarily weakened, green-fly might endanger human life.

H. Bastin

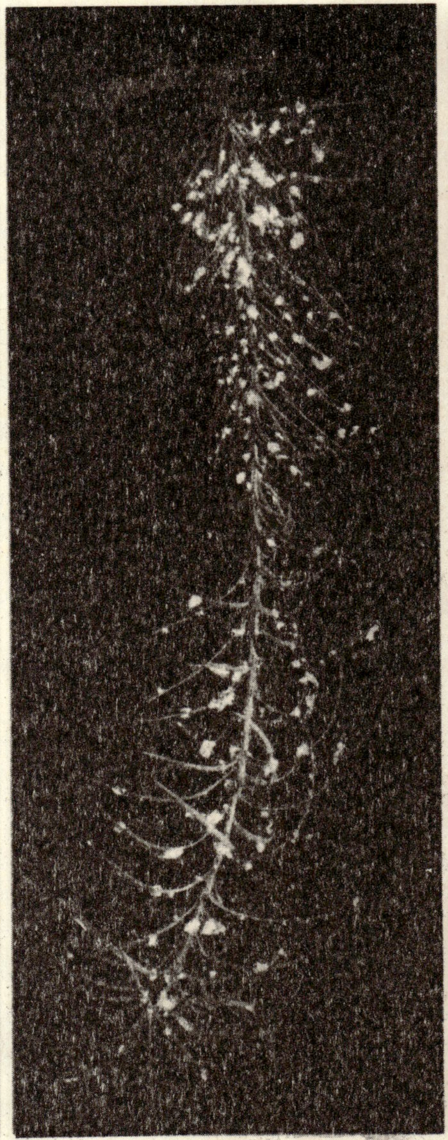

H. Bastin

J. J. Ward

GREEN-FLY WHOSE PROLIFICACY IS A DANGER TO PLANT LIFE SEEN WITH THE ANTS THAT "MILK" THEM

In the left-hand illustration is a part of a raspberry cane, greatly magnified, which is infested with green-fly Their cast skins litter the surface of the cane and it will be noticed that the hairs on the stem do not in the least prevent the green-fly from attacking it. The central photograph shows a spray of larch, natural size, which is being attacked by these voracious insects. On the right we see ants preparing to drive off to their underground nest the green-fly—which are also sometimes called ant cows because the ants suck the honey-dew secreted by them. This liquid is secreted by two tubes at the hinder end of the green-fly's abdomen. As the insect does not stop feeding when it is full the ants are able to "milk" their "cows" without injuring them.

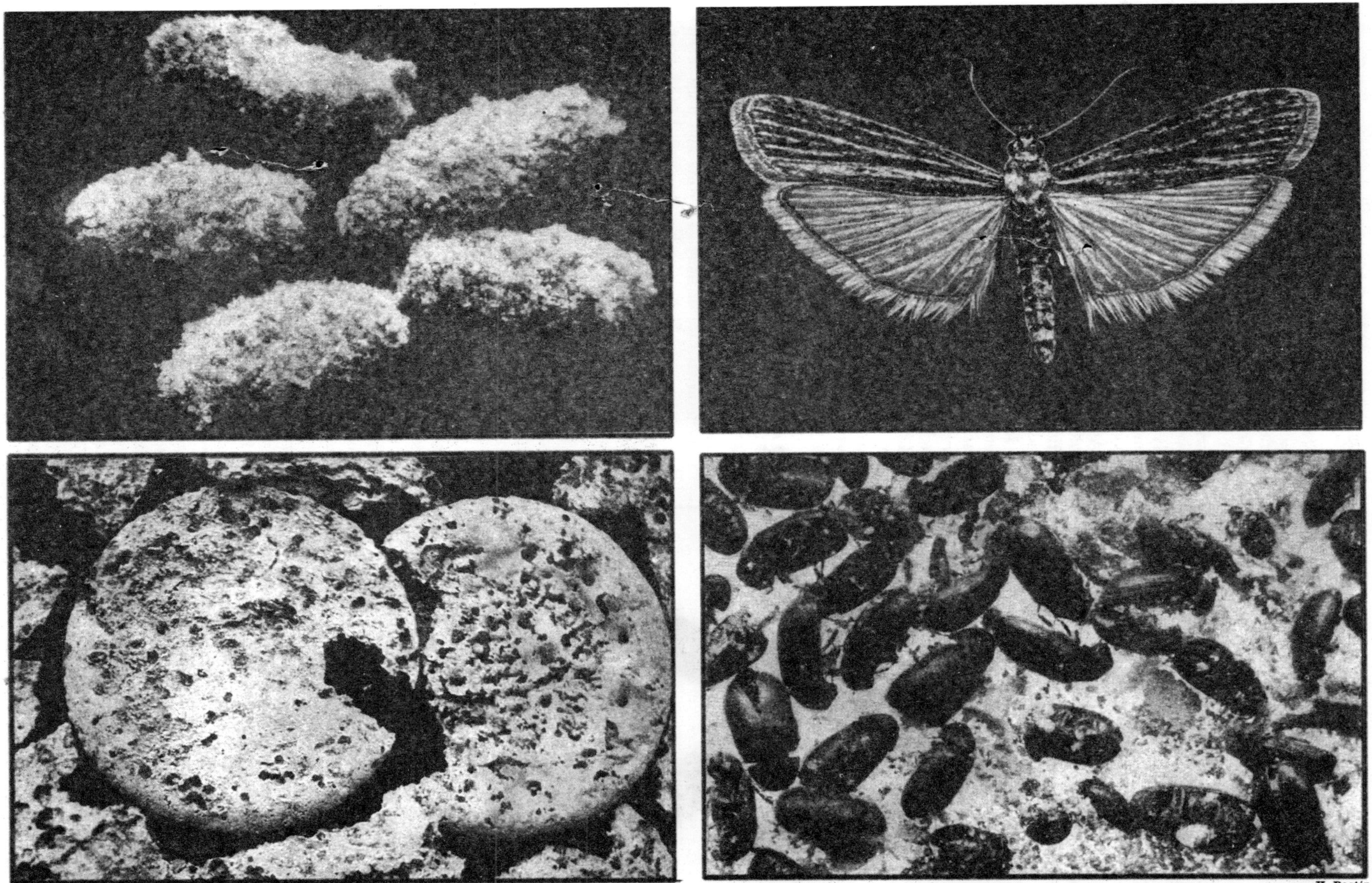

H. Bastin

DESTROYERS OF HUMAN FOOD STUFFS: THE BREAD BEETLE AND THE MEDITERRANEAN FLOUR MOTH

"Weevilly biscuits" are a well-known nuisance on ship-board and the two lower photographs here show the results of activity on the part of the weevil *Anobium*, called the bread or paste beetle. On the left we see biscuits damaged by the borings of the grubs and on the right some sweepings consisting of biscuit dust and dead weevils. Another pest of human foodstuffs which has adapted itself to living on artificial instead of natural food is the Mediterranean flour moth (upper photograph). On the left are some cocoons made by the grubs while in the flour and coated with it. Eventually those cocoons will split and from them emerge the fully developed moth to fly away and lay eggs and then die. On the right is one of these moths considerably magnified.

Pygmies that Threaten the World

E. A. Botting

J. J. Ward

POTENTIAL FERTILITY ALMOST BEYOND BELIEF

These are two views of a slipper animalcule, much enlarged. One, kept for experiment, produced in five years 3,029 generations. If every individual had survived, this would have meant a bulk of protoplasm 10,000 times the Earth's bulk.

Turning now to the beetles, we find that the grain-borer (*Rhizopertha dominica*), if Lea's figures are correct, has the following high potential rate of increase: supposing that there are five broods per season, that the sexes of the offspring are evenly distributed, and that all survive and multiply, the number of beetles at the end of the season would be 152,894,295,300.

In the case of another beetle, the rice-weevil (*Calandra oryzae*), Duvel estimated that one pair might theoretically produce in the space of six months 10,000 million pairs.

In certain small parasitic wasps the reproductive rate is tremendously increased by a peculiar phenomenon, polyembryony, in which one egg, deposited in the body of the host, gives rise to a very large number of young. Among the mammals similar cases occur regularly in the armadilloes, and certain types of twins in human beings are susceptible of the same explanation. Silvestri has especially studied the little parasitic wasp, *Litomastix.* In this insect the fertilised female produces nothing but female offspring —one egg may produce more than a thousand larvae. It thus follows that one such female, laying only forty eggs, may have no fewer than 40,000 female young which in their turn can produce as many as 1,600,000,000 offspring.

Among vertebrate animals, fishes are remarkably prolific. Lull found that in four herrings the eggs varied in number from 20,000 to 47,000. A cod may produce six millions of eggs, a turbot nine and a ling no fewer than 28 millions. Thus since ling maintain themselves at about the same numbers from year to year, the chance, as Lull remarks, of a ling's egg surviving and producing a young fish which will reach maturity is one in fourteen millions.

Compared with such figures the number of eggs laid per year by any bird is insignificant indeed. Yet Barrows has shown that a single pair of English sparrows are theoretically capable of producing in ten years, 275,716,983,698 offspring.

RABBITS, according to Lull, may have as many as six young in a litter and four litters a year; and the young begin to reproduce at the age of six months. Here again is material for the calculation of a phenomenal rate of increase. Rats and mice breed even more quickly, as man has discovered to his cost.

It is, of course, perfectly obvious that the unchecked multiplication at the theoretical rate of any of the animals just discussed would be utterly disastrous. The original realization by Malthus that such also would be the case with man led Darwin into the train of thought which culminated in the setting up of the famous hypothesis of organic evolution by means of the natural selection of favoured races in the struggle for existence. Darwin believed, and accumulated a vast body of evidence influencing others to believe, that such prodigious theoretical rates of increase coupled with the observed fact that on the average and under ordinary circumstances the population of a given species does not increase, proved the existence of a strenuous struggle for existence, a severe competition which ensured that only the most vigorous and best-adapted individuals survived to leave offspring in their turn, to inherit the accumulated favourable qualities.

Before we pass on to examine the nature of these checks, which are the agents of natural selection, we must examine, if possible, how far the theoretical rates of increase are realized in practice if the checks are removed. This is naturally a difficult problem, but Graham-Smith (1916) has tackled it in the case of flies. This very careful observer allowed blow-flies to lay eggs on dead rabbits in a large open-air net cage. The flies which emerged and their descendants were thus protected from natural enemies and very largely from other adverse conditions, and they were supplied with abundant food. The results may be summarised in the author's own words: "According to Fabre the blow-fly lays about three hundred eggs in one batch and therefore the first generation resulting from a hundred parent females ought to have consisted, had adults matured from all the eggs deposited, of at least 30,000 individuals. The total number, which emerged under apparently favourable conditions, was 2,789." The final result of the experiment was that "The descendants of the hundred females, which emerged from winter pupae, numbered during the season about 13,000 adults, instead of the 101,250,000,000 postulated in four generations by the calculation employed by Howard, or to put the matter in figures which can be more readily understood, the descendants of each female during the season numbered 130 instead of 1,012 millions." While it is difficult to be sure that all adverse circumstances had been obviated, the discrepancy here between actual and theoretical results is so very great that it is obvious the latter are exaggerated, and that there exist intrinsic factors which limit increase much below the possibilities calculated on the number of eggs.

Further light has been thrown on this question by the researches of Thompson and Parker on the corn-borer (*Pyrausta nubialis*), a moth-caterpillar tunnelling the stalks of maize. These writers distinguish as intrinsic controlling factors "those characteristics of structure and habit peculiar to the species, by reason of which a high mortality occurs in certain phases of existence, even in the normal environment." Such factors limit the increase of the corn-borer more than any other single group of adverse outer influences. Apart altogether from environmental checks "Only a very small fraction of the population represented by the eggs actually reaches maturity."

Let us then freely admit that estimates of potential increase based on the number of offspring may be exaggerated and misleading. It still remains true that without external checks almost any animal species would increase beyond all bounds. This holds true even of animals with an extremely low rate of increase. Thus the fulmar petrel lays only one egg; yet it is believed to be the most numerous bird in the world (Darwin). In fact, so far as actual increase is concerned, other factors may be much more important than mere fecundity.

IN fishes, like those instanced above, the spawn is deposited more or less at random and a stupendous number of eggs is necessary to ensure that one or two young per parent may survive. In the case of internal parasites like the tape-worm the voided eggs must be swallowed by an intermediate host, and its flesh in turn devoured by the final host. The chances against success are here so great that an even more phenomenal number of eggs must be produced. But in those insects which deposit their eggs actually in the midst of an abounding food-supply; in birds which shelter their eggs in a nest and feed the newly-hatched young; and above all in the mammals (including man) which suckle their offspring and tend them carefully until they can fend for themselves—in all these higher organisms the need for such extreme fecundity is gone, and the population is maintained by means of a higher survival rate among the much fewer young.

There is, then, a very definite check on the increase of all animals, ensuring that their populations ordinarily remain stable. Thus Cooke found in the north central United States that there were about eleven nesting pairs of English sparrows to every hundred acres of land. During a five-year period, when an accurate census was made, this number fluctuated only from nine to thirteen. Yet, adopting the rate of increase cited in our first section, we should expect each hundred acres of land to give rise to 575 sparrows every year; but the number remained constant. Since we know of no intrinsic limiting factors in this case, we may agree with Chapman that "This difference between the potential number of sparrows and

H. Bastin

GRAIN WEEVIL AND ITS WORK

Grain weevils have a very dangerously high rate of reproduction. From one rice weevil, for instance, there could be produced, at any rate in theory, 10,000 million pairs in six months. Here we have the grain weevil (top) and its work (bottom.)

H. J. Shepstone

W. S. Berridge

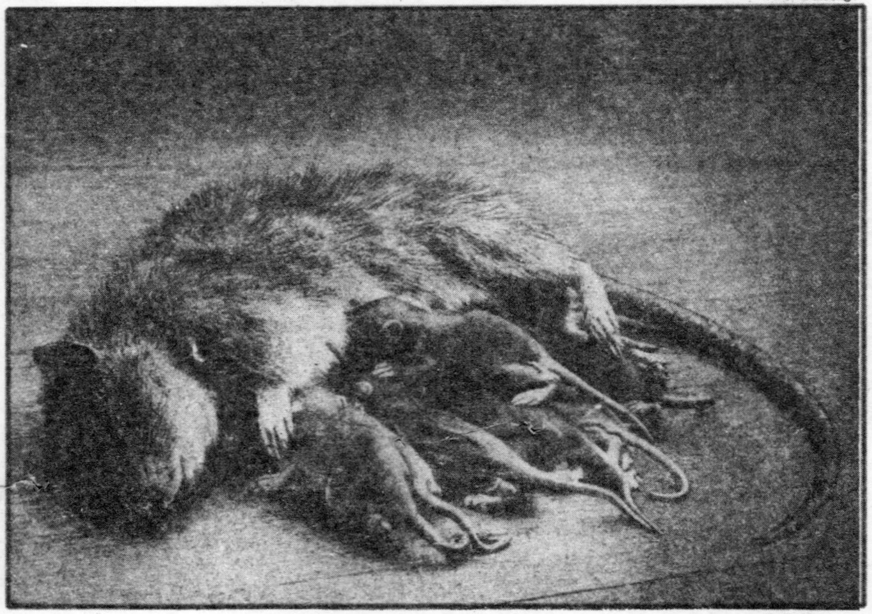

J. T. Neuman

NUISANCES TO HUMANITY: RATS THAT BREED AT AN ALARMING RATE AND ONE CAUGHT IN A PARIS SEWER

Rats can increase under conditions favourable to them in an alarming way as man has found to his cost. Being very versatile—they are virtually omnivorous, can board ships and get transported from one end of the Earth to the other and can adapt themselves quickly to great changes of conditions—their tenacity of life is great. Sewers are proverbial haunts of the rat and there are many stories of the "sewer rats." There is, of course, no special sub-division of the rat family which lives habitually in sewers and the numbers of those that do are often exaggerated. About forty or fifty drowned rats are found every day on the grids at Barking Outfall which serves the whole of London north of the Thames. On the right are (bottom) a brown rat and (top) a black rat.

H. Bastin

CORNSTALKS THAT ARE ATTACKED BY QUICK BREEDING ENEMIES, INCLUDING THE CORNFLY AND SAWFLY

Of these photographs, which are mostly of magnified subjects, the lower row shows the destructive work of the goat, or ribbon-footed cornfly. On the left is a cornfly larva just before pupating. In the centre photograph is the pupa safely ensconced in a groove cut in a wheat stalk. The right-hand illustration is of half a dozen ears of corn. On the left is a normal ear, then, moving to the right, specimens damaged by the cornfly, Hessian fly, wheat midge and sparrows. The upper row of photographs is of the corn sawfly and shows, from left to right, how the larva cuts out the inside of the cornstalk just before pupating; the attacked stalk opened to show the cocoon at its base; a larva in the stem and, beside it, a stem showing how the joint has been bored through.

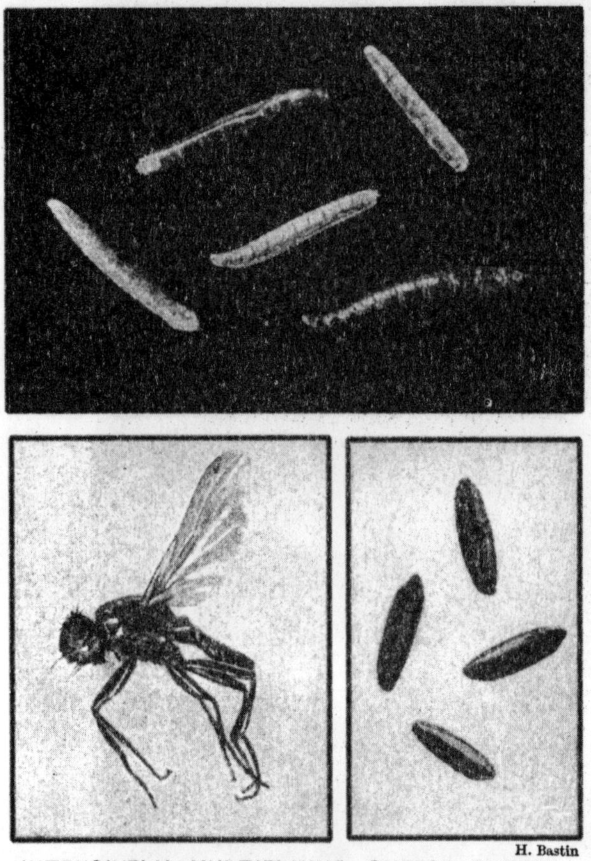

H. Bastin

INTENSIVELY MULTIPLYING CHEESE SKIPPER

The cheese skipper is a fly (bottom left) that lays its eggs on cheeses whose larvae (top) bore their way within and feed until they are ready to become pupae (bottom right). The potential increase from one female is 240 to the power of thirty, annually.

the actual number must be a measure of the toll taken by the environment."

It has remained for man, in certain circumstances, to give to a number of animal species the opportunity of realizing more nearly their potential rates of increase. As Darwin first suggested, a very striking example of rapid multiplication in the absence of many of the customary checks is afforded by the progress of animals and plants introduced intentionally or accidentally into new countries. Thus the horse, imported into America by the Spaniards, very rapidly spread through a great part of the New World; the prickly pear introduced into Australia speedily covered and rendered agriculturally useless a huge area which is now increasing at the rate of one million acres per year; rabbits first introduced into New Zealand some time previous to 1838, were already in 1866 referred to as "That great scourge to our large run-holders." At the present day "The economic waste caused by the vast increase of rabbits in New Zealand is incalculable, and certainly represents a loss in the stock-carrying capacity of the country which probably runs every year into millions of pounds" (Thomson, 1922). The sugar cane leafhopper (*Perkinsiella saccharicida*) was accidentally introduced into the Hawaiian Islands about 1897. By 1902 it had increased to such an extent that sugar production on one infested plantation fell in three years from 19,000 to 7,000 tons.

There are other means also by which man inadvertently renders conditions favourable to animal increase. He does this especially by increasing their food-supply. Agriculture consists in nothing more nor less than a systematic attempt to favour, over large areas, the growth of certain limited species of plants to the detriment of their natural competitors, which automatically become weeds. Animals feeding upon these cultivated plants are commensurately encouraged. The balance of Nature is disturbed. A striking instance occurred in Australia during the War, when unparalleled stocks of wheat were accumulated. At one port alone, in three yards, five million bags were stacked. This led to a plague of rats and mice, which was succeeded by one of weevils (*Calandra*). At certain times the latter swarmed from the stacks and piled up four or five inches deep on the ground. "In Wallaroo yard alone, when the plague was at its worst, up to one ton of weevils per day were gathered up and destroyed."

How is man with his industries to fare in this welter of proliferation? He is now endeavouring, in one of the most interesting biological experiments of the present century, to tackle the problem fundamentally. Where a destructive animal has been introduced into a new country and its natural enemies are lacking, he imports enemies from the original home.

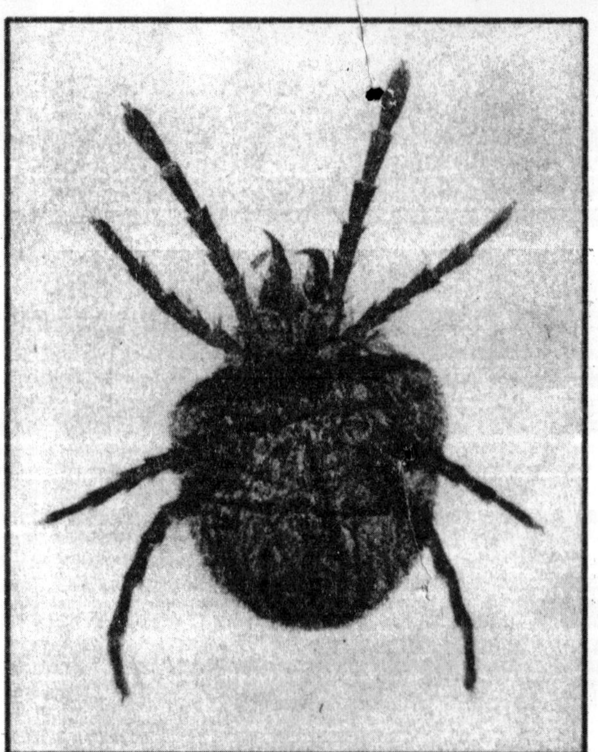

J. J. Ward

HARMFUL MITE CALLED "RED SPIDER"

According to careful calculations the progeny possible to one of the Indian mites, called "red spiders," might be 3,500,000 mites from one female in four weeks. Natural causes reduce its numbers, but this mite does great damage to crops.

Chapter CXIV

The Wonder of Mother Love Among the Animals

By Frances Pitt

Author of "Woodland Creatures"

MOTHER love among birds and beasts is a marvellous force, driving the most timid creatures to desperate deeds for the sake of home and young. I have known of a mother rabbit turning upon a stoat in defence of her family; and I have seen a tiny merlin attack a great raven because the latter came too near her nest.

It was in the Shetland Islands that I saw the latter episode. The merlin had a nest on the hill-side, or rather had taken possession of an old hooded crow's nest, and had therein five greyish-white eyasses, the quaintest most witch-like little birds, that looked out from their home on the hillside over the wide heathery expanse of moor and island. The two old merlins watched over their family with greatest care. Let anything strange appear, even in the distance, and the keen-eyed cock saw it instantly, giving warning to his mate with a chattering call. She was, after the manner of hawks, bigger and stronger than he, but still she was only a small bird, no larger, in fact, than a mistle-thrush, yet she was a marvel of pluck and determination.

One day when I was lying among the heather on the hilltop, watching the wild life of this barren, wind-swept spot, I saw a great black raven flapping over. The ominous bird came onwards on his sable pinions, flying slowly and majestically, until almost over the merlin's nest, when out from her eyrie shot the little hawk. Straight as an arrow she came, driving at the raven with utmost determination. Beside his black majesty she looked no bigger than a sparrow, and in real fact she was little larger than a thrush; yet she went at the raven with indomitable resolution—she was not going to allow any black robber near her young family.

Again and again that merlin flew at the raven, getting above him and diving down, when he turned and twisted and tried to elude her, flapping his great wings and making off as fast as he could go. The plucky little mother had fairly put the intruder to flight, he swerved before her attacks, and flew off faster than ever; but she was not satisfied. She followed him up, and pursued him far across the valley, until she was almost lost to sight, and the raven was but a speck in the distance.

AT last the merlin was satisfied, left her quarry, turned about and came home, gliding up in the beautiful, effortless flight of this hawk, to close her wings and alight on a rock near the nest. Here she sat and rested. I watched her preening her ruffled feathers and putting her apparel to rights, but all the while she was on the look out, and her dark eyes took in everything that stirred. When at last I moved from my hiding-place she was instantly upon the wing, following me across the moor, and chattering angrily the while. But even she drew the line at attacking a person.

Yet there are some birds that have the pluck to do this, and one of them is that dark-coloured robber gull, known as the great skua. The great skua haunts the northern seas, where it gives other gulls an unhappy time, harrying and hunting them for the fish they have caught. In the spring-time it resorts to wild and wind-swept islands, where it lays its dark eggs, and hatches two olive-coloured chicks. For those quaint roly-poly babies it will dare a very great deal. I well remember helping a friend who wished to take snapshots of some skua chicks, and what a lively time the old birds gave us. They dashed towards us, darting over our heads with a mighty rush of wings, and at last, as my friend was stooping over her camera, one skua, shrieking "sku-arr, sku-arr!" as it came, dived headlong at her, and hit the side of her face with its webbed feet. It was a real smack. My friend had a sore face for days after.

ANOTHER courageous bird is the homely brown or tawny owl, that fluffy, comfortable bird that is so common in woodlands throughout Europe. An old owl will venture much in defence of her owlets, as when I was stooping over a hole in a hollow tree, trying to inspect the owl family at the bottom of it, and received a resounding smack in the middle of the back. Not having seen or heard anything I jumped up much startled, but not a thing was to be seen. Still mystified, I turned to have a second look at the owlets, when bang, something gave me another thump, I sprang around in time to see a large owl gliding off. Of course, with its downy, muffled wings it had been able to attack suddenly and unheard. I retreated, feeling very respectful towards the irate and formidable mother.

Indeed, she deserved respect, for many birds, bigger, stronger and better armed, would not have displayed the mother love that she did. Even the magnificent golden eagle in its mountain eyrie might not have attacked an intruder, nor would many another large and fierce-looking bird of prey.

We find, however, some brave mothers among the four-legged beasts, no mammal being more courageous in defence of its young than the cat, and the homely, everyday cat at that. Puss is indeed a wonderful study in mother love; watch the devoted care with which she tends her kittens, licking and dressing them, cuddling them to her furry flank, and, as they

Neville Kingston

W. S. Berridge

MOTHER LOVE AS EXHIBITED AMONG THE MONKEYS: FOSTER PARENT AND REAL PARENT

Since this South-American monkey (left) had no young one of its own it adopted a marmozet. The instinct to mother something was too strong to be denied and had to find an outlet. Humouring the more delicate feelings of the animals is one of the tasks that those who look after modern zoos set themselves, thereby finding their captives happier and healthier animals. Our right-hand photograph shows a pig-tailed macaque. It is up against the wire netting of its cage with its young. Some monkeys, when they have young ones, become very suspicious of visitors; but they usually find that more than the ordinary share of good things is theirs for the sake of the very maternity which has made them withdraw from the bars.

get older suffering their teasing, when they pull her tail and bite her ears in their playful glee in life; but, when any danger threatens, what a change! Is there a greater fury than an angry cat with kittens to defend? Brave, or rather very foolish, is the dog that would venture near that family. With no thought of danger, utterly regardless of self, the mother flies at the intruder, using her claws with such fiery wrath that hardly any dog can withstand her onslaught.

If this fury animates our household puss when danger, fancied or real, threatens her kittens, what of the true wild cats, whether it be one of the wild cats that are found in the mountains of Scotland and other parts of Europe, or the different wild cats found in various parts of the globe? Most of them are among the bravest of mothers, ready to dare and do anything for their little ones, rushing upon what seems like certain death if their babies appear imperilled.

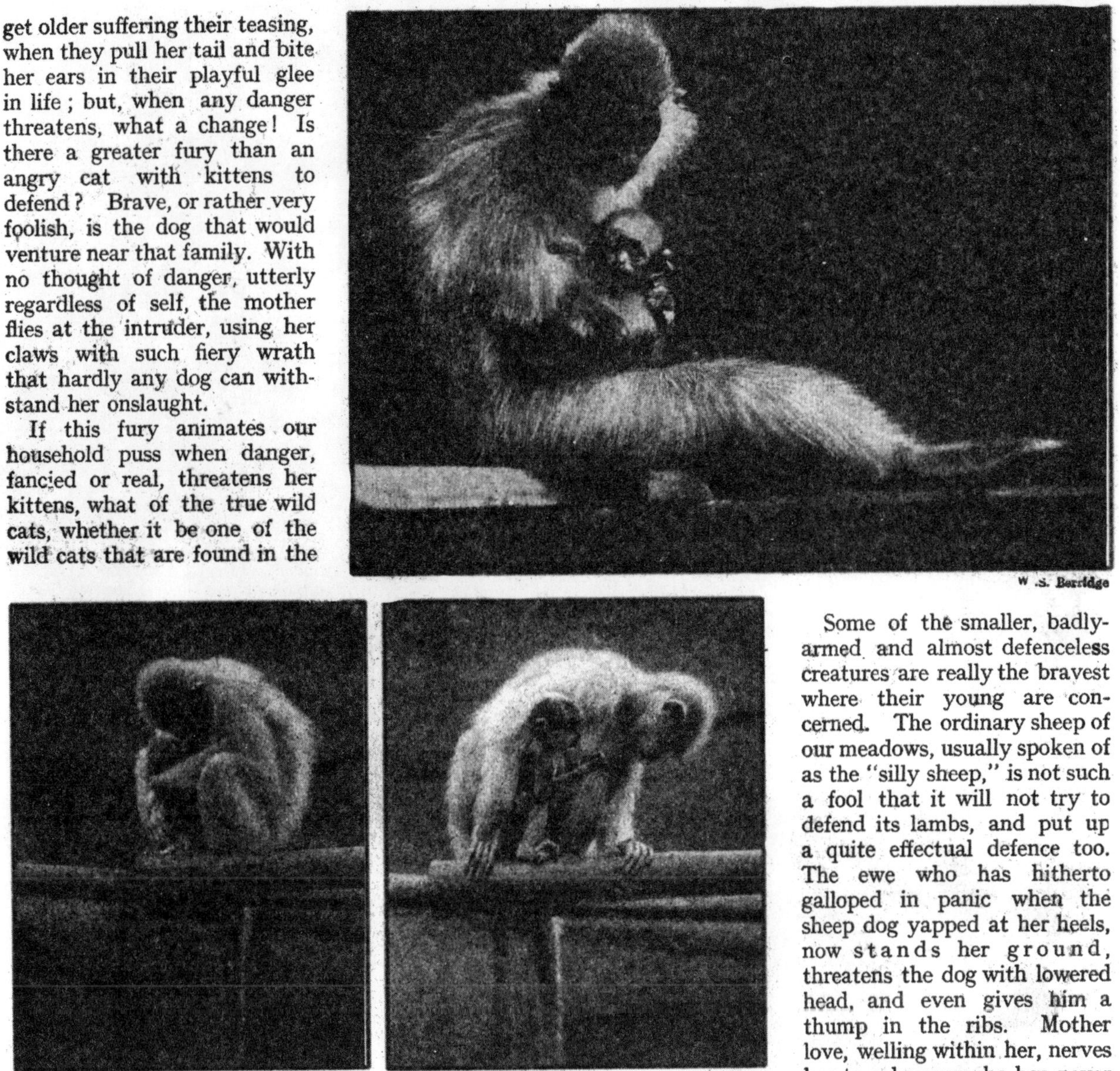

W. S. Berridge

H. Bastin

CAPPED LANGURS AT THE LONDON ZOO

These very interesting studies of female capped langurs and their young come from the London Zoo, where the photographs were taken. Below, on the left, the mother is crouching on a perch and stooping attentively over the young one, which is held between the knees. In the next photograph (bottom right) the attention is wandering. But, above, the nine-days-old baby is being held firmly to the breast by its mother.

In saying this, I am speaking of the smaller cats, for courage in the cat tribe does not seem to increase with size. Of course a tigress or lioness with cubs to defend is a dangerous beast, not to say a very dangerous one, but if its courage was as proportionately great as that of our little house puss, well, it would win in every contest and dominate the jungle.

Some of the smaller, badly-armed and almost defenceless creatures are really the bravest where their young are concerned. The ordinary sheep of our meadows, usually spoken of as the "silly sheep," is not such a fool that it will not try to defend its lambs, and put up a quite effectual defence too. The ewe who has hitherto galloped in panic when the sheep dog yapped at her heels, now stands her ground, threatens the dog with lowered head, and even gives him a thump in the ribs. Mother love, welling within her, nerves her to a bravery she has never known before.

Perhaps one of the bravest performances in defence of the young is that commonly spoken of as the "broken-wing trick," which certain birds go through in an endeavour to lure a foe away from their offspring. I have seen many different species of birds do the trick, Arctic skuas when their nesting colony on a wind-swept island moor was invaded, partridges in an English meadow, a pintail duck on a bog in the Scandinavian mountains, golden plover on a Shetland hillside, and so on.

The pintail duck did the trick particularly well. I had seen her on this part of the bog before, and was searching the marshy ground, wading backwards and forwards across its uncertain surface, peeping and peering into the tussocks, in the hope of finding her nest, when the duck flew up, or rather floundered

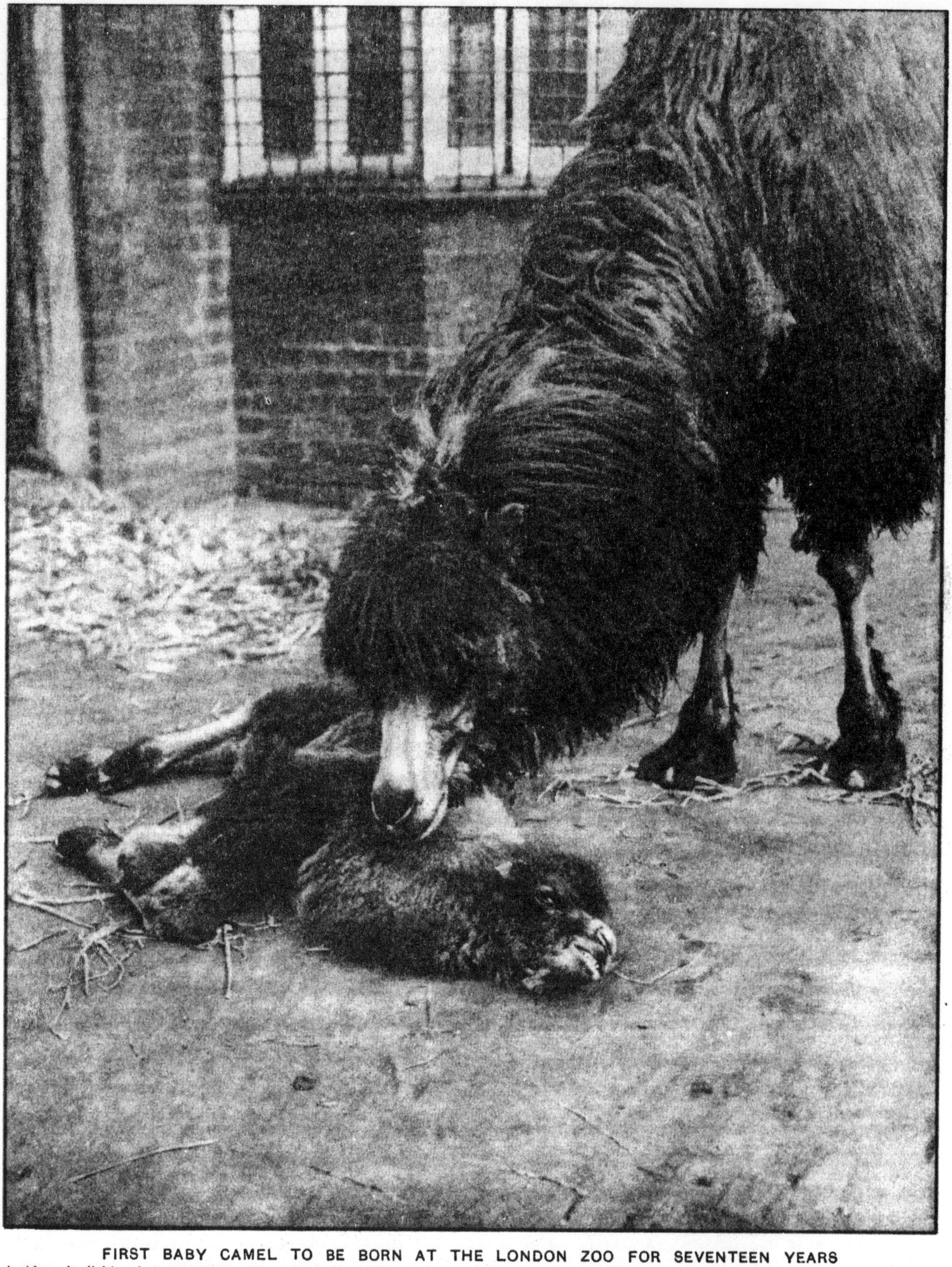

FIRST BABY CAMEL TO BE BORN AT THE LONDON ZOO FOR SEVENTEEN YEARS

Assiduously licking her young one, this animal gives us a sight of mother love as practised by that most unaffectionate of domestic beasts, the camel. It is always something of a triumph when certain of the wild animals are induced to breed in captivity, and it seems the more surprising that a domesticated animal like the camel should so seldom bear young at the London Zoological Gardens. Yet this is so, for the infant camel seen here was the first born at " the Zoo " for seventeen long years.

YOUNG ZEBRA COLT GIVES ITS MOTHER AN AFFECTIONATE LICK

Among animals the first and the most constant association between mother and offspring is licking. This cleansing action is also soothing to the new born and nervous animal, and takes the place of the caress of a human mother to her baby. Naturally enough this young zebra pays its mother back in her own kindly coin. Perhaps when the effects of a few maternal bites have been felt, there may be more reciprocation but of a less charming kind. But animal mothers are usually very patient.

W. S. Berridge

W. S. Berridge

ARABIAN CAMEL WITH ITS DELICATE CALF: CONGO MARSHBUCK AND ITS LATEST BORN

Arabian camels have one calf at a birth, and it runs with its mother and suckles for a year or even more. Very young camels are rather helpless creatures, and when large camel herds are kept, as they are for instance in the Sudan, the young ones are often slung by a net to the back or side of full-grown animals when the herds are driven northward in the rainy season. The mothers are very fierce and defend their offspring with their teeth—the camel's most dangerous weapon. Our right-hand photograph shows a Congo marshbuck with its little one just two days old. The legs of the calf are not so very much shorter than the mother's but its body is only about a quarter the size. The legs have to develop quickly so that mother and offspring may keep together.

Neville Kingston

FEMALES OF THE LLAMAS AND BARBARY SHEEP THAT BOTH MAKE GOOD MOTHERS

Llama mothers apparently have an arduous life with the young, for it is said that they are not unusually suckling two generations at the same time. However, only one offspring is born at a time, in the ordinary way, so that the strain of the length of time before weaning is partly compensated for by the small size of the family requiring nourishment. It is to be noticed in the left-hand picture that the young llama is dark all over, while the mother has the foreparts, legs and neck, white. Young Barbary sheep (right) need most tender care, for they are brought up in the wildest and most inhospitable parts of the North African uplands. But the parents, like all wild sheep, will defend their offspring very courageously.

up at my very teet. I had almost stepped on her and her ducklings. There they lay, flat on the peaty soil, such quaint, rather sandy-hued youngsters, with that snaky aspect which is characteristic of the adult pintail. However, I barely glanced at the ducklings for the old duck took my attention. She was floundering on the bog like a creature sorely wounded, flapping about as if almost helpless. Her actions were not so much those of a bird with a broken wing, as of one with all limbs broken. I am sure a dog, fox or cat would have been completely deceived by the way she " carried on."

I stood quite still while she floundered and tumbled off across the marsh, but when she found I was not following her she came back and again tried to lure me away. This time I walked after her, while she tumbled ahead, with frantic quacks and much flapping. Of course, she led me away from the ducklings, but the further we went the quicker became her actions, until she was half-running, half-flying across the watery ground. Finally she spread her wings, rising with what sounded like a derisive quack, and flew off towards a little stream. I turned about and walked back towards the ducklings which brought the pintail duck after me. She flew from the stream, alighted near, and began to tumble about again.

Thinking it might be possible to get a photograph of her performance, I ran back to the house to fetch a camera, being away less than twenty minutes. On returning I went straight to the spot where I had left the little ducklings hiding, but they had gone. Their devoted mother had got them away. In vain did I search up and down the bog, not a trace of those ducklings could I find. The old duck flew up, but maae no attempt to do the broken-wing trick. Did she know that she had defeated me, and had hidden her tamily where I could not discover them ? It looked like it. But what love and devotion had inspired her previous actions !

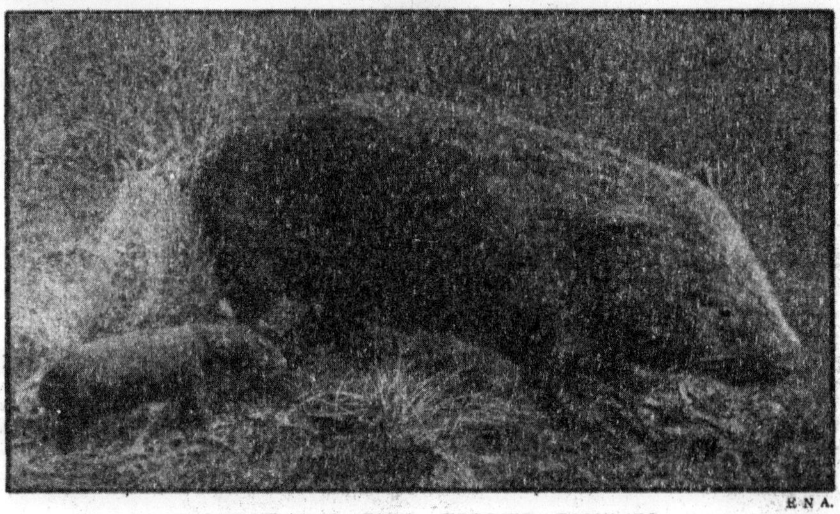

E N A.

WOMBAT AND BULL TERRIER FAMILIES

Wombats have only a short period of gestation, the young being transferred to a marsupium or pouch in which to finish their development, just as in the case of the kangaroo and other Australian marsupials. The lower illustration is of a wombat in the Australian bush. Above is a much more familiar kind of mother, a bull terrier with her litter.

It is an interesting question how far such a performance is instinctive and how far intelligent. Is it the result of unreasoning impulse arising from fear combined with love for the little ones, or is it a

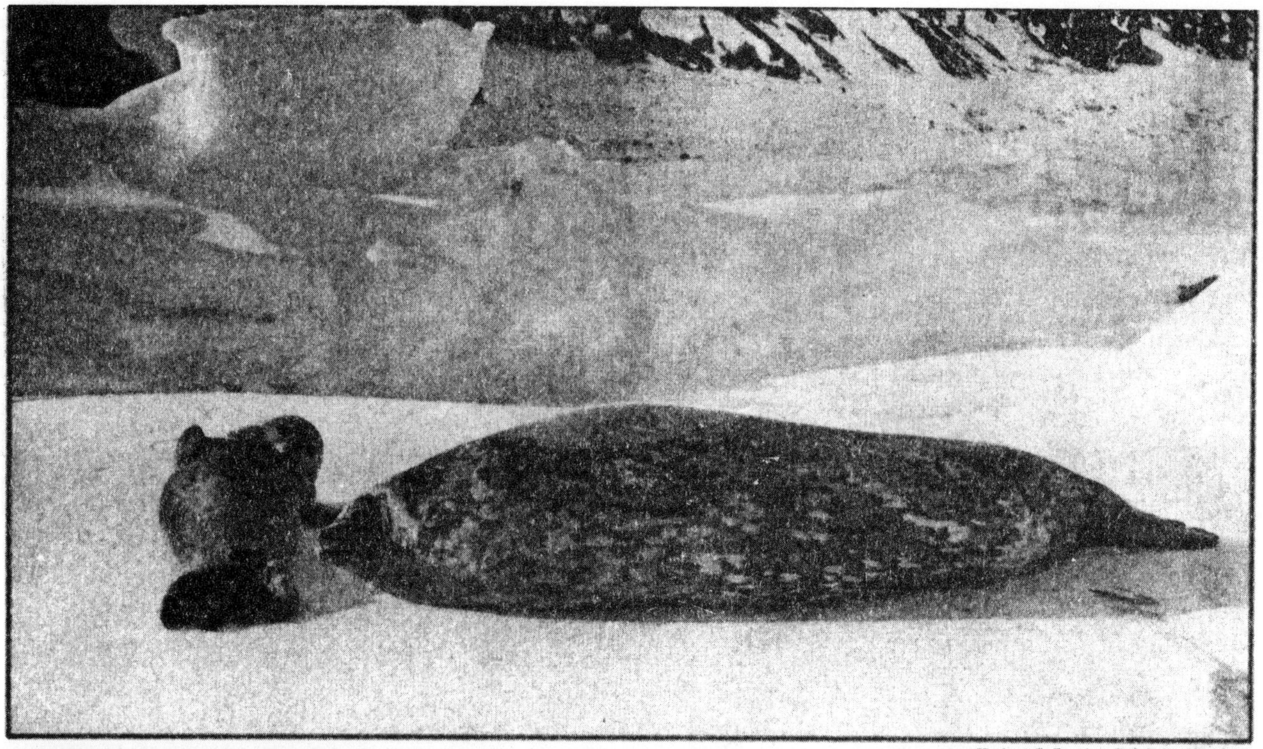

Herbert G. Ponting, F.R.P.S., Copyright

SEAL PARENTS THAT CAREFULLY TEACH THE WAYS OF THE SEA TO THEIR YOUNG

Seals are most affectionate and painstaking mothers and very interesting to watch. In the lower photograph we have both a mother and a father seal using their best endeavours to persuade their pup to enter the water. This, unexpectedly enough, it is very unwilling to do, although we find that this is usually the case with young seals. They do not take readily to the sea, and have to be taught the various lessons of the life by their mothers. Above is a Weddel seal and its pup in the Antarctic.

W. S. Berridge

W. S. Berridge

ANIMAL MOTHERS OF INDIAN HIGHLAND AND LOWLAND WITH THEIR OFFSPRING

High up in the Himalayan mountains in the tract of rock and scrub between the ending of the forest and the snow line, the markhor (bottom), that fine wild goat, brings forth and rears its young. On the other hand, the nilgai, the largest antelope found in India (top), lives in the lower hills or else in the plains. Our photograph shows a young one only ten minutes old. Nilgai mothers look after their offspring on the community system, going about in herds together, separate from the males.

James

SECURE RESTING PLACE FOR A LITTLE KANGAROO: A FOUR-HORNED SHEEP FAMILY

Among mothers of the animal world kangaroos are very prominent in popular fancy because of the interesting pouch in which they carry their young. The sight of the little one looking out at the world from the comfortable warmth of a kind of watch pocket in its mother's coat is always most attractive to visitors to the kangaroo cage or paddock in any zoological garden where these animals are kept. The upper photograph shows two parents and a lamb of the curious four-horned sheep of India.

W. S. Berridge

WILD ASS AND MONGOLIAN WILD HORSE WITH THEIR FOALS

Of the Asiatic asses the finest and largest is the kiang (lower photographs). The males and females feed together with their young in a herd, with a sentinel to keep guard. The period of gestation lasts about twelve months with these animals. In the upper photograph we have a Mongolian wild mare feeding her foal. The foal has to run with its mother, and the legs are capable of sustaining it quite soon after birth. The mother teaches by force of example, and her care is no less impressive for being silent.

FOND MOTHERS FROM AMONG CATTLE DOMESTICATED IN ENGLAND AND FAR TIBET

Upon an English farm near Peterborough, this cow (bottom) successfully gave birth to three calves at once, and we see that both the mother and the triplets are doing well. Attention is sometimes forcibly drawn to mother love in the animal world by its appearance, in the guise of ferocity, in the usually placid cow. Cases of cows molesting human beings can usually be traced to fear or anxiety in connection with a calf. Above we see a relative of English domestic cattle, the yak of Tibet, which is itself domesticated in its own country.

W. S. Berridge

W. S. Berridge

CAT AND DOG AS FOSTER MOTHERS OF STRANGE FOUNDLINGS

A twist in the normal course of things often brings strange and startling results when it occurs to interfere with the maternal affections of the animal. The lower photograph gives us a strange instance of this with a cat that brought up a squirrel given to it in exchange for drowned kittens. In the same way a retriever is seen playing foster mother to a litter of timber wolves (top). But the gulf between the animals in this case is nothing like as great as exists between cat and squirrel.

thoughtful series of actions? I am inclined to think it is a combination of the two. I have seen a mallard duck, a tame bred one, which I knew had never been in trouble before, when surprised on her nest by an otter, tumble off and do the broken wing trick to perfection. She had no experience whatever, yet when the otter sprang at her as she sat on her eggs, she instantly behaved as if she knew all about it, floundering into the water and splashing the length of the pond in front of the pursuer, so that she drew the otter away from her treasures. It was only when she had lured it right away that she took wing, leaving the otter looking thoroughly silly.

A. H. Willford

THRUSH PARENTS ATTENDING TO THEIR NURSERY

Birds being, as we say, lower down the scale of life than mammals, have to go out and get food for their young when they are mothers. The work is very hard and very exhausting for the parent. All through the spring day it never ceases. A cluster of gaping beaks waits, shrieking impatience, the successful end to each little hunting excursion.

In the case of that duck it was obvious she acted on impulse, an inherited predisposition to respond in that way when panic-stricken, and that there was no thinking out what she was about, but when a bird returns again and again, as my pintail duck did, and as I have seen a golden plover do, deliberately to repeat its endeavour to draw peril to itself and away from its offspring, surely we see intention as well as instinct—true mother love driving the parent to dare even the final sacrifice for her young ones?

MOTHER love has queer manifestations at times, as when under stress of extreme fear and excitement the distraught old one destroys her own family. I have seen a meadow vole (the little furry brown field mouse known to scientists as *Microtus agrestis*) slay her young ones, biting each in turn until she had killed it; and have known cases of the domestic pig, dog, ferret, rabbit, badger and other mammals destroying their offspring. Some perversion of their love, perhaps the feeling that they must keep their babies safe, drives them to the awful deed. But from such a horrid subject let us turn to more pleasant things, for instance the manner in which various animals care for their young ones.

Birds, of course, take first place with regard to elaborate nurseries, their wonderful and beautiful nests having no parallel among the mammals. Such nests as that of the weaver bird, or the European long-tailed tit are exquisite structures. The latter is a marvel of bird architecture. I examined one, the whole nest weighing less than an ounce, and found its walls were a thin but elastic structure of moss, spider cocoons and lichen, while it was lined with feathers. These feathers were drawn out one by one and carefully counted. They numbered 1,144! What a nursery for the delicate eggs, and the little birds that hatched from them. Even a common song-thrush's nest is an elaborate structure, with its grass walls and clay-lined cup; but however hard the birds work on behalf of their coming young ones, preparing wonderful nurseries, it is nothing to the way they work afterwards when the babies have to be fed. There is no rest for the parents then, life becomes one long labour collecting caterpillars and other grubs to push down the ever eager beaks, beaks that open so wide, and are held up in such anxious appeal. With those hungry beaks always waiting for more, the poor devoted parents have to work harder than ever. No wonder that when the spring days wane many a little mother bird finds herself almost worn out by her unflagging devotion.

YET devoted as bird parents are, despite the anxious care they give to their nestlings, there is one thing the majority cannot do, and that is move the family to a new home. The bird's nest must be occupied until the nestlings are ready to go

Harold Shepstone

BIRDS ONCE HELD TO BE SHINING EXAMPLES OF MATERNAL CARE: A PEACEFUL COLONY OF PELICANS

In the days when the animals were considered to have certain almost fairy qualities—they might, for instance, suddenly begin to speak, and usually very much to the point—moral lessons were frequently drawn from them and many birds and beasts had each a special virtue or failing. The pelican was the great example of maternal virtue. The bird was supposed to feed its young, if necessary, with its own flesh and blood. Actually, what happens is that it opens its beak and lets the fledglings swallow the fish in its huge pouch. Our illustration shows a pelican colony on an island and is from a photograph by the American Museum of Natural History, New York.

C. Reid

SWAN FATHER AND MOTHER, WHICH DEFEND THEIR FAMILY WITH THE UTMOST FEROCITY

Let anyone who doubts the power of motherly care interfere with a swan when she is on her nest or has her cygnets with her. Swans have always been noted for truculence, and they may treat the owner of a piece of ornamental water who has given it them for a home as rudely as any interfering terrier. Here we see a family afloat on an English river. The mother will deign to receive food for herself and family, but all the time the wings will be a little raised and spread as though the bird might fly into a rage at any moment. Swan mothers have an alarming habit of flying so that their wings hit the water in a series of terrifying claps when they wish to drive off an intruder.

F. Vear

MOTHER HEDGE SPARROW FEEDING ITS HUNGRY CHILDREN

Low down, near the ground, the hedge sparrow—which is no relation to the house sparrow—builds its nest of moss or roots lined with hair or wool. Its care for its little ones is shown in the painstaking labour with which this hedge cradle is constructed, and afterwards by the ceaseless hunt for food. Hedge sparrows often have an extra burden thrust upon them, for the cuckoo is very fond of a hedge sparrow's nest—probably because of its easy accessibility—as a place in which to lay its changeling egg.

forth into the great world; but the four-legged creatures think nothing of changing house.

One of the prettiest removals I have seen was that of a squirrel family. There was a tall and very thick fir tree close to the house, and in the top of this spruce was a squirrel's nest, or, to use the correct word, a " drey," but I did not know it was a nursery until one morning when I was looking out of a window and saw something red moving in the tree-top. Watching, to see what the squirrel was about, I saw her come running down the trunk, but more slowly and carefully than a squirrel usually moves. She neither sprang from bough to bough, nor dashed headlong downwards; then as she came to an open space, where I could clearly see her golden-red form through the dark green fir branches, the reason of her care was apparent, she was carrying a little squirrel in her mouth! It was quite a well-grown youngster, and as much as she could carry. No wonder she had to descend with care. She bore it by the loose skin at the back of its neck, as a cat carries a kitten, and it hung limply in her grasp, its little red tail curled up and curved over her head. Slowly she went down the tree, slipping the last few inches of trunk and landing on the turf with a run, when she scampered off across the lawn, to the shrubbery on the further side, where she disappeared with her burden into the bushes and trees.

Waiting and watching I presently saw her reappear, race back across the turf, ascend the spruce, and bring down another youngster, which was carried off like the first. How many she had taken before I cannot say, but she was evidently removing the entire family. Why, is another question. Was the old nest too close to the house, in too public a position, and did she therefore build a new drey in the plantation? I cannot say, all I know is that the new nest, which I subsequently found, was an elaborate one, well built and bulky, up a Scotch fir, and it must have been hard work carrying her well-grown babies up to it; but, then, mother love does wonders.

MANY mother animals will carry their young away from what they consider a dangerous neighbourhood to a new home, creatures so diverse as foxes, wolves, lions and tigers, doing so after the manner of the household cat, that is, bearing each baby by the " scruff of its neck." It is a curious fact that little animals never kick or struggle when picked up by this loose skin. They seem to have the notion implanted in them that this is the right part to be carried by, and even when they have become adults they never forget it. If you are handling a wild animal, and can get hold of it by the back of the neck, it usually stops struggling, and hangs limply in your grasp as if it remembered its infancy.

F. Vear

Mondiale

FALCON AND MISTLE THRUSH, FIERCE DEFENDERS OF THEIR BROODS

A nest-full of young birds takes a deal of looking after. Our lower photograph is of a falcon which has just brought home a tasty morsel for its hungry brood. Above we have a mistle thrush with its young. This bird is extremely courageous in defending the nest from such bandits as jays and magpies, birds considerably larger than itself. It will fly at these enemies without hesitating, and seems always to succeed in driving them off. There are usually about four or five eggs laid at a time and, in the South, two broods are raised each summer.

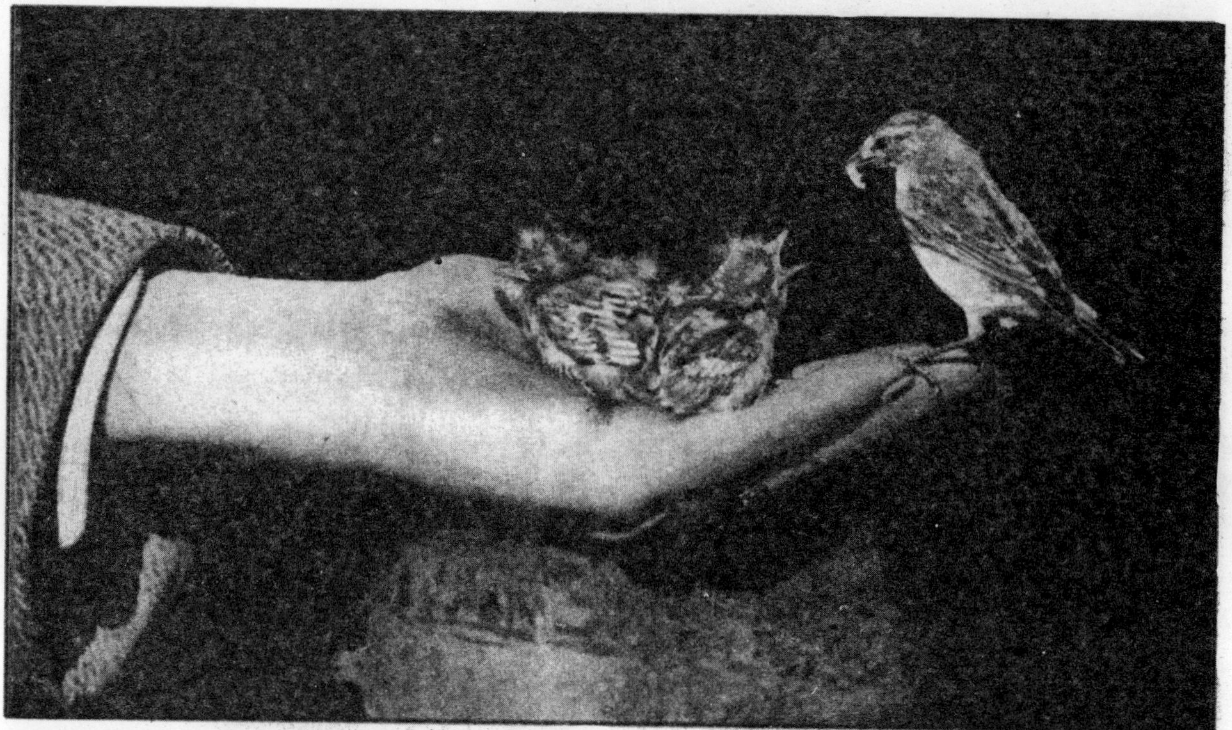

F. Vear

G. J. Shepstone

EGRET AND WILLOW WREN MOTHERS

Young egrets (bottom) have nowadays a little less chance of being starved because the mother has been killed for the millinery value of her feathers. Above is a willow wren whose matronly care has conquered distrust of the human hand.

But it is not of adults, as such, but of mothers and their young that I wish to write, and in particular of the cosy quarters some creatures prepare for their babies. The common rabbit makes the warmest of nests for its litter, either scratching a special hole, or using one already made, and carrying a considerable quantity of grass to the end of the tunnel. This bedding, however, does not content the doe; she proceeds to line the nest, plucking the soft, silky wool from her chest and underparts until the most perfect of couches has been prepared, so soft and warm that even the naked, blind, helpless young rabbits are kept perfectly snug and cosy. Yet even then their mother is not contented, and when she leaves the family, does her best to close the door behind her, so that cold air, to say nothing of enemies, may not enter. She scratches back all the soil she loosened when excavating the burrow, and fills up the mouth of the hole with this earth. Only when all is level does she venture to go away and nibble some grass.

In contrast with the care the old rabbit devotes to her little ones, the hare seems a casual mother; but then the latter's young ones are born fully clad, the prettiest of furry mites, and it does not matter to them if they have to sit out in an open " form " in the middle of a wind-swept field.

Of course, the most undeveloped of young mammals at birth are those of the kangaroos and certain other marsupials, but in their case the dam is mother and nursery in one, carrying her helpless babies in a special pouch, to which they cling for some time, even after they have grown comparatively strong and active. It is very quaint to see a kangaroo mother, with two or three little ones peeping forth at the world from their snug refuge.

Chapter CXV

The Marvel of the Mammoth and the Mastodon

By J. R. Ainsworth-Davis

Formerly Professor of Zoology, University of Wales

One of the most interesting of the extinct monsters of the past was a huge elephant, the mammoth (*Elephas primigenius*), which ranged through the Northern Hemisphere for perhaps half a million years in those remote times when Siberia was continuous with Alaska, the North Sea was a fertile plain, and the British Isles were part of the Continent of Europe. The race died out completely somewhere about 15,000 years ago, its last stronghold being in Northern Siberia, among the frozen wastes known as tundras.

Prehistoric man, in the Age of the Mammoth, was a wandering hunter, using stone implements and weapons, and leading a precarious existence among formidable wild animals. But he nevertheless possessed a strong artistic sense, as attested by many engravings on ivory, bone and stone, together with spirited drawings on the walls of caves, these being particularly abundant in France and Spain. In May, 1864, the French scientist Lartet discovered, in the cave of La Madeleine (Department of Dordogne), a fragment of mammoth tusk on which some early hunter had scratched a rough but vigorous outline of the tusk's owner, obviously a hairy elephant. This created much discussion, for existing elephants are notably devoid of well-developed hirsute covering. The subsequent discovery of similar engravings on the walls of other caves in the same district added further evidence as to the former existence of such a creature. These interesting representations were probably executed by the "medicine men" of the period, as magical spells for securing success in hunting, if we may judge from practices of the kind still resorted to by some primitive peoples.

Smithsonian Institution

MAMMOTH'S FORE FOOT

Although mammoths were, on an average, not so high in the leg, and therefore not so tall as the African elephant of to-day, they were much bulkier beasts. This forefoot is nearly as large as a man. The bone structure can be seen.

Our knowledge of the mammoth is now pretty complete for Nature has anticipated the methods of refrigeration which now enable Australian beef and New Zealand mutton to compete with our home-grown products, and mammoths which have been in cold storage in north Siberia for many thousands of years are from time to time discovered. Ides, a Dutch collector of mammoth ivory, came across a frozen head and foot as far back as 1707, but the first complete cold storage specimen was found on the banks of the River Lena in 1799, and was very gradually thawed out in the course of a few years.

Baron von Meydell discovered no fewer than three such frozen animals in north-east Siberia in the course of 1869, since when others have been brought to light. So perfectly have these prehistoric creatures been preserved that dogs, foxes, and wolves devour their flesh with gusto, and in at least one instance it was possible to find the nature of the last meal eaten by examining the contents of the stomach. It is extremely probable that mammoth steak has now and then been eaten by human beings in comparatively recent times, and there is a legend to that effect among American Indians.

Smithsonian Institution

PART OF A MAMMOTH DISCOVERED ON A CLIFF

Whereas the ordinary weight for a tusk of an African elephant is from forty to fifty pounds—though exceptional specimens may weigh a good deal more—the mammoth sometimes had tusks ten feet long and weighing two hundred pounds. Here we see part of a mammoth carcase discovered on a cliff. The body was covered with a reddish wool in life.

These extinct monsters apparently came to grief by falling into snow-filled ravines from which they were unable to extricate themselves, ultimately getting frozen up. The evidence afforded by them enables us to form a good idea of what the mammoth was like, and how it lived. It may be described as a super elephant, for though average specimens were not much more than nine feet high, some attained a much greater stature and the curved tusks sometimes reached a length of nine or ten feet, and a weight of from 180 to 200 pounds. In the existing African elephant an average tusk weighs from forty to fifty pounds, though this may be greatly exceeded in exceptional specimens.

The body of the mammoth was thickly covered with a kind of reddish wool and long black hair, and this is intelligible when we remember that the climate of the Northern Hemisphere was much more rigorous in those days than it is at the present time, and the contemporary "woolly" rhinoceros was also provided with a great-coat. The ears were comparatively small and the tail short, while the little cunning eyes resembled those of an ordinary elephant. Like all his kindred, the mammoth was a vegetarian, subsisting chiefly on the leafy branches of pine, fir and willow though he did not disdain a meal of grass, wild thyme, and even flowers, for seeds of poppies and buttercups have been found in his stomach or sticking in his teeth.

The mammoth was not only contemporaneous with man, but also contributed to prehistoric human diet, for his bones—some of them cracked for the extraction of marrow—are sometimes found associated with flint implements. Probably the ancient hunters constructed huge pitfalls for the undoing of their huge quarry, whose extinction is by some attributed partly to human agency.

The nature of the skeletons of this great creature found in Europe long ago was often misunderstood. One discovered in the eleventh century was identified with Pallas, son of Evander, a mythical giant of classical times: the "Giant of Lucerne" (1577) 19 feet high, and the "Giant of Dauphiné" (1613) were merely mammoths; and heated debates arose about some mammoth bones disinterred near Gloucester in the reign of James I, and asserted by some enthusiasts to be of giant human nature.

From very remote times mammoth ivory has been an important article of commerce, the early Greeks, for example, being well acquainted with the tusks as a

Smithsonian Institution

PARTIALLY EXCAVATED CARCASE OF A MAMMOTH IN SIBERIA

Siberia was the last dwelling place of the mammoth before it became extinct about 15,000 years ago. The representatives of the race which have come down to us are those which accidentally fell into depressions hidden by snow and were unable to get out. The one seen here, partially excavated, was a fine specimen. In the lower view it is photographed from behind and we can see the hollow body-cavity and the hindquarters nearest the camera. Above is a side view. The animal is leaning over on one flank.

The Mammoth and Mastodon

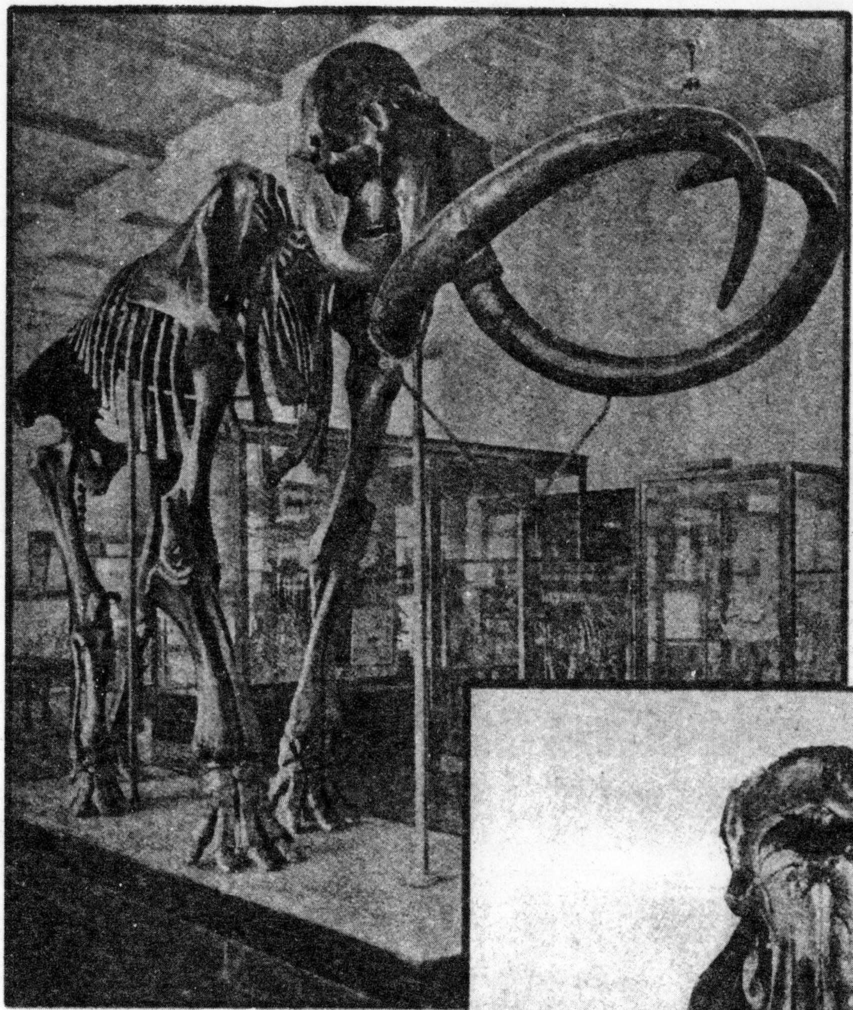

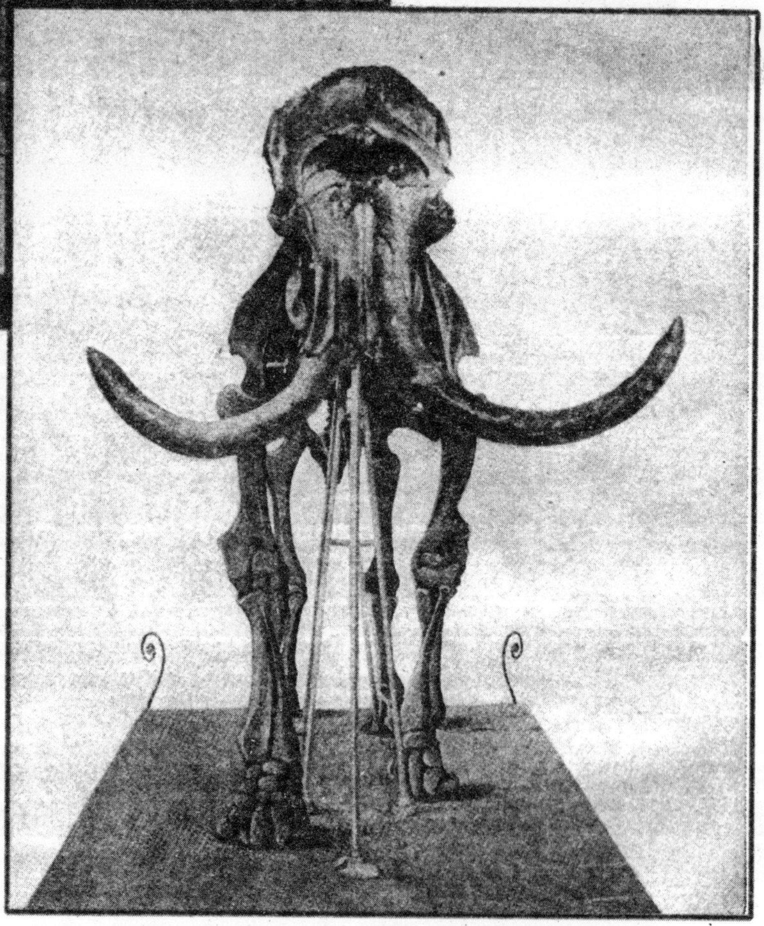

SKELETONS OF SIBERIAN AND AMERICAN MAMMOTHS

In the lower photograph we have a mammoth's skeleton dug up at Beresovka in Siberia. It is now in a museum at Leningrad. Notice the outward curving tusks. The tusks of the American mammoth (top) from Indiana, are nearly semi-circular in shape. This animal was ten feet six inches high at the shoulder.

valuable commodity. Even at the present day they are an important source of ivory, and Bassett Digby has recently written a most interesting book about his experiences as a hunter of mammoths in north-east Siberia, especially in the New Siberian or "Ivory" Isles of the Arctic Ocean. There are many curious beliefs about the mammoth among the primitive races inhabiting Siberia. It is thought to be a gigantic burrowing rat, whose tunnelling movements are responsible for earthquakes. When a specimen is discovered, weird incantations precede any attempt to secure the tusks, for the supposed "rat" is also regarded as a powerful and malign demon.

Much research of the most interesting kind has been devoted to working out the genealogy of elephants. One interesting species, the straight-tusked elephant (*Elephas antiquus*), was an ancestor of the mammoth that lived in Britain before the onset of the long cold period known as The Great Ice Age. It attained a height of twelve feet seven inches, and part of a skeleton has been mounted in the Natural History Museum at South Kensington.

Still older are the mastodons, which once ranged through the Northern Hemisphere. In these the grinding teeth were sr aller and simpler than those of the mammoth, and there were tusks in the lower as well as in the upper jaw. A very remarkable member of this group is the "shovel-toothed mastodon" discovered by the American scientific expedition to Mongolia. The remains were found in a hill range adjoining a vast desert, which was a lake long ages since, fringed at that

Smithsonian Institution

James

MAMMOTHS RECONSTRUCTED BY TAXIDERMY AND PAINTING

At a museum in Leningrad we may see the famous Beresovka mammoth mounted in the exact position in which it was found (top). The terrific cold of Siberia—the lowest temperatures on record have been found there—has been responsible for the wonderful state of preservation in which these mammoth carcases have been kept for something like one hundred and fifty centuries. The lower illustration is from a painting representing a mammoth in its natural surroundings of the frozen Siberian wastes.

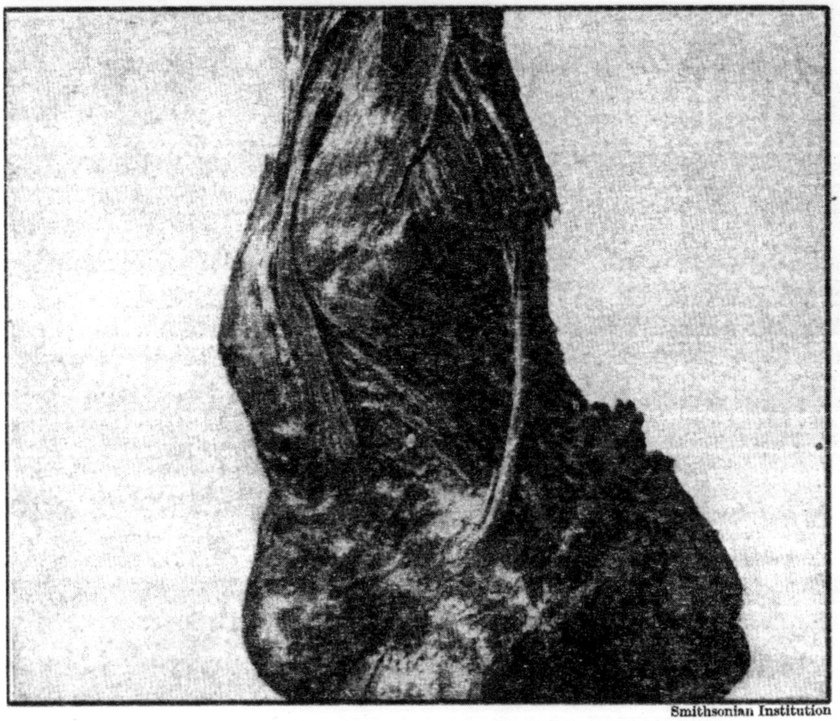

Smithsonian Institution

FOOT, AND SKULL WITH FOOD STILL IN THE TEETH

Nature's cold storage has wonderfully preserved the mammoth remains in Siberia. Here (bottom) we have a right hind foot, while above is a skull, photographed where it was unearthed. And here we find an amazing thing. The food of the monster's last meal, 150,000 years ago, is still between its teeth, and is marked in the photograph with a cross.

time by luxuriant vegetation. The lower tusks of this new find were flattened out into what looks like a coal scoop over six feet long, provided with a cutting edge in front, and narrowing behind into a "handle." This peculiar apparatus was apparently used for cutting through and shovelling up into the mouth the succulent plants growing at the edge of the lake. Both trunk and tongue must have helped in the operation.

Many other kinds of four-tusked elephants are known, the older ones, like our shovel-toothed friend, having long chins and elongated lower tusks, while in the youngest members of the series the chin and lower teeth were quite short. The grinding teeth became larger and more complicated as time went on. The mammoth and existing elephants were derived from the last four-tuskers by still further

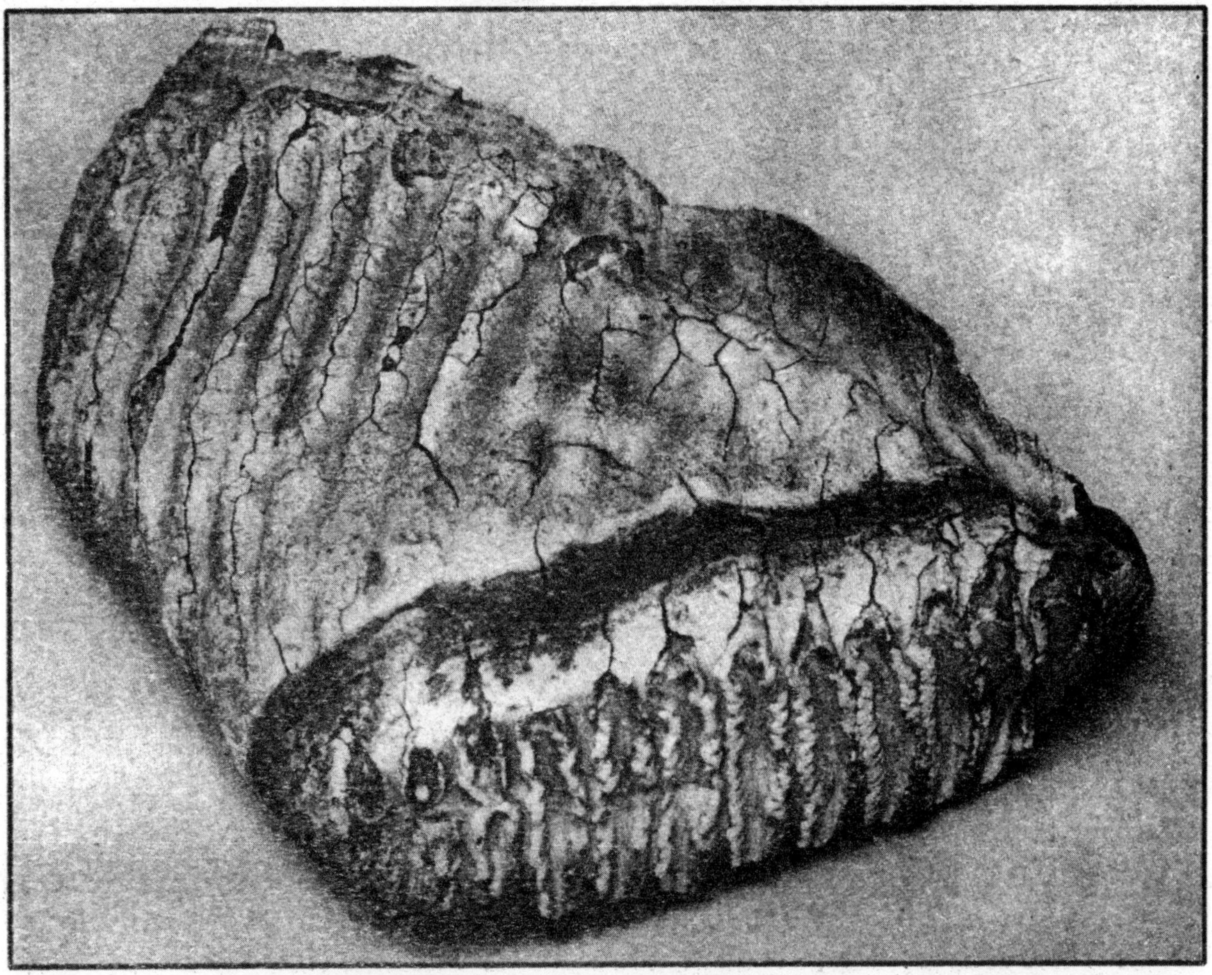

ONE OF THE ENORMOUS TEETH FROM A MAMMOTH'S UPPER JAW

As reproduced here this tooth is about one quarter of the natural size. It is one of the huge molars in the upper jaw and its long surface consists of a series of irregular ridges worn down by the constant grinding of the vegetation which formed the mammoth's food. The tooth came from a carcase found in the frozen tundra of Siberia and is now in a private collection. It measures about eight inches along the top or grinding surface, which is about two and a half inches broad, and its greatest length is about eleven inches. It weighs some twelve pounds.

shortening of the chin and suppression of the lower tusks; while the grinding teeth increased in size and complexity, so that ultimately only four of them could be in place at the same time.

DURING the heyday of the mastodons a curious creature, the dinotherium, came into existence in Europe and Asia, as a sort of unsuccessful experiment in the evolution of elephants, for it became extinct without leaving descendants. Here the upper tusks were suppressed, while the end of the lower jaw bent sharply downwards and bore a pair of sharp backwardly curved tusks possibly used for digging.

We have seen how ordinary elephants have taken origin from mastodons, and must now enquire where and how the latter came into existence. Our evidence on these points is derived from fossil remains found in the ancient fresh-water deposits of Egypt. Here we find the bones of an extinct creature, palaeomastodon (meaning "old mastodon"), which was about the size of a small elephant and possessed a short trunk. There were two small tusks in the upper jaw, and two pointed front teeth in the elongated lower jaw, used for grubbing in the ground. The grinding teeth were smaller and more numerous than in mastodons, and much like those of a pig.

This species, in its turn, was preceded by a much smaller and less specialised form, moeritherium, which appears to have resembled a tapir in size and appearance. There was a short trunk, and strong tusks in both jaws. We see in this creature the first beginnings of the characters that distinguish elephants and their kind. The subsequent stages in evolution are easy to understand. There was a gradual increase in size, and the necessary support for a bulky body was secured by the conversion of the limbs into strong pillars lacking flexibility, and with no external trace of digits save small hoof-like nails.

At the same time some of the front teeth were converted into weighty tusks, the evolution of which was incompatible with an elongation of the neck sufficient to bring the mouth down to the ground to graze. Hence the development of the snout into a flexible trunk for seizing food.

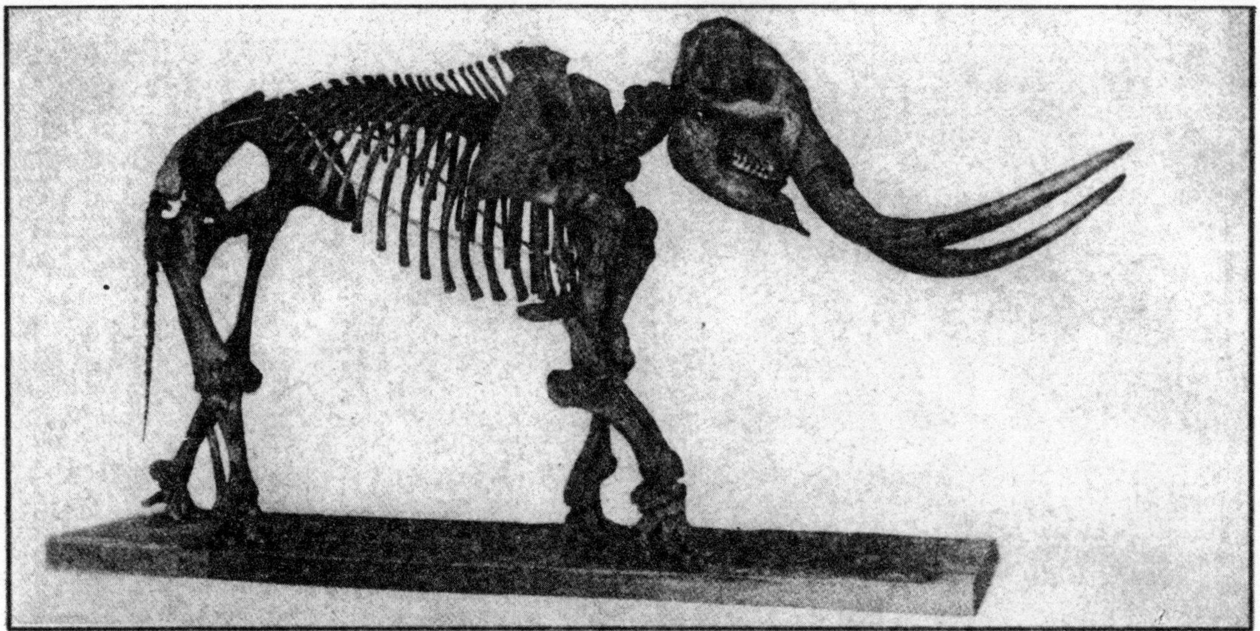

Natural History, N.Y.

Natural History, N.Y.

CAREFUL RESTORATION OF AN AMERICAN MASTODON AND A SKELETON

Based on an exhaustive survey of muscles and other anatomical details and from very precise measurements of skeletons, this is a restoration of an American mastodon, an animal much older than the mammoth, which had much smaller and less elaborate teeth. The mastodon had a hairy coat to withstand the severe climate in which it lived. This specimen lived in New York State in the Ice Age and may have been as common then as the buffalo in the early nineteenth century. Above is a mastodon skeleton nine feet two inches high.

Natural History, N.Y.

James

MASTODON REPRESENTED IN ITS NATURAL HAUNTS, AND A MUSEUM MODEL

Mastodons were, like their distant relatives, the elephants of our own day, fond of water, and this picture, painted from scientific data (bottom) shows the kind of surroundings which the mastodon liked. Above is a model of a mastodon in the American Museum of Natural History in New York. It was a shorter animal than the elephant and there were, in some kinds of mastodons, tusks in the lower as well as the upper jaw. The name mastodon means "breast-toothed" and refers to the conical tubercles on the teeth.

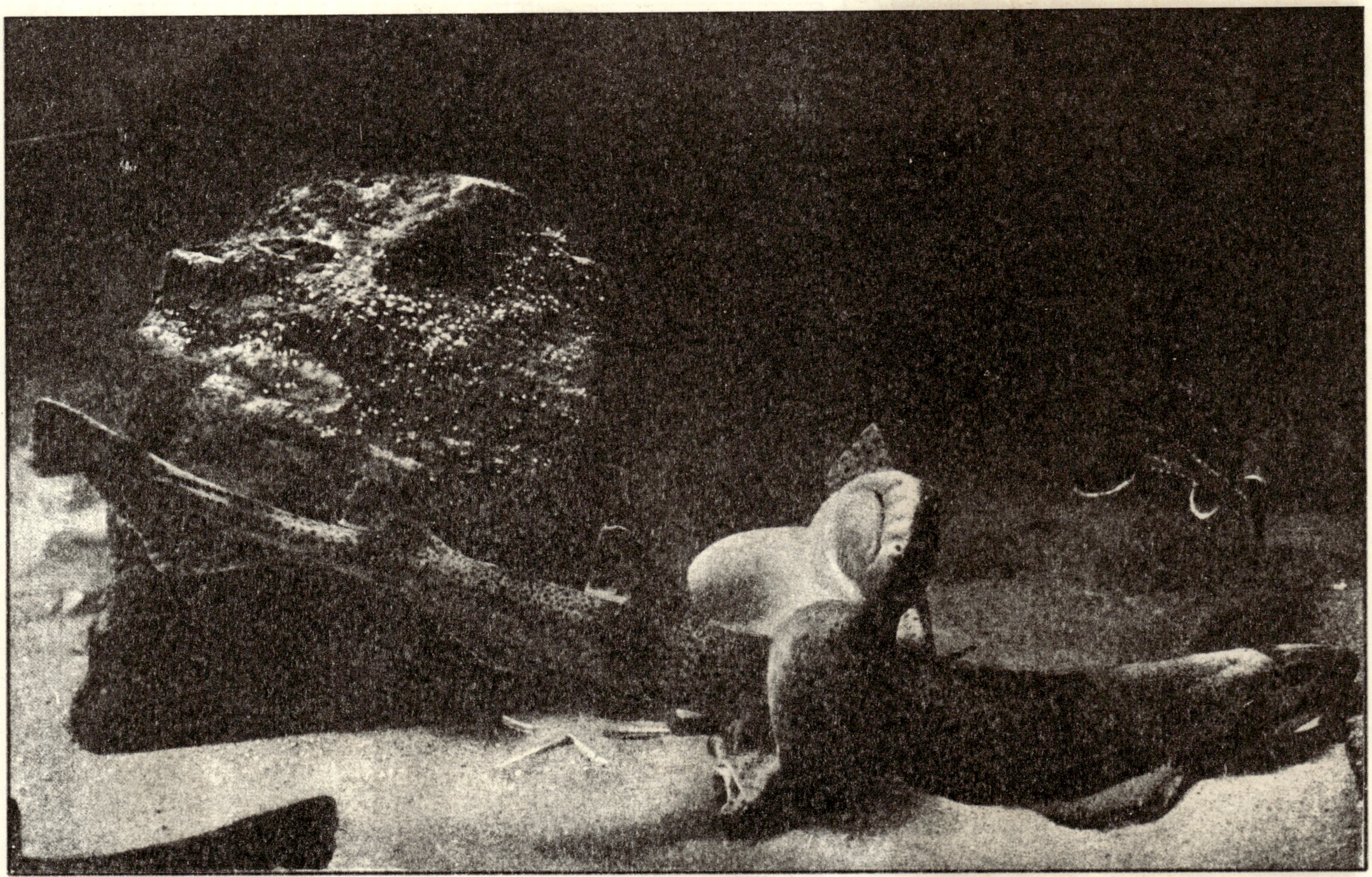

COURTSHIP CONTORTIONS OF THE HANDSOME SPOTTED DOG-FISH THAT SWIMS THE NORTH SEA

Growing to a length of not much more than two feet, the spotted dog-fish is the smallest member of the shark family found in the North Sea. It is an elegant fish, and its smooth, grey sides are softly tinted with red and decorated with handsome markings in the shape of spots. Although related to the viviparous sharks—those that bring forth their young alive as complete individuals—the spotted dog-fish lays its eggs in brown purse-like objects which are attached to seaweed. From April to June both male and female become very lively and swim about excitedly, the male biting his mate's fins and butting her with his nose and going through antics most extraordinary for a fish, as we see here. Photograph by F. Schensky of the Biological Station, Heligoland.

Chapter CXVI

Courtship Display in the Animal World

By R. I. Pocock, F.R.S.

Of the Zoological Department, British Museum

One of the first lessons in natural history the child learns is that male and female animals often differ in size, colour, voice and other particulars, and that the superiority in these respects is on the side of the male. He is taught to distinguish the lion from the lioness by his mane, the stag from the hind by his antlers, and the cock from the hen by his gaudy colouring and plumed tail, his crow and perhaps by the spurs on his legs.

These and many similar differences between the males and females of other beasts and birds are called secondary sexual characters; but although their origin and meaning have for many years been subjects for discussion amongst naturalists, there is still much to be learnt about them.

According to their functions most of these characters may be assigned to one of two categories. The first comprises organs, like horns, tusks and spurs, which have to do with the law of battle, with the contests between the males of a species for the possession of the females. The second comprises bright colours or plumes, sounding organs or odours, which are more directly concerned with courtship itself and apparently serve the purpose of stirring appropriate emotional responsiveness in the females at the breeding season.

Since the subject of this chapter is the part played by plumes, colours and other garments in courtship, we must restrict our remarks mainly to those organs of the second category which were believed by Darwin to influence the female in the way described and to have been brought to their present state of perfection by the preference of the female, continued generation after generation, for the more gaudily attired males. Darwin, however, also thought it possible that horns and antlers of male antelopes and deer might be included in this category. But although these weapons admittedly add greatly to the handsomeness of the males from the human point of view, their function for their owners is now considered to be solely combative.

W. S. Berridge

WEDDING GARMENT OF THE TAHR

When they go out to find a mate the male tahrs have their long, shaggy beards at their finest. During the summer the older males leave the females in their flocks and herd by themselves. We see one here in its shaggy wedding-garment.

One little point about them must be referred to, nevertheless. It is not to the advantage of a species that an older and, for the time being, stronger male should kill his younger rival. Hence the antlers of deer carry accessory branches which act as guards against serious injury. It is well known in fact that fights between two stags seldom end fatally. Similarly, wild boars are provided with warts or shields of thick skin as a protection against the tusks of opponents. This suggests that the lion's mane, although enhancing the splendid appearance of the animal, is to be interpreted as a mat of hair guarding the neck and throat from the claws and teeth of a rival. At all events, there is no evidence that a lion displays his mane to the lioness or that a lioness in any way prefers a larger-maned to a smaller-maned lion as a mate.

The mane of the male hamadryas baboon possibly serves the same purpose as that suggested for the lion; but we do not know the meaning of many of the secondary sexual characters of mammals. The adult male mandrill, another species of baboon, is much more brilliantly tinted with red and blue on the face and other naked parts than the females or young males; the male nilgai antelope upon reaching maturity turns iron-grey, the females remaining tawny; and the male blackbuck assumes either seasonally or permanently a black coat, the female retaining through life the characteristic sandy tint of all the gazelles. But there is no display of these colours by the males; nor is there any justification for the belief that their development has been fostered by female preference.

It was facts of this nature that influenced Wallace, who, in opposition to Darwin, believed that in no class of animals has female choice exercised an influence upon the secondary sexual characters of males. He held that horns, manes, crests and plumes are indications of superior strength and vitality in virtue of which those males were more successful in securing mates than their less favoured rivals, quite irrespective of female preference. He also thought that a tendency to produce bright colours and patterns is inherent in both sexes and that where the females differ from the males in that respect, as in the case of the wild duck in the winter and the pheasant throughout the year, the development of colour has been arrested by natural selection in the female to enable her to escape observation while nesting. General opinion, however, favours Darwin's view that the decor-

B.N.A.

G. Hearn

THE VIPER'S COURTSHIP

When vipers prepare to wed they find some quiet and sunny place where they can bask side by side (bottom). The pair then go through a number of evolutions, chasing and twisting round each other as we see in the upper photograph.

ations of males are specialised developments; and in one species of bird, the ruff, as we shall show, recent observations attest preference on the part of the females for the finest males. Evidence on this head is, however, extremely scanty and nothing is more noticeable to those who watch the courtship of birds than the apparently complete indifference of the hens to the elaborate display of beauty presented to them by the cocks.

Neither of the theories above epitomised explains all the facts. Some still remain a puzzle awaiting solution; and of these none is perhaps more baffling than that presented by the immense horns on the head and thorax of the males of the great tropical beetles known as the hercules and atlas beetles. An interesting fact about these horns is that their size depends upon the size of the individuals that carry them, the dimensions increasing not in simple proportion, but in a rapidly increasing ratio; and this, we may add, is a very general rule with similar appendages throughout the animal kingdom, the proportionate weight of the appendage to that of the body being mathematically fixed, thus attesting the existence of a law of growth of which we do not know the explanation.

Now the function of the horns in the hercules and atlas beetles is quite unknown. They are not weapons for fighting—for, apart from their unsuitability for that purpose, the insects are not pugnacious—and they cannot be regarded as ornamental. Their arrangement and size suggest that they may be prehensile, possibly for holding the female; but they never show any signs of wear or use in any way, and we must leave them at that. On the other hand, the horns of the male stag beetle, which are enlarged jaws, serve the double purpose of grasping the female and of fighting with rival males, thus coming in this respect into the same category as the antlers of deer, which they resemble.

The marked difference between the males and the females of the beetles quoted shows that secondary sexual characters may be as highly developed in some classes of invertebrate animals as in beasts and birds; but only in one group of invertebrates, apparently, have we positive evidence of display of bright colours and ornamental tufts by the males to the females such as occurs in birds. This group is that of the spiders. There is a large family of spiders, called the Attidae, remarkable for the possession of a pair of immense eyes occupying almost the whole area of the face. They stealthily stalk flies and catch them with a leap, a proceeding demanding keenness and precision of vision found in no other families of this order.

THE KINGFISHER GOES COURTING IN A LIVERY OF BRILLIANT COLOURS

When the time comes for pairing, the kingfisher's gorgeous plumage is seen at its best as the bird flashes over stream or lake. The female can be distinguished by the duller and greener feathers while the immature birds which have not yet reached the age to go courting, are of a browner tone. Besides its bright back and wing feathers, the kingfisher sports a jaunty moustache at the base of its beak.

James

POLAR BEARS AND CATTLE DISPLAY AFFECTION BEFORE MATING

Most of the higher animals go through some sort of courting ritual though in some it seems to be merely a question of forceful capture. Polar bears, however, display great affection, playing together and suffering the usual foolishness characteristic of courtship. The upper photograph shows a bull and a cow of a breed of English park cattle. Preliminaries for mating consist of mutual, though gentle, buttings and rubbings of nose against nose. Often the cow makes most of the advances.

E.N.A.

The males of many of these spiders differ strikingly from the females in the gaudy colouring of the fore parts of the body and limbs, and, when courting the female, the male performs fantastic antics in front of her, unmistakably displaying his beauty by presenting to her view only those parts which are specially decorated. It is true that there is no proof that the female prefers the most gaudily attired of her suitors, but it is impossible to doubt that the display has some effect upon her choice, and it is particularly significant that this display is practised only by spiders with well-developed visual powers capable of seeing clearly the decorations.

The sexes also differ in colour in some insects. As instances may be cited the common orange-tip butterfly, so called from the presence of a conspicuous orange patch on the wing of the male which is absent in the female, and the chalk-hill blue in which the wings are azure blue in the male and brown in the female. Since butterflies are known to have good vision, capable of distinguishing flowers from foliage, it may well be that the females of these species, by preferring to mate with males showing orange or azure tints, have by a long process of selection brought about the marked differences by which the sexes can be distinguished at a glance.

E.N.A.

MAN-OF-WAR AND FRIGATE BIRDS

Frigate birds in mating time are most entertaining to watch. The male searches about until he has found a good nesting site and then sits upon it and inflates a skin pouch under the beak. It looks like a blood-red balloon and the bird agitates it, to and fro, till some female arrives to make him happy. Below are man-of-war birds courting.

Turning to the vertebrate animals, the mammals have already been dealt with, and call for no further mention, because there is no evidence that the males of any species, even when differently coloured from the females, make any attempt at display. This is somewhat surprising, seeing that the mammals are usually considered to be the most highly organized class of this sub-kingdom.

In the most lowly organized class, the fishes, on the other hand, there are reasons for thinking that the males of some kinds display special colours and ornaments before the females. Even in such species as the common tench and roach the colours of the male become intensified at the breeding season, and in a Chinese fish (*Macropus*) the male is not only more brilliantly tinted than the female, but during courtship expands his brightly-coloured fins and leaps about with great vivacity.

Still more significant is the case of the sword-bearer (*Xiphophorus*), in which the lower edge of the tail-fin in the male is developed into a long, brightly striped filament; and since this is not provided with muscles, and is therefore useless for swimming, it is regarded as purely ornamental. Also, the male dragonet (*Callionymus*) differs from the female not only in being more brilliantly striped and spotted with vivid blue on the head, but has the dorsal fin extraordinarily elongated. These special growths and brighter tints, accompanied by active movements on the part of the males in the presence of the females at spawning time, favour the view that they have been developed by female preference.

The class above the fishes, the amphibia, presents an analogous case in the newts, common in ponds, where they breed, in the spring and summer. The males at those seasons become more brilliantly yellow below, and acquire a soft, erect crest along the back and tail which disappears during the winter.

In the higher class, the reptiles, we also meet with somewhat similar but persistent dorsal crests in the males of some lizards, whereas in others the males are provided with a brightly-coloured dilatable throat-pouch which is expanded and exhibited only during the breeding season.

W. S. Berridge

H. Bastin

BIRD OF PARADISE AND THE OSTRICH'S PROPOSAL

The head ornament of the Superb bird of paradise (bottom) is of an extraordinary shape. The birds of paradise are famous, but this particular kind is prominent even in such company. The upper photograph shows a cock ostrich displaying before the hen.

But it is in birds, the courtship of which has been more closely observed than in other animals, that we find the greatest evidence in favour of Darwin's hypothesis. Whether the sexes are alike or different in colour, they behave towards one another at the breeding season in a variety of ways which appeal to the senses of hearing, touch or sight. In guillemots, for example, in which the sexes are alike, the pair interlock their necks and bills, nibble each other, bow and wag their heads, and sway their bodies from side to side. In this instance, as in that of the great crested grebe, where again the sexes are alike, the courtship is mutual, both male and female going through a remarkable sequence of actions. But when the sexes differ considerably in colour and adornment, as in the ostrich, peacock, birds of paradise and many others, the courtship display is practised by the cock, the part played by the hen being passive. Each type of bird has its own method, and it is only possible to mention one or two in detail.

The male ostrich, which differs from the greyish-brown hen in being black-and-white, goes through a remarkable performance. Taking a position facing the hen, he drops on his hocks in a squatting attitude, spreads his wings, lowers his tail, and throwing his neck over his back, sways slowly and rhythmically from side to side, swinging his neck to right and left and often setting his wings ashake. This may go on for ten or more minutes. Then, suddenly rising to his feet, the cock rushes towards the hen with wings outspread and sometimes repeats the performance at close quarters, sometimes bringing it to a close by stamping on the ground like a soldier rapidly marking time. The hen, on the contrary, does not pay the slightest attention to his antics, but treats him and his behaviour with the most supreme indifference.

The beauty and display of the peacock are familiar to all. The full-grown bird has a brilliant bluish-green throat and breast and develops for the courting season a train of immensely long feathers, each adorned at the tip with the well-known "eye-mark"; and this train, generally but wrongly called the tail, is raised during display and spread like a great fan, the true tail, which is beneath, being raised and spread at the same time to support it. With the train thus spread, the wings drooped and the

indications of exuberant vitality. No two ruffs are alike in colour; each, however, acquires for the breeding season a great fan of feathers on the sides of the neck—whence the name. But they vary in decorativeness, and it is only the fully adorned ruffs that come to the fore on the courting-ground, the shabbier individuals keeping disconsolately in the rear and remaining completely unnoticed by the reeves, or females.

W. S. Berridge

DRAGONETS THAT HAVE ELABORATE COURTSHIPS

So brightly coloured are the male dragonets that one could think they came from the tropic seas. Here we have a female (bottom) and a male (top). But most species live in the north temperate zone. These fish are very active at mating time and the males have brilliant markings and long, projecting filaments on the fins.

beautiful neck to the fore, the bird presents the most gorgeous and striking appearance as he faces the hen; but she, as in the case of the hen ostrich, is apparently quite unimpressed by the splendid spectacle.

The turkey cock is particularly interesting when studied in connection with the peacock, because the attitude of the two assumed in display is the same. In detail the display is different because the adornment of the turkey's neck is due to the brilliant colouring of the naked skin and there is no resplendent train to be lifted by the upraised expanded tail; but no one who compares the two birds while courting can doubt that the display of the turkey represents an early phase in the display of the ancestors of the peacock, before the wonderful train was developed.

The cock Argus pheasant excels even the peacock in feather development, although not in brilliance of tint. He also faces the hen during courtship; but other pheasants behave differently. They run in half-circles in front of the hens, so as to display at a time the beauty of only one side of the body.

Equally varied and elaborate are the attitudes assumed by cock birds of paradise, which are most beautifully decorated with coloured plumes, iridescent patches and other ornaments; and even the tiniest of all birds, the humming birds, which rival the birds of paradise in their gorgeous apparel, go through the most intricate manoeuvres to display their beauty to the females when courting them.

The last case we have space to allude to is that of the ruff, a polygamous plover; but it is particularly important in supplying evidence, as shown by Mr. E. Selous, of preferential mating on the part of the female, or reeve, as she is called. This plover has several scientific names, such as *Machetes* and *Philomachus*, based upon the seemingly desperate combats in which the males, or ruffs, indulge; but these fights are harmless affairs and, like the other antics practised, such as frantically darting about, leaping, kicking, whirring the wings and so forth, are merely

There is one other aspect of sexual display to be considered. Since in the case of the spiders no one probably will dispute that the behaviour of the males during courtship is purely instinctive and not prompted by a knowledge of their beauty, we are led to inquire if the same is not true of birds. There are many facts supporting this conclusion. In the first place cock birds in full feather will not uncommonly go through all the phases of display characteristic of the species when hens are nowhere at hand. Sometimes they display to one another, sometimes to nothing at all. Taking the peacock as a type, these birds have been seen to show off in the presence of sparrows and to an old felt hat on the ground. Again, most birds in which the two sexes are alike behave in the breeding season in a way that would be called display if they possessed any special ornamentation to show. These facts seem to suggest very forcibly that the strange behaviour of birds during courtship is instinctive, is the outcome of the physiological disturbance that affects their entire organization when the breeding fever holds sway.

In describing the display of cock birds most naturalists write under the belief that they assume particular attitudes for the purpose of showing off their colours or plumes. In other words, the birds display because they are decorated. But we shall probably be nearer the truth if we invert the idea and say that decorations are developed on particular areas because the cocks pose in a particular manner. The decorations, that is, are adapted to the display.